AN INTRODUCTION TO SCIENCE AND HYGIENE FOR HAIRDRESSERS

*

AN INTRODUCTION TO
Science and Hygiene
FOR
Hairdressers

O. F. G. KILGOUR BSC, MIBiol
and
MARGUERITE McGARRY BSC

*

FUNK & WAGNALLS
NEW YORK

Library of Congress Catalog Card Number: 68–14061
Published by Funk & Wagnalls, A Division of Reader's
Digest Books, Inc., by arrangement with William Heinemann Ltd.

PRINTED IN GREAT BRITAIN

Contents

Plates

Acknowledgements

It is my pleasure to acknowledge with gratitude the help I have received from Miss B. M. Marshall who typed the manuscript; Mr R. H. Pritchard, B.A., who read the work; my colleague, Mr G. Williams, B.Sc., who made valuable suggestions for this reprint; and from friends and colleagues who gave their kind criticism. In particular, I acknowledge the considerable help and guidance given by Miss Clarice Morris of William Heinemann Ltd. Finally, I am indebted to my wife Barbara, for her assistance and continual encouragement, to whom I dedicate my section of this book.

I am also grateful to the following for the use of their photographs and diagrams, and for giving valuable technical information:

A. Boake, Roberts & Co. Ltd (Plate 15)

British Insulated Callender's Cables (Figure 7.15)

British Launderers Research Association (Plate 2)

J. A. Crabtree & Co. Ltd (Figures 7.14, 9.9, 9.10, 9.14)

Englehard Hanovia Ltd (Plate 12)

Fox & Oxford Ltd (Plate 7)

Glass of Mark Ltd (Figure 13.9)

Instron Ltd (Plate 5)

International Woo Secretariat (Plates 19, 20, 22)

La Reine Ltd (Plate 4)

W. B. Nicolson Ltd (Plates 6, 8, 9, 10)

Osborne, Garrett & Co. Ltd (Plate 11)

Pifco Ltd (Figures 8.8, 10.14, 11.9)

Unilever Ltd (Plates 1, 13, 14, 16, 17, 18, 24, 25, 26, 27)

G. H. Zeal & Co. Ltd (Plate 3)

Dr R. Lassé, Dr J. Cunz, and CIBA Ltd (Plate 21)

O.F.G.K.

I wish to express my thanks to several people who have helped at various stages in the preparation of the book:

Dr T. A. G. Wells and Mr W. H. Southern without whose initial help I should not have started this work; Mr J. Small for reading the manuscript and offering valuable suggestions; Mrs F. Sugarman for reading part of the manuscript; Dr R. Barrass for his advice on the drawings; and finally, Mrs R. Barrass for typing the manuscript.

I am also grateful to the following for providing photographs and illustrations:

I.C.I. Pharmaceutical Department (Plate 33)

Mr R. Kay (Plate 32)

Longmans, Green and Co. Ltd (for allowing me to base Figures 21.7, 22.3, 22.5, 22.6, 23.3, and 23.4 on figures in Gray's *Anatomy*)

The Rank Film Library (Plate 28)

Reckitt and Sons Ltd, Hull (Plates 29, 30, 31) which were reproduced from their filmstrip *Elementary Bacteriology 'Part I'*.

M.M.

PART I
Physics

1 MEASUREMENT OF VOLUME, WEIGHT, DENSITY, AND SPECIFIC GRAVITY

Science is a word that means knowledge; it may also mean the study of matter. It is important at the beginning of your course to realize that words and their meaning are of importance to all who are studying science. To a scientist the exact meaning of a word or term is called a *definition*, and often the scientific definition of a word will not convey the same meaning as its meaning in everyday conversation. The definition or scientific meaning of the word *matter* is: *anything that occupies space and has weight*. For example, a brick has weight and also occupies space; therefore it is matter. This definition of the word *matter* does not convey the same meaning as the everyday meanings of the word (for example, pus from an infected wound). It is therefore important to understand and remember all definitions or meanings of words used in scientific language that you come across in this book.

Scientific investigation into the composition and behaviour of products and appliances is being used to help the consumer and shopper in his choice by such bodies as the Consumers' Association, publishers of *Which?* Thus science helps us to select products on a basis of sound scientific fact, rather than on wide generalizations.

A knowledge of science helps a person to experiment and to investigate for himself whether the advertised claims of a product are true or false. For example, an advertiser may claim that a hairdressing preparation can grow hair on a bald pate. The immediate reaction of a person trained in science is to test the preparation and find out whether the claim is true or not.

BRANCHES OF SCIENCE

The study of science or the knowledge of the earth and its surrounding atmosphere is so vast that it has to be split up into branches, of which the following are especially important to hairdressers:

Biology: science *or* knowledge of life.
Chemistry: science *or* knowledge of the composition of matter.
Physics: science *or* knowledge of the behaviour of matter; it includes heat, electricity, light, and mechanics.
Mathematics: science *or* knowledge of space and number.

HAIRDRESSING SCIENCE

This is science applied to hairdressing and its related processes. This knowledge has been gathered from the following branches of science:

Branch of Science	Contribution to Hairdressing knowledge
Biology	Hair structure and growth. Hair disease and treatment. Salon hygiene. Human anatomy and physiology.
Chemistry	All hairdressing preparations and shampoos. Cold-waving lotion. Water treatment. Hair dyes and conditioners, etc.
Physics	Electricity and electrical appliances. Electrical treatments. Hair waving. Heat. Water heating. Ventilation. Light and illumination of salons. Ultra-violet ray treatment.

CLASSIFICATION OF MATTER

All matter exists in one of three physical states, namely: solids, liquids, and gases. The differences between the states of matter depend on the fact that all matter is made up of tiny particles called *molecules* that are arranged in different ways, as shown in Plate 1.

Solid molecules are packed together in an orderly manner, as in hair.
Liquid molecules are less closely packed together, as in water.
Gas molecules are far apart, as in air.

DIFFERENCES BETWEEN SOLIDS, LIQUIDS, AND GASES

Solid	Liquid	Gas
Ice	*Water*	*Steam*
Definite shape; molecules packed together and remain in definite position.	No definite shape; molecules move about and take on the shape of a container, e.g. jelly-mould.	No definite shape; molecules move very freely and fill container of any size, e.g. smell of perfume spreads rapidly in a room.

MEASUREMENT OF MATTER

We shall consider this under three headings: length, volume, and weight.

The metric system of measurement is used in all scientific work.

MEASUREMENT OF LENGTH

The metric unit of length is called the *metre* (m). This was formerly defined as the length of a rod of platinum–iridium alloy kept in the National Archives in Paris; an optical standard is now used.

The metre is divided into one hundred parts called *centimetres* (cm):

$$1 \text{ m} = 100 \text{ cm}$$

Each centimetre (cm) is divided into ten parts called *millimetres* (mm):

$$1 \text{ cm} = 10 \text{ mm}$$

The instrument commonly used for measuring length is the metre rule, a wooden ruler.

MEASUREMENT OF VOLUME

Volume is the amount of space occupied by matter. The metric system unit of volume is the *litre* (l). It is equal to one thousand *cubic centimetres* (cm³):

$$1 \text{ litre} = 1{,}000 \text{ cm}^3$$

As an alternative to the cubic centimetre (cm³) the *millilitre* (ml) is often used:

$$1 \text{ litre} = 1{,}000 \text{ ml}$$

For practical purposes the cubic centimetre and millilitre can be regarded as equivalent.

Note. One cubic centimetre is the same as the volume of a small box with sides of one centimetre.

One millilitre is a thousandth part of a litre.

Apparatus used for measuring volume

Measuring cylinders are available in various sizes ranging from 10 cm³ to 2 litres (Figure 1.1). They are fairly accurate instruments and are used for general purposes and for measuring ingredients for cosmetic preparations.

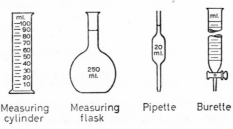

Measuring   Measuring   Pipette   Burette
cylinder   flask

Figure 1.1

Pipettes are available in various capacities from 1 cm³ to 50 cm³. The liquid is drawn into the pipette by sucking, the index finger being placed over the open end to retain the liquid. Pipettes are used for measuring definite volumes of liquid accurately, as for testing hardness of water (Figure 1.1).

Burettes are available in sizes from 10 cm³ to 100 cm³. They deliver accurate amounts of liquid by way of the tap, and are mainly used for testing hardness of water.

Graduated and measuring flasks, available in capacities from 10 cm³ to 3 litres, are used for making solutions of known strength. They are useful for making up solutions of dyes where small quantities of the dye are dissolved in definite volumes of liquids.

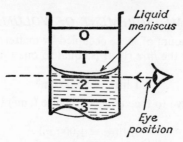

Figure 1.2. Reading the level of liquid in a measuring instrument

When reading the level of the liquid in any measuring instrument, hold the instrument at eye level and read the lower line of the *meniscus* or liquid surface (Figure 1.2).

USES OF MEASURING INSTRUMENTS IN HAIRDRESSING

Instrument	Accuracy	Uses
Measuring cylinder	Fairly accurate	General purposes. Measuring ingredients of cosmetics. Measuring lotions for hairdressing treatments.
Pipette	Accurate	Measuring *small* amounts of liquid. Making up perfumes. Determining hardness of water.
Burette	Accurate	Determining hardness of water.
Graduated flask	Accurate	Making up solutions of known strength.

All hairdressing lotions and preparations used in a salon should be measured in *glass* apparatus, because metal containers are liable to corrosion.

MEASUREMENT OF WEIGHT OR MASS

Weight is the pull of gravity on a body. *Mass* is the amount of matter contained in a known volume of substance.

For our purposes weight and mass are equal to each other, although the weight of a body can vary slightly in different parts of the earth, because of the differing pull of gravity. The mass or amount of matter in a body never alters.

The unit of mass or weight is the *gramme* (g). There are one thousand grammes in one *kilogramme* (kg):

$$1{,}000 \text{ grammes} = 1 \text{ kilogramme}$$
$$1{,}000 \text{ g} = 1 \text{ kg}$$

Instrument for measuring weight

The direct-reading balance is the simplest type of instrument for measuring weight. The object to be weighed is placed on the pan and its weight is directly indicated on the scale.

Rules for weighing:

(a) Weigh powders on to a piece of clean paper covering the balance pan.
(b) Waxy and greasy solids should be weighed directly into a previously weighed beaker.
(c) Wipe up all spilt materials immediately.
(d) Allow all hot objects to cool before weighing.

DENSITY AND SPECIFIC GRAVITY

DENSITY

Given blocks of iron, aluminium, and cork of identical size, we should immediately notice the difference in their weights. Similarly a bottle of mercury is considerably heavier than a bottle of water of equal size. If we wish to compare the heaviness of substances we must take *equal volumes* of them.

Density means the weight in grammes of one cubic centimetre of a substance:

$$\text{Density} = \frac{\text{Weight in grammes}}{\text{Volume in cm}^3}$$

$$\text{Density} = \text{grammes per cubic centimetre (g/cm}^3)$$

This is the way a scientist describes heaviness and lightness, namely by using the word *density*.

DENSITIES OF SOME COMMON SUBSTANCES

Substance	Density g/cm³
Mercury	13·6
Iron	7·9
Aluminium	2·6
Glycerine	1·26
Sea-water	1·05
Water	1·0
Olive oil	0·9
Ethyl alcohol	0·8
Acetic acid	1·05
Acetone	0·80
Amyl acetate	0·87
Ethyl acetate	0·89
Castor oil	0·96
Petroleum	0·64
Triethanolamine	1·13
Turpentine	0·86
Almond oil	0·91
Peanut oil	0·92
Methylated spirit	0·83
Liquid paraffin	0·87

From the table it can be seen that (a) mercury is heavier than glycerine and (b) ethyl alcohol or methylated spirit is lighter than water.

All substances with a density less than 1·0 g/cm³ will *float on water*, and those with a density greater than 1·0 g/cm³ *sink in water*.

Since the density of water is 1 g/cm³, therefore 100 grammes of water equals 100 cm³ of water.

It is easier to measure water by volume than to weigh it.

Experiment

To find the density of glycerine or any other liquid:

Obtain a clean dry 100-cm³ measuring cylinder and find its weight using a direct-reading balance. Carefully record the weight of the empty measuring cylinder. Fill the measuring cylinder with glycerine to the 100 cm³ mark and obtain the weight of the glycerine and cylinder by means of the direct-reading balance, again recording the weight.

Results:

$$\begin{aligned} \text{Weight of glycerine plus measuring cylinder} &= 176 \text{ g} \\ \text{Weight of empty measuring cylinder} &= \underline{50 \text{ g}} \\ \text{Weight of 100 cm}^3 \text{ of glycerine} &= \underline{126 \text{ g}} \end{aligned}$$

$$\text{Density of glycerine} = \frac{\text{Weight}}{\text{Volume}} = \frac{126 \text{ g}}{100 \text{ cm}^3} = 1\cdot26 \text{ grammes per cm}^3.$$

SPECIFIC GRAVITY

Specific gravity or S.G. is the weight of a known volume of substance divided by the weight of the same volume of water.

$$\text{Specific gravity} = \frac{\text{Weight of substance}}{\text{Weight of equal volume of water}}$$

Specific gravity can also mean the number of times a substance is heavier or lighter than water. Therefore, if the specific gravity of lead is 11 it means it is eleven times heavier than an equal volume of water.

The *hydrometer* is the instrument (Figure 1.3) used to find the specific gravity of a liquid. It consists of a weighted bulb and stem marked with the specific gravity scale. The hydrometer is allowed to float in the liquid, and the depth to which it sinks indicates the specific gravity on the stem scale.

Figure 1.3.
A hydrometer

APPLICATIONS OF SPECIFIC GRAVITY IN HAIRDRESSING

1. The specific gravity of the strongest ammonia solution that one can obtain, namely 35 per cent, is 0·880. The term 'eight-eighty ammonia' is thus used by the chemist to describe the strongest ammonia.

SPECIFIC GRAVITIES OF AMMONIA SOLUTIONS

S.G.	% Ammonia
0·880	35
0·900	28·5
0·950	12·5
1·000	0·0

Note: As the specific gravity increases to 1·0 the percentage strength of ammonia decreases until only water (S.G. 1·0) remains. Ammonia is used in preparing various hairdressing lotions.

2. Specific gravity is used to describe the state of *battery acid* used in car batteries.
3. Methylated spirit or ethyl alcohol, used in cosmetic and friction

lotions, is sold at different strengths determined by specific gravity hydrometers.

4. In certain *recipes for hairdressing preparations* the weight of a liquid ingredient is given. Since it is preferable to measure the volume of liquids it is an advantage to calculate the volume of liquid from a given weight and S.G.

$$\text{Volume} = \frac{\text{Weight}}{\text{Specific gravity}}$$

Example

A recipe suggests 100 g of methylated spirit of S.G. 0·8. Calculate its volume.

$$\text{Since volume} = \frac{\text{Weight}}{\text{Specific gravity}}$$

$$\text{volume} = \frac{100 \text{ g}}{0·8} = 125 \text{ cm}^3$$

Conversion from weight to volume calculations

Most recipes and formulae list the ingredients of the preparation together with their respective amounts as parts of 100 or 1,000. It is therefore necessary to calculate the conversion weight to volume from the recipe as follows:

1. Hair lotion preparation:

0·880 ammonia solution	25
Methylated spirit	700
Tincture of quillaia	275
	1,000

All are *liquids*, and their volumes can therefore be measured in cm³ directly without conversion.

2. Talcum powder preparation:

Talc	840
Chalk	70
Boric acid	45
Magnesia	45
	1,000

All ingredients in this recipe are *solids*, and each is therefore weighed directly.

3. (*a*) Skin lotion—wet and dry ingredients:

Ingredient	Amount	Physical state	Conversion
Calamine	150	Solid	150 g
Zinc oxide	50	Solid	50 g
Glycerine (S.G. 1·26)	50	Liquid	$\dfrac{50}{1·26} = 40$ cm³
Water (S.G. 1·0)	750	Liquid	$\dfrac{750}{1·0} = 750$ cm³

In this recipe the *solid* ingredients are *weighed*, and therefore their amounts in the recipe converted to grammes (g).

The liquid ingredients are always *measured by volume*. Therefore it is necessary to convert the recipe amount to cubic centimetres (cm³).

(*b*) Hair preparation—wet and dry ingredients:

Ingredient	Amount	Physical state	Conversion
White wax	3	Solid	3 g
White oil (S.G. 0·85)	85	Liquid	$\dfrac{85}{0·85} = 100$ cm³
Borax	1	Solid	1 g
Water	11	Liquid	$\dfrac{11}{1·0} = 11$ cm³

★ ★ ★

SUGGESTIONS FOR PRACTICAL WORK

1. Determine the capacity in cm³ of various containers that you use in the salon. Fill the container with water and pour off the water into a measuring cylinder, then read the volume of water in the measuring cylinder. Tabulate your results.
2. Determine the density of the following liquids, using the method described in the experiment: (*a*) liquid paraffin; (*b*) methylated spirit; (*c*) castor oil; (*d*) carbon tetrachloride (used for cleaning wigs).
3. By means of a hydrometer provided by your instructor determine the specific gravities of the liquids listed in question (2).

QUESTIONS ON CHAPTER 1

1. Draw and describe the type of measuring instrument you would use to measure the following amounts of substances: (*a*) 100 cm³ of water —accurately; (*b*) 36·5 cm³ of methylated spirit; (*c*) 250 cm³ approximately of glycerine.

2. The following is a recipe for a lotion:

Sugar   25
Water   75
Glycerine (S.G. 1·25)   25

Describe (a) the physical state of each ingredient; (b) the instrument you would use to measure each ingredient; (c) how you would calculate the correct weight or volume of each ingredient.
3. Explain the following terms, giving definitions wherever possible: (a) science, (b) density, (c) matter, (d) specific gravity, (e) molecules, (f) gramme, (g) litre.
4. One ingredient in a hair lotion is described as 'ammonia solution 0·880' followed by the amount 10 g. Explain the figure 0·880. Calculate the volume of the ammonia solution in the question.
5. The recipe for lotion X is:

Olive oil (S.G. 0·9)   30 g
Water   60 g
Alcohol (S.G. 0·85)   25 g
Lard   10 g
Glycerine (S.G. 1·25)   30 g
Common salt   36 g

Calculate the volume of each of the liquid ingredients from the weights and specific gravities given. Describe the measuring instrument you would use to measure these liquids.
6. Draw and describe the main use of: (a) a hydrometer; (b) a graduated flask; (c) a pipette.
7. Briefly describe an experiment to find the density of liquid paraffin.

2 PRESSURE IN FLUIDS

Fluids are substances that can *flow*, for example, water and air. The term 'fluid' is used to describe liquids and gases.

Pressure is something that we have all experienced at some time, e.g.,

(a) we notice water pressure when we try to hold back the water from an open tap;
(b) solid pressure is experienced when someone stands on your toes;
(c) gas pressure is felt when holding the blowing end of a vacuum-cleaner tube.

PRESSURE EXERTED BY SOLIDS

Imagine three people of similar weight who are wearing different kinds of shoes walking across wet sand: person *A* wears shoes with 6-inch stiletto heels, *B* wears broad-soled and heeled walking shoes, while *C* wears large boards strapped to his shoes.

Each person's shoes will make impressions in the wet sand similar

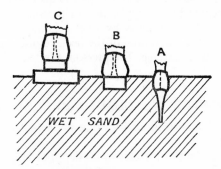

Figure 2.1. Shoe impressions in wet sand to show the relation
between weight and surface area of the shoes

to those shown in Figure 2.1. It will be seen that *A* sinks deeply into the sand because her weight is supported on the very small surface area of her shoes. *B* sinks into the sand to a lesser extent, because the surface area of the soles and heels of his shoes is greater. *C* sinks very little because of the large surface area of the boards tied to his shoes.

11

Conclusion:

The pressure exerted by the human body on the feet depends on the weight of the body and the area of the feet. The *greater* the surface area of the feet the *less* will be the pressure upon them.

Units of Measurement of Pressure

Pressure is equal to weight divided by area, or, weight per unit area:

$$\text{Pressure} = \frac{\text{Weight}}{\text{Area}}$$

For example, pressure = Pounds weight divided by area in square inches

Or pressure is measured in pounds per square inch (lb/in.^{2}). These are the most common units used in Britain for expressing pressures of solids, liquids, and gases.

APPLICATIONS

1. Tired feet are caused by long periods of standing in shoes that are a poor fit. To overcome this, shoes should be of sufficient surface area to accommodate the weight of the body. Also, the heels should be low.

2. During scalp massage the weight of the operator's body exerts pressure on the scalp by way of the operator's finger-tips.

3. Digital pressure or finger pressure is used to stop bleeding, as when rendering first aid. The tourniquet is also used as a means of controlling bleeding by the application of pressure.

4. Damage to floor surfaces by stiletto heels is due to the body weight acting on the small area of the heel, resulting in considerable pressure on the floor surface. The pressure exerted is between 80 and 140 lb/in.^{2}.

WATER OR LIQUID PRESSURE

The following demonstrations illustrate important characteristics of water pressure.

1. The pressure of water increases with depth or height, as illustrated in Figure 2.2.

2. Water 'finds its own level' (Figure 2.3). This apparatus shows that when the rubber tube is lowered a water fountain at high pressure is obtained. When the open end of the rubber tube is at the same level as the water in the tank the water ceases to flow, since the water has now 'found its own level'.

Head of water means the vertical distance between the level of water in the tank and the level at the open end of the rubber tube. This term is used by water engineers and is a means of indicating water pressure (in feet).

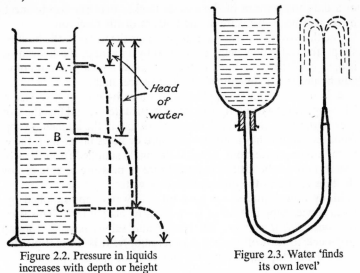

Figure 2.2. Pressure in liquids increases with depth or height

Figure 2.3. Water 'finds its own level'

APPLICATIONS OF WATER PRESSURE

1. *The hairdressing salon water supply* (Figure 2.4)

Many parts of the country receive water from mountain reservoirs which are situated at a much higher level than the town or village they

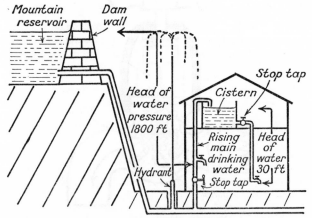

Figure 2.4. Domestic water supply

supply. Therefore, the water will flow from a high level to a low level. If the vertical distance between the level of water in the reservoir and level of water in the house tap is great, the water pressure or head of water will be high and the water can be driven through the main pipe by this pressure to all parts of a town or village. In the construction of a dam the bottom of the dam is thicker than the top to meet the increasing water pressure at the bottom of the reservoir.

The thick-walled main water pipe brings the water to the houses and shops, the water flow being controlled by a *hydrant*. If a hydrant valve is open or if there is a burst in the main pipe, a great fountain of water will be produced sometimes twenty-two feet high.

A house or salon is supplied with water by way of a service pipe. This supplies the drinking-water tap in the kitchen and fills the storage tank in the attic. Since the drinking-water tap in the kitchen is supplied from the main it has a greater pressure or flows faster than the cold-water tap in a bathroom, which is normally supplied from the storage cistern tank in the attic. This difference in pressure or rate of flow at the taps is due to the different head of water.

Many houses and shops have all cold-water taps supplied by the main service pipe instead of from the attic cistern tank. This is called the '*intermittent system*'. All houses and salons have a stop-tap or stop-cock to turn off the main water supply. It is normal practice to turn off the stop-tap if a pipe bursts or a tap needs repairing.

2. *Water tap or 'bib' tap*

Before examining any tap see that the water is turned off at the main tap. The movable part of a bib tap (Figure 2.5) is called the '*jumper*'.

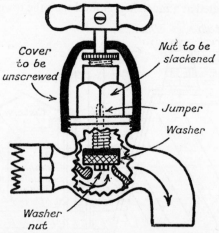

Cover to be unscrewed

Nut to be slackened

Jumper

Washer

Washer nut

Figure 2.5. Water tap showing the 'jumper' and 'washer'

This controls the water flow and is supported by the '*washer*'. In a cold-water tap the washer is made of leather, but in a hot-water tap the washer is of composition fibre and is red or black in colour.

3. *Water supply in flat districts*

Water is pumped by mechanical means to the top of a large water tower which provides the necessary head of water to supply surrounding towns and villages.

AIR PRESSURE

The earth is surrounded by a layer of air or atmosphere that is approximately 500 miles high. This layer of air has *weight* and is continually pressing on the earth's surface, resulting in *air pressure* or *atmospheric pressure* (Figure 2.6).

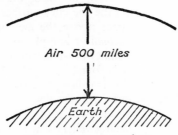

Figure 2.6. The atmosphere

Experiments

To illustrate air pressure:

1. Fill a glass tumbler to the brim with water and cover the top with a sheet of paper. Press the paper with the palm of the hand, making sure that no air-bubbles remain. Carefully turn the tumbler upside down (Figure 2.7). The water does not fall out of the glass because the air pressure is acting on the paper; its pressure is greater than the water pressure.

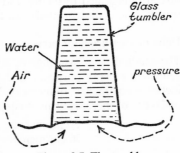

Figure 2.7. The tumbler experiment

2. *Crushing can.* A tin can containing a small amount of water is heated; this produces steam that drives out the air from the can. A rubber stopper is used to close the can, the source of heat being withdrawn. When the can is allowed to cool the steam condenses, leaving an empty space or vacuum within the can. The greater air pressure outside causes the can to be crushed.

MEASUREMENT OF AIR PRESSURE

The instruments used to measure atmospheric pressure are called *barometers*.

1. *Simple mercury barometer*

Take a thick-walled glass tube, about three feet long, and fill it carefully with liquid mercury. Placing the index finger over the open end of the tube, invert the tube in a dish of mercury (Figure 2.8).

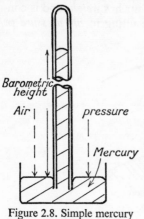

It is seen that the mercury is kept up to a certain height by the air pressure acting on the mercury surface in the dish. The space above the mercury in the tube is a *vacuum* or completely empty space. If the height of mercury in the tube is measured, it is found to be about 30 in. or 76 cm; this is called the barometric *height*. (Mercury will discolour and corrode gold and silver jewellery. It is advisable not to wear such jewellery when handling mercury.)

Figure 2.8. Simple mercury barometer

2. *The aneroid barometer*

This is the type of barometer used in houses and shops. The barometer consists of a small metal box from which some air has been removed. When the air pressure is high it will tend to crush the box. Similarly when the air pressure is low the box will expand. The movements of the metal box are magnified by chains and levers which operate a pointer that travels over a dial printed with the words 'stormy', 'wet', and 'dry'.

Units of measuring air pressure

The method of measuring the length of a mercury column is convenient for many purposes; the pressure is thus measured either in inches or centimetres of mercury. Normal air pressure is equal to 30 in. or 76 cm of mercury; this is equal to *one atmosphere*:

$$30 \text{ in. mercury} = 1 \text{ atmosphere}$$
$$76 \text{ cm mercury} = 1 \text{ atmosphere}$$

It is important to know that the average air pressure is approximately fourteen and a half pounds per square inch:

$$\text{Average air pressure} = 14\tfrac{1}{2} \text{ lb/in.}^2$$

Imagine a column of air 500 miles high one square inch in area. This would weigh $14\tfrac{1}{2}$ lb.

Air pressure and the human body

As already stated, the air pressure is $14\frac{1}{2}$ lb/in.[2]; therefore this pressure acts on every square inch of the human body. The total pressure acting on the human body is between *5 tons* for young children and *16 tons* for adults. This, of course, depends on the total surface area of a person. The human body can withstand this great atmospheric pressure because comparable pressures are exerted within it.

Altitude. As an aeroplane ascends the air pressure becomes less. The effect of this on the human body is to cause bleeding at the nose and ears, and temporary deafness may be experienced. This high-altitude effect is overcome by equipping aeroplanes with *pressurized* cabins in which a pressure similar to that at ground level is maintained.

Changes in altitude may be detected during a car drive by the sensation experienced in the ears. This may be overcome by yawning.

The weather and its changing moods depend on the atmospheric pressure. When it is fine and dry the atmospheric pressure is *high*. As the weather worsens the atmospheric pressure becomes *low*. Meteorological stations record the air pressure in order to forecast the weather. The continuous-recording barograph is a useful instrument for providing a continuous record of air-pressure changes.

AEROSOL SPRAYS

(See also page 209)

Aerosol sprays are used for many purposes, which include hair lacquer, perfume, and deodorant sprays. The aerosol dispensers contain extremely volatile liquids called *propellants*. These readily change into gases, which create a gas pressure inside the dispenser that is far

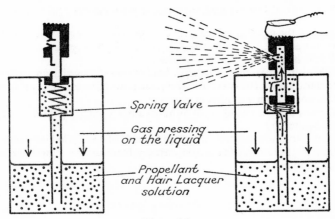

Spring Valve

Gas pressing on the liquid

Propellant and Hair Lacquer solution

Figure 2.9.

c

greater than the air pressure outside. The pressure of the gaseous propellant, above the liquid to be sprayed, is responsible for driving the
liquid out of the container when the spring valve is pressed down
(Figure 2.9). Aerosol spray dispensers should be kept in a cool place
as extreme heat will cause the container to explode.

★ ★ ★

SUGGESTIONS FOR PRACTICAL WORK

1. Find out where the main stop-tap or stop-cock is situated in your college
   or salon.
2. *How to replace a cold-water-tap washer.* A continually dripping tap
   indicates the need for a new washer:
   (*a*) Turn off the main stop-cock or the stop-tap from the attic cistern
   tank.
   (*b*) Unscrew the cover of the tap to expose a nut and slacken this exposed
   nut with a shifting spanner.
   (*c*) Lift out the jumper and slacken and remove the nut at the base of the
   jumper. Refit the washer of the correct size and material.
   (*d*) Reassemble the jumper and tighten on the cover of the tap. It is
   advisable to call in an experienced plumber to replace a hot-water-
   tap washer, for this may involve draining the hot-water storage tank
   and pipes.
3. Investigate the origin of your water supply. Find out what the head of
   water pressure is in the town main supply and to your drinking-water tap.
4. Keep a daily record of (*a*) atmospheric pressure, (*b*) the type of weather
   for a period of four weeks.

QUESTIONS ON CHAPTER 2

1. Explain the meaning of the term *atmospheric pressure*. Explain how it is
   measured. Briefly describe the effect of atmospheric pressure changes on
   (*a*) the human body, (*b*) the weather.
2. What is the meaning of the term *head of water*? Describe an experiment
   to illustrate your answer. Briefly outline how the water supply is brought
   to a house from a mountain reservoir.
3. Explain how you would deal with: (*a*) a burst water pipe; (*b*) a dripping
   cold-water tap.
4. Write short notes on the following: (*a*) head of water; (*b*) blood pressure;
   (*c*) digital pressure; (*d*) simple mercury barometer; (*e*) pressurized aircraft cabins.

3 SURFACE TENSION, CAPILLARITY, AND ELASTICITY

SURFACE TENSION

Surface tension is the force of attraction that exists between solid and liquid surfaces.

Examples illustrating effects of surface tension

1. Water drops will cling to a greasy window-pane.
2. The free surface of a liquid in a glass beaker resembles a skin. The margins of the free liquid surface creep up the sides of a beaker; this is called the *meniscus* of the liquid (Figure 3.1).

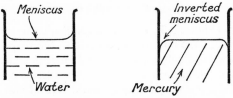

Figure 3.1. Liquid meniscus for water and mercury

3. Take a sewing needle, smear it with 'Vaseline', and place it on a piece of blotting-paper. Gently lower the blotting-paper on to the surface of the water in a bowl. The blotting-paper will sink but the

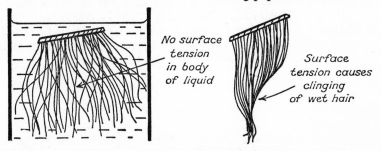

Figure 3.2. Surface tension and wet hair

needle will remain floating on the water surface, supported by surface tension.
4. Dip a postiche of hair into a beaker of water and observe the way the hair spreads itself in the water. This spreading effect is due to the

19

absence of surface tension forces in the body of the water. Remove the hair postiche and observe how the hairs cling together owing to the surface tension of the water film on the hairs (Figure 3.2).

5. Fit a small piece of camphor into the stern of a small celluloid boat and place it on the surface of the water in a large bowl. The small boat dashes over the surface of the water owing to the surface tension between the solid camphor and the water.

6. Attach two pieces of cotton thread to two pieces of stiff wire, as in

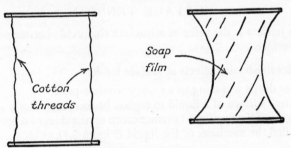

Figure 3.3. Soap-film tension

the diagram (Figure 3.3). Place in a soap solution and observe the tension between the cotton threads due to the soap film.

7. Sprinkle flowers of sulphur on to the surface of water in a beaker. Note how the sulphur powder floats on the surface owing to surface tension. Add a few drops of shampoo detergent and note how the sulphur powder sinks, because the surface tension of the water has now been lowered.

APPLICATIONS OF SURFACE TENSION

1. *Sebum* is a natural greasy secretion from the *sebaceous* glands situated in the hair follicle. This greasy material serves to waterproof the hair and repel the water, thus preventing the hair from becoming soaked. This function was of greater importance to primitive man than his less hairy descendants of today (Figure 3.4).

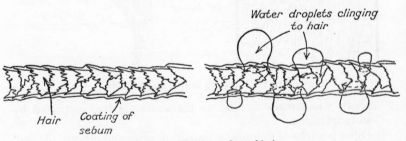

Figure 3.4. Waterproofing of hair

2. *Lanolin* is the natural coating of the wool in sheep and serves primarily as a waterproofing agent. All mammals and birds groom or preen themselves in order to maintain the water-repelling powers of their coats or plumage.
3. Other methods of *waterproofing* materials involve the use of:
    (*a*) Oily materials, such as linseed oil in fishermen's oilskins, or
    (*b*) *Silicones*, chemical compounds derived from sand, used to showerproof rainwear. Silicones repel the water from the fibres.
4. Shampooing or washing of hair involves the removal of the natural greasy coating of the hair and its attendant dirt. The soapless detergent shampoo serves to *lower* the surface tension of the grease and allows the grease to float away as tiny droplets, the dirt particles being suspended in the shampoo foam (see Plates 2 and 26).
5. Sulphonated castor or Turkey red oil is used to protect the permanently waved portions of the hair from further action of permanent-wave lotion. The oil coats the hair and repels the permanent-wave lotion.

CAPILLARITY

Capillarity is the phenomenon of liquids rising in narrow tubes of *hair-like* dimensions [*capilla*—hair (Latin)].

Take a number of glass capillary tubes of different bores and support them in a dish of water coloured with ink. Observe how the water rises to a greater height in the narrowest capillary tubes, and the least rise is in the widest tube (Figure 3.5). This rising of the water by capillarity is due to surface-tension effects. The narrowest tube has a *hair-like* bore.

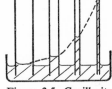

Figure 3.5. Capillarity in glass tubes

APPLICATIONS

1. *Rising damp* in brick walls is due to water rising through the tiny capillary tubes present in the porous bricks. By inserting a

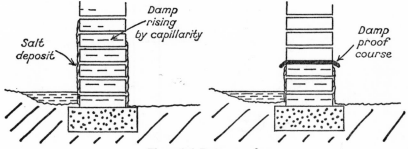

Figure 3.6. Damp-proof course

damp-proof course in the first layer of bricks near to the foundations, the rising damp is prevented. The damp-proof course can be either of sheet lead or waterproofed felt (Figure 3.6).

2. *Towels and blotting-paper* allow liquids to rise by capillary action through the fine spaces between their fibres (Figure 3.7).

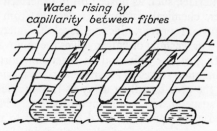

Figure 3.7. Capillary rise in towels

ELASTICITY

Elasticity is the property that enables a substance to change its shape when a force is applied to it and to recover its shape when the stretching force is removed, provided that the elastic limit has not been exceeded.

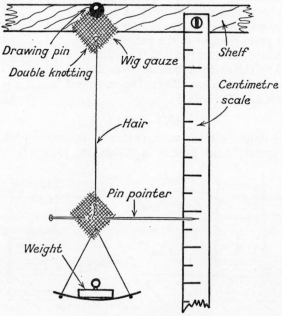

Figure 3.8. Elasticity of hair

Hair is a natural elastic fibre and its elastic property is of importance to hairdressers.

Experiment

To measure the elasticity and breaking force of hair:

Obtain a human hair, at least 6 in. long, and tie each end to a small piece of wig gauze using a double knot. Attach a light metal weight-pan to one piece of wig gauze together with a pin to act as a pointer. Firmly fix the other piece of wig gauze to a wooden shelf by means of a drawing-pin. Arrange a metre rule parallel with the supported hair strand as in Figure 3.8.

1. Carefully measure the length of the supported hair.
2. Add $\frac{1}{4}$-oz weights to the pan, allowing the hair to stretch fully before adding more weights. An interval of three to five minutes should be allowed before adding further weights.
3. Continue to add weights, noting the extension of the hair.
4. When the hair snaps, note the weight that was required to break it.
5. Repeat the experiment several times with other hair samples.

Results:

Experiment	Original length of hair (A)	Length at breaking-point (B)	Elasticity $= \dfrac{B - A}{A}$	Breaking force
	cm	cm		oz
1	22	29	$\dfrac{29 - 22}{22} = \dfrac{1}{3}$ approx.	$2\frac{1}{4}$
2	18	22	$\dfrac{22 - 18}{18} = \dfrac{1}{4}$ approx.	3
3	27	32	$\dfrac{32 - 27}{27} = \dfrac{1}{5}$ approx.	4

Conclusion:

The elasticity or stretching power of hair is between one-fifth and one-third of its original length. The force required to break hair is between 2 and 4 oz.

The elastic limit of hair can be determined by adding and removing weights and noting whether the hair regains its original length on removal of the stretching force. When the hair does not recover its original length the weight required for this over-stretching is noted.

The weight required to exceed the elastic limit of hair, or to cause over-stretching, is between 1 and 2 oz. Care should therefore be taken when winding hair on to rollers in order to prevent over-stretching the hair by exceeding its elastic limit.

Factors affecting the elasticity of hair and its application to hairdressing practice

1. *Wet* hair is more elastic than *dry* hair. This is an important factor in making a temporary wave or water wave. Steaming the hair increases its elasticity considerably.
2. *Heat* increases the elasticity of hair. This is the main factor that governs hot iron or marcel waving.
3. *Chemical substances* such as ammonium hydroxide, amines, sodium sulphide, sodium sulphite, and ammonium thioglycollate change the chemical composition of hair and increase its elasticity. These substances are important ingredients of waving lotions.
4. The physiological condition or health of a person is an important factor affecting the elasticity of hair.

Plate 5 illustrates the apparatus used for accurately measuring the strength, toughness, and elasticity of hair and other fibres.

★ ★ ★

QUESTIONS ON CHAPTER 3

1. What is meant by surface tension? Give at least two examples of surface-tension effects. How does sebum waterproof the hair? What happens to the natural grease of hair during shampooing?
2. Explain the term *capillarity*. Describe how rising damp is caused in a brick wall, and show how it can be remedied. By what process does a towel dry wet skin and hair?
3. Why is hair called an elastic substance? Describe an experiment to determine the stretching power and weight required to break hair.
4. Why is a knowledge of the elasticity of hair important in hairdressing practice?
5. 'Hair should be washed once every three weeks using a mild shampoo and should not receive any greasy dressing but should be lightly brushed.' Give a brief account (*a*) in support, and (*b*) against this statement.
6. Explain the following: (*a*) A sheep-dog's coat should not be shampooed. (*b*) A seagull that has become fouled with tar and oil and has been washed with a soapless detergent cannot float.

4 HEAT AND TEMPERATURE

Heat is a form of *energy*. The heat from a coal fire can be employed to drive a steam engine, which in turn can do work by drawing railway carriages.

Energy is the capacity for *doing work*. This definition applies equally to the energy required by the human body in order to do work.

Energy is of two main kinds:

(*a*) *Potential* or stored energy, e.g. steam contained in a boiler, or energy stored in food.

(*b*) *Kinetic* energy or active energy in motion. For example, steam released from a boiler that sets an engine in motion, or energy released from food during exercise and resulting in movement of body muscles.

The main forms of energy are shown in the following table:

Form of energy	Uses
Heat energy	Drives engines, resulting in movement of cars, etc. Also used to make electricity and coal gas.
Electrical energy	Gives heat, light, and power to drive motors and electrical appliances.
Atomic energy	Gives heat for electricity generation. Medical purposes.
Light energy, mainly from the sun	Used by all green plants for making food for themselves and animals that depend on them.
Chemical energy	From burning coal, coal gas, and petroleum; used to provide electrical, mechanical, and light energy.
The sun's energy is the primary source of energy for the earth	Gives energy to all living plants; their remains form coal and petroleum which are the main sources of energy used in everyday life.

METHODS OF PRODUCING HEAT

1. *MECHANICAL METHOD*

Friction produces heat when two rough solid surfaces are rubbed together. This is the method employed to produce local surface heat during scalp massage. Manual massage involves the use of the finger-tips rubbed into the scalp. The electrical vibrating massage appliance can be used instead of the manual method. The frictional heat produced serves to stimulate the blood circulation to the scalp and improve the nutrition of the hair.

Frictional heat is produced by the action of brake blocks on wheels. It is required to ignite matches.

Friction opposes motion between solid surfaces, but it can be reduced by the use of *lubrication*. The most effective lubricants are oils such as liquid paraffin and almond oil. These are the main ingredients of muscle oils or massage oil and serve to prevent friction between the masseur's fingers and the patient's skin.

Friction lotions used for scalp massage contain as their main active ingredient industrial spirit, which serves to a slight extent as a lubricant, its main action being due to its cooling effect.

2. *CHEMICAL METHOD*

Many chemical changes give out heat and are called *exothermic* changes.

Coal, paraffin, and coal gas and other fuels all produce heat by burning or *combustion*. This heat is used for producing light and power, and for heating purposes.

Food is the fuel for the human body. It releases its energy during the process of respiration.

Permanent-waving chemical pads produce heat by exothermal chemical action when moistened with a suitable chemical reagent.

3. *ELECTRICAL METHOD*

This is the method mainly used in hairdressing establishments for the production of heat. Various electrical appliances are used.

4. *ATOMIC ENERGY*

This is mainly in the form of heat and harmful rays—obtained by the natural breakdown or *fission* of radioactive material such as uranium which is used as fuel in the atomic power station.

EFFECT OF HEAT ON SOLIDS

1. Solids *expand* on heating and *contract* on cooling. This can be shown using the brass bar and gauge experiment. Before heating the bar fits easily into the gauge. After heating the bar increases in size and no longer fits the gauge.

2. *Invar* metal alloy does not expand on heating. If a *bimetal* strip, made of strips of brass and invar joined together, is heated, it curves owing to unequal expansion of the two metals, the brass expanding more than the invar (Figure 4.1).

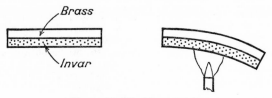

Figure 4.1. The bimetal strip

APPLICATIONS OF EXPANSION OF SOLIDS

1. *Fire alarm.* A bimetal strip is connected to a battery and electric bell as in Figure 4.2. A candle is allowed to burn beneath the

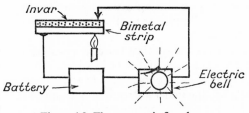

Figure 4.2. The automatic fire-alarm

bimetal strip, causing it to bend and touch the metal contact, and this results in the ringing of the bell. This type of automatic fire alarm is fitted to most business premises.

2. *A thermostat* is a device used to keep temperatures steady. The main part of any thermostat is the bimetal strip (brass/invar). The following experiment serves to illustrate the action of a thermostat (Figure 4.3):

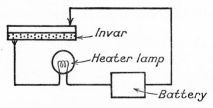

Figure 4.3. Thermostat experiment

A 12-volt lamp is connected to a suitable battery and the bimetal strip made to touch the contact point. The heat produced by the lamp causes the bimetal strip to bend and the lamp is switched off. The cooling of the bimetal strip causes the lamp to switch on again. Some uses of thermostats are shown in the following table:

Thermostat	Use
Room thermostat	Controls room temperature and prevents overheating. Prevents waste of coal gas or electricity.
Water-heater thermostat	Serves to switch off the coal gas or electricity when water is hot and switch on the heater when the water cools.
Automatic thermostatic valve	This is fitted in the water system leading to the water hair-spray. It controls the water temperature and prevents sudden surges of scalding hot water.
Appliance thermostats in hair-dryers, steamers, hot-perm machines, drying cabinets, disinfecting cabinets, kettles, and irons	All appliances that produce heat are controlled by fitted thermostats, which serve to prevent overheating and subsequent burning-out of the heating unit.

3. Some general applications of expansion are found in the gaps left between rails in railway lines to allow for expansion and prevent the lines being buckled.

Telegraph wires and overhead electricity cables are slack in summer owing to expansion and tight in winter owing to contraction.

Tight-fitting caps or stoppers on jars and bottles can be eased off by alternate heating under a stream of hot water to expand the cap, followed by contraction under a stream of cold water. This method cannot be used for containers with volatile contents such as spirit and similar liquids.

EFFECT OF HEAT ON FLUIDS

Expansion of liquids on heating can be demonstrated using the apparatus shown in Figure 4.4. The liquids used are paraffin, methylated spirit, and water coloured with ink. When the water-bath is heated the levels of the different liquids in the tubes are seen to rise.

Different liquids expand by *different amounts* for the same rise in temperature.

Expansion of air can be demonstrated with the apparatus shown in Figure 4.5. When the flask is gently heated bubbles of expanding air issue from the glass tube. On cooling, the contracting air draws in water to replace the air expelled by expansion.

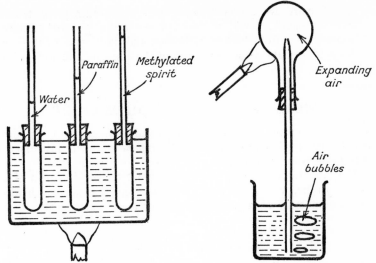

Figure 4.4. Expansion of liquids   Figure 4.5. Expansion of air

APPLICATIONS OF EXPANSION OF FLUIDS

1. Hot water will float on cold because water increases in volume on heating, therefore, its density $\left(\dfrac{\text{weight}}{\text{volume}}\right)$ becomes less than 1g/cm^3.
   This is noticed when cold water has been run into a hot bath and the person entering the bath feels the cold-water layer beneath the hot-water layer.
2. Hot air expands on heating and will therefore rise. Its density is less than cold air. This explains the movement of air *currents*.
3. Water on cooling contracts but between 4°C and 0°C it *expands*, causing, for example, bursts in pipes. This can be shown by partly filling a test-tube with water and marking its level, then placing it in a freezing-mixture of salt and ice. Remove it from the freezing-mixture and note the new level of the frozen water (Figure 4.6).

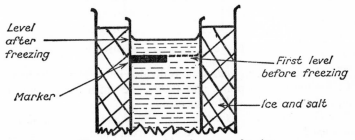

Figure 4.6. Expansion of water on freezing

4. Liquid hairdressing preparations, such as hydrogen peroxide and
0·880 ammonia, should be stored in *cool dark* cupboards or store-
rooms, away from boilers, radiators, and direct rays of the sun.
Such heat could cause expansion of the contents and subsequent
bursting.

MEASUREMENT OF TEMPERATURE

Temperature means the relative hotness and coldness of a body compared to melting ice or boiling water. *Thermometers* are the instruments
used to measure temperature.

The laboratory mercury-in-glass thermometer consists of a glass
capillary tube, with a *bulb* and graduated *stem*. The stem is divided
into a number of *degrees* according to the thermometer scale.

TEMPERATURE SCALES

Thermometer scales have two *fixed points*, namely the *lower fixed point*,
or temperature of melting ice, and the *upper fixed point*, or temperature
of boiling water (Figure 4.7).

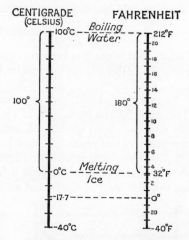

Figure 4.7. Temperature scales

The Celsius or *Centigrade* scale is divided into 100 degrees between
0°C, the lower fixed point, and 100°C, the upper fixed point. This
temperature scale is used by scientists.

The *Fahrenheit* scale is divided into 180 degrees between 32°F, the
lower fixed point, and 212°F, the upper fixed point. This temperature
scale is used mainly by doctors, nurses, engineers, and hairdressers.

CONVERSION OF FAHRENHEIT AND
CELSIUS TEMPERATURES

Although the Fahrenheit scale is used to indicate the temperature of many hairdressing processes, Celsius (Centigrade) temperatures may be quoted in process instructions. It is therefore useful to be able to convert from one scale to another to suit the thermometer in your possession.

(a) Conversion from the Fahrenheit to the Celsius scale:

Subtract 32 and multiply the answer by $\frac{5}{9}$

Example: What is 59°F on the Celsius scale?

$$59 - 32 = 27 \times \tfrac{5}{9} = 15°C$$

(b) Conversion from Celsius to Fahrenheit:

Multiply by $\frac{9}{5}$ and *add* 32 to the answer.

Example: What is 45°C on the Fahrenheit scale?

$$45 \times \tfrac{9}{5} = 81$$
$$81 + 32 = 113°F$$

TYPES OF THERMOMETERS

1. **The laboratory thermometer.** This is a mercury-in-glass thermometer of considerable accuracy graduated with the Celsius or Fahrenheit scale. This type of thermometer is used for accurate work by chemists and physicists.

2. **Room or wall thermometer.** This is either a mercury or coloured spirit-in-glass thermometer mounted on a wooden scale. Rooms should be kept at 60° to 65°F for comfortable warmth. This temperature can be maintained by the room thermostat mentioned earlier.

3. **Bimetal thermometers** are fitted with a bimetal coil whose movements are indicated by a pointer travelling over a thermometer scale. These thermometers are used to indicate the temperatures of the heating bars of wireless-waving machines. They usually read from 50°F to 300°F.

   Desk thermometers and continuous recording thermographs are also fitted with a bimetal coil mechanism.

4. **Bath thermometers** are useful for measuring temperature of either

bath or hair-washing water. The most suitable working temperatures are indicated on the thermometer as follows:

Hot	110°F
Warm	100°F
Tepid	90°F
Temperate	80°F
Cool	70°F
Cold	50°F

5. **The clinical thermometer** is a mercury-in-glass thermometer with a
range of about 95°F to 110°F, the normal body temperature being
98·4°F as shown in Figure 4.8. An important feature is the *constriction* in the capillary tube which breaks the mercury thread when
the thermometer is removed from a patient, allowing a reading to
be made at leisure. The mercury can be returned to the bulb by a
sharp shake.

A clinical thermometer should be rinsed in cold water or disinfected, and should never be immersed in hot water.

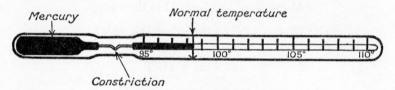

Figure 4.8. Clinical thermometer

6. **The maximum and minimum thermometer** is used mainly for recording the highest (maximum) and lowest (minimum) temperatures
experienced during a period (Plate 3). It is used mainly by meteoro-
logists for weather forecasting purposes. The temperatures are
recorded by small iron indicators that can be reset by means of a
magnet.

IMPORTANT TEMPERATURES

	Fahrenheit	*Celsius*
Freezing	32°F	0°C
Cold water	50°F	10°C
Cool water	70°F	21°C
Room temperature	60°–65°F	15°–18°C
Temperate water	80°F	27°C
Tepid water	90°F	32°C
Body temperature	98·4°F	36·9°C
Warm water	100°F	38°C
Hot water	110°F	43°C
Cool heat—hair-dryer	100°F	38°C
Medium heat—hair-dryer	120°F	49°C
Hot heat—hair-dryer	140°F	60°C

In gases or vapours the molecules are widely separated, except at moments of elastic collision. There is little or no attraction between them and they have great mobility

In liquids or solutions the molecules are in constant motion. There are cohesive forces between them which affect their motions, but only in special cases, for specific solutions, are the forces strong enough to produce crystalline arrangements in the liquid

In solids strong forces operate between the molecules and they are held in predetermined regular patterns

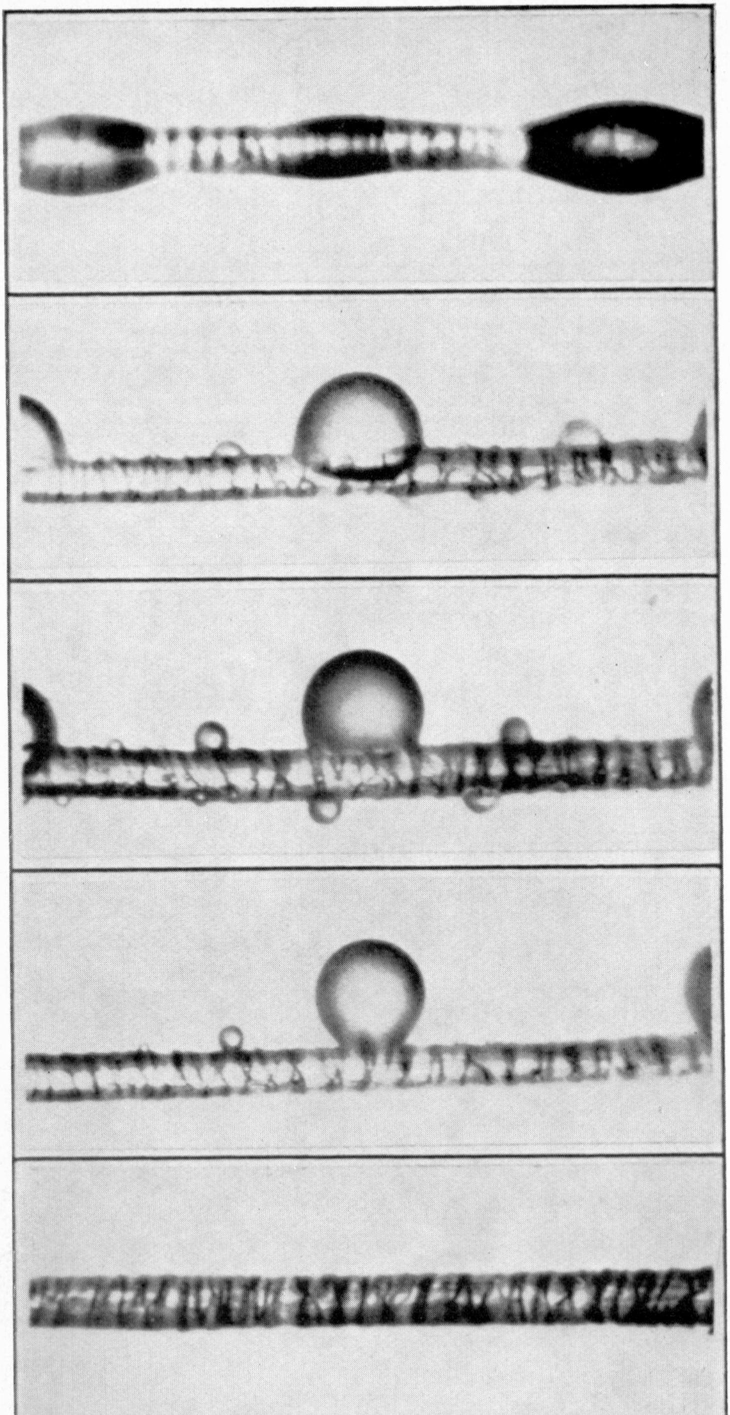

2. Detergent action on grease

MEASUREMENT OF HEAT

Heat is measured in units called *calories* or British Thermal Units (Btu).

The *calorie* is the quantity of heat required to raise the temperature of one gramme of water by one degree Celsius. This unit is used by scientists.

The *British Thermal Unit* is the quantity of heat required to raise the temperature of one pound weight of water by one degree Fahrenheit. This unit is used by engineers.

The *therm* is the unit used by gas companies and is equal to 100,000 Btu.

Heat and the heating value of fuels are measured by means of a *calorimeter*.

Gas bills

The amount of gas used by a consumer is measured in cubic feet by means of a *gas meter*. (The method of reading a gas meter is the same as for the electric meter and will be explained in Chapter 8.)

The number of *therms* used, as shown on the gas bill, may be calculated if the number of British Thermal Units of heat produced by burning one cubic foot of coal gas is known. This is between 450 and 500 Btu. One therm of gas costs 2*s*. 7*d*. approximately (1964).

Cost of operating a gas appliance

Cost of operating a gas appliance =

$$\frac{\text{Cubic feet of gas used} \times \text{Calorific value} \times \text{Rate per therm}}{100,000}$$

★ ★ ★

SUGGESTIONS FOR PRACTICAL WORK

Using the equipment supplied by your instructor set up and perform the experiments outlined in this chapter.

1. Obtain a chemical permanent-waving sachet or pad and place it in a small beaker (100 cm³). Moisten the pad with the appropriate reagent and determine the maximum temperature that the pad produces, using a laboratory thermometer (0°–250°C) to record the temperature rise.
2. Using both a Celsius and a Fahrenheit thermometer determine the temperatures of the following: a room, a cup of hot tea, cold water from the tap, the hottest water from the tap, the temperature of the air out of doors, the temperature of the hair-dryer at various heat settings.
3. Find out what your temperature is, using a clinical thermometer, being careful to reset and clean it after use.

D

4. If your room is fitted with a room thermostat check its efficiency by means of hourly readings of a wall thermometer.
5. Tabulate the number of appliances used in your hairdressing room that are controlled by thermostats.

QUESTIONS ON CHAPTER 4

1. Explain the structure and function of a thermostat. Give examples of the use of thermostats in hairdressing practice.
2. Draw and describe a room thermostat and a clinical thermometer. Explain how they work.
3. Give the approximate Fahrenheit temperatures of the following and convert them to the Celsius scale: (a) body temperature, (b) room temperature, (c) warm water.
4. Convert the following temperatures to the Fahrenheit scale: 60°C, 80°C, 40°C.
5. Explain the meaning of the following terms, giving examples in each case: (a) friction, (b) energy, (c) therm, (d) exothermal, (e) heat, (f) temperature.

5 HOW HEAT TRAVELS

Heat may travel from one point to another by three methods (Figure 5.1):

    (*a*) conduction,
    (*b*) convection, and
    (*c*) radiation.

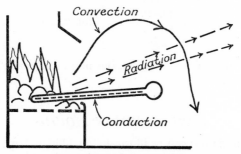

Figure 5.1. How heat travels

Conduction is the method by which heat travels through the handle of a poker.

Convection is the method by which heat rises from the fire, producing the shimmering heat effect.

Radiation is heat travelling as invisible rays straight out of the fire.

CONDUCTION

Conduction is the process of heat passing from molecule to molecule in solids or fluids without the molecules moving bodily. We may compare it to a torch being passed along a row of people until it reaches the end of the row.

When the Marcel waving iron is heated, the heat travels along the iron from molecule to molecule until it reaches the handle.

CONDUCTION IN SOLIDS

Conduction in solids can be demonstrated by using an apparatus consisting of a tank with rods of different materials fitted into the sides.

Small ball-bearings are attached to the ends of the rods by means of 'Vaseline' and the tank is filled with boiling water. The heat is conducted along the rods and melts the 'Vaseline', causing the ball-bearings to fall off.

The order in which the ball-bearings drop is noted; this indicates the relative *conductivities* of the various materials.

Order of conductivity of various substances:

1. Silver ⎫
2. Copper ⎪
3. Aluminium ⎬ Metals
4. Zinc ⎪
5. Brass ⎪
6. Iron ⎭
7. Glass ⎫
8. Plastics ⎪
9. Cloth ⎬ Non-metals
10. Hair ⎭

All metals are good conductors, but non-metal materials are poor conductors of heat.

CONDUCTION IN LIQUIDS

Conduction in liquids can be illustrated by filling a large boiling-tube with cold water and inserting a cube of ice weighted with wire gauze. The *top* of the boiling tube is heated and the water is made to boil while the ice remains unaffected. This shows that water is a poor conductor of heat (Figure 5.2).

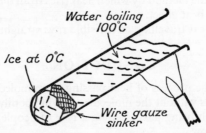

Figure 5.2. Experiment to show that water is a poor conductor of heat

CONDUCTION IN GASES

Conduction in air or gases is difficult to demonstrate by simple methods. Air is a *very bad* conductor of heat, as is shown by the fact that a Bunsen burner flame temperature is 600°C, yet the air temperature 6 in. away from the flame is 25°C. If the air were a good conductor its temperature near to the flame would be much greater.

Experiment

To compare insulation powers of different materials (Figure 5.3):

Fill a number of copper containers with different insulating materials, e.g. sawdust, glass wool, powdered cork, human hair, and commercial samples of insulating material. Fit each container with a thermometer and stopper. Place the containers in the water-bath and gently heat the water. After 30 minutes record the temperatures of each container.

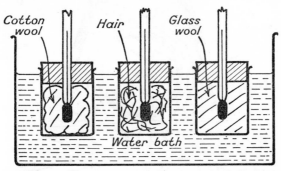

Figure 5.3. Experiment to compare insulation properties

The best insulator will show the *least* rise in temperature; the insulating powers of the other materials will be indicated by their rise in temperature.

APPLICATIONS OF CONDUCTION

1. Handles of teapots, saucepans, and heating appliances are made of poor conductors or insulators of heat, such as wood and plastics.
2. Clothing keeps the body warm by means of the air pockets between the clothing materials. For this reason loose-fitting garments are warmer than tight-fitting garments.
3. Hair is a very *poor conductor* of heat. This is obvious during the process of marcel waving, since the heat does not conduct along the hair shaft and cause scalp burns. The original purpose of human hair was to preserve body warmth by means of the layer of non-conducting air entangled between the interlocking hair. The insulating effect of hair on the head is noticed after a particularly short hair-cut.
4. Thermal caps made of plastic material are used to cover the hair during cold-wave permanent waving in order to keep in the natural

body heat. The hot permanent-waving machine (Plate 4) or wireless-waving machine is an example of the use of conductors and insulators in hairdressing practice. The aluminium heater clips (Figure 5.4) are good conductors of heat. They are heated by conduction from the heater bars of the machine. The hot heater clips are picked up by their non-conducting plastic handles and attached to the hair curl, which is previously covered in aluminium foil that allows the heat to be conducted through it into the hair beneath. The insulating rubber pads protect the scalp from burns.

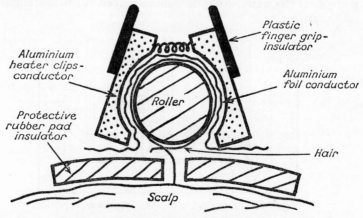

Figure 5.4. Hot permanent-waving clip

5. Buildings and houses can be insulated by laying proprietary insulating materials on the floor of the attic to prevent heat being lost by conduction through the ceiling. The outer walls of modern houses are not solid but are double with an air space between, and are called *cavity walls*. The air space, being a good insulator, serves to prevent heat loss through the walls of the building. Hot- and cold-water pipes and water-storage cylinders in houses and hairdressing establishments should be covered with insulating materials to prevent heat loss.

CONVECTION

Convection is the process in which heat travels by the *movement* of the heated molecules in fluids.

CONVECTION IN LIQUIDS

Convection currents in liquids can be demonstrated by the apparatus shown in Fig. 5.5, which resembles a model hot-water system. The

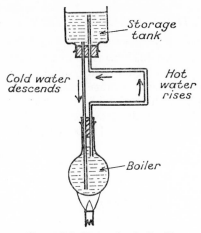

Figure 5.5. Convection in liquids

upper container or cistern is filled with coloured water; the boiler flask and connecting tubes contain cold water. When the boiler flask is heated it is seen that the coloured *cold water descends* to the boiler flask while the *hot water rises* to the upper container.

CONVECTION IN GASES

Convection currents in air can be shown by the glass chimney apparatus (Figure 5.6). A lighted candle is placed beneath one glass chimney

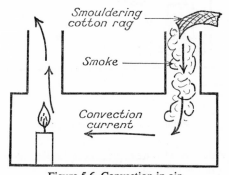

Figure 5.6. Convection in air

and a piece of smouldering rag is held over the other. The smoke is seen to be drawn down with the cold air and rises with the hot air as a continuous convection current.

If the tissue wrapping paper from an orange is placed on a table and lit with a match, it will be seen that the ash remaining will rise in the convection current produced by the burning paper.

APPLICATIONS OF CONVECTION CURRENTS

1. The *low-pressure* hot-water system (Figure 5.7) is usually fitted in most hairdressing establishments and often has an electric immersion heater built into the hot-water cylinder.

Water from the attic storage cistern supplies the hot-water cylinder and pipes. This tank is at a higher level in order to provide the necessary head of water pressure to supply the system.

The immersion heater is fitted into the base of the cylinder so that

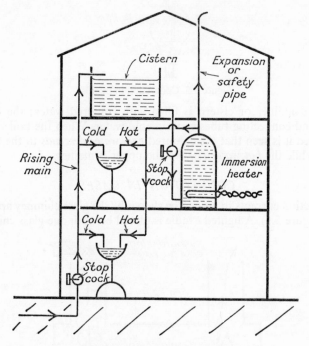

Figure 5.7. The hot-water system

the heated water rises to the top of the cylinder, allowing cold water to be drawn in for heating.

As previously mentioned, it is advisable to cover the storage tank, hot-water cylinder, and main cold-water pipe with insulating material or lagging.

Drinking water is obtained from the main cold-water service pipe, because cold water from the attic storage tank may be contaminated with dust, etc.

The expansion pipe is a safety outlet to allow steam to escape from the system into the attic space or directly through the roof into the air.

2. Convector heaters (Figure 5.8) operate by coal gas, electricity, or oil. The cold air is drawn over the heater unit and the hot air rises by convection out of the appliance.

3. Ventilation of rooms using a heating apparatus depends on the formation of convection currents, illustrated in Figure 5.9. The warm stale air rises and flows out through the top part of the window, while the cool fresh air flows in through the lower part of the window.

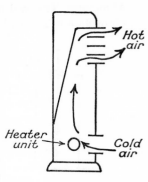

Figure 5.8. Convector heater

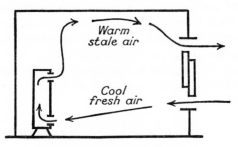

Figure 5.9. Room ventilation

RADIATION

Radiation is the process by which heat travels from one point to another by means of waves or rays that can travel through empty space or a vacuum.

The earth receives its energy from the sun, which radiates electromagnetic waves which travel 92 million miles across empty space towards the earth. Similarly, all hot bodies give out heat rays or *infrared* rays that can travel through a vacuum. The heat of a coal fire reaches us by radiation; this can be experienced by holding out the hands towards the fire.

Experiments

To demonstrate radiation and its relationship to surface texture:

1. Obtain two clean tins of identical size, polish the surface of one and paint the other tin black. Fill the tins with cold water and arrange them at equal distance from an electric radiant heater (Figure 5.10).

Observe the rise in temperature of the water in each tin after 45 minutes. This will indicate which tin has gained most heat by absorption of radiated heat.

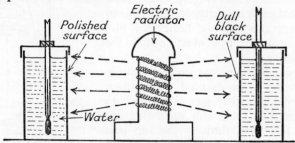

Figure 5.10. Radiation experiment

2. Fill a polished and a black tin with boiling water and fit each tin with a lid and thermometer. Take the temperature readings of each tin and allow them to cool for one hour, then take further temperature readings to determine which tin has lost most heat by radiation.

It is seen from these two experiments that:

(1) A dull black surface is a good radiator and absorber of heat.

(2) A polished surface is a poor absorber of heat but a good reflector of heat.

APPLICATIONS OF RADIATION

1. Radiant heaters operate by electricity, oil, and coal gas. The radiated heat from the heating unit is reflected from a highly polished reflector. In addition some of the heat leaves the heater by convection as shown in Figure 5.11.

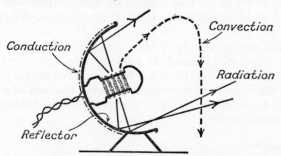

Figure 5.11. Heat loss from electric fire

2. Infra-red heaters have an electrical heating element covered with a glass-like silica sleeve. When the heating unit is red-hot it gives out heat rays or infra-red rays that are produced from all hot bodies.

3. Radiators can be water- or oil-filled and thermostatically controlled. They give out 80 per cent of the heat by convection and therefore are incorrectly described as radiators. The best surface for radiator heaters is a dull black enamel to provide maximum radiant heat.
4. The polished metal surface of the heating rods of the wireless hot permanent-waving machine should be kept bright to prevent heat loss by radiation, since this appliance heats the clips by conduction.
5. Radiant heat or infra-red treatment is used to direct localized warmth on to any part of the body surface. The heat induces the blood to flow to the skin surface and thereby improves circulation. It is used in the treatment of rheumatism and for relieving pain (see Chapter 11).

★ ★ ★

SUGGESTIONS FOR PRACTICAL WORK

1. Determine the insulating power of hair and wool using the method described in this chapter.
2. An alternative method for comparing insulating powers of different materials is as follows: Fill a large tin with insulating material such as hair or cotton wool (Figure 5.12). Embed a small tin in the insulating material and fill it with boiling water. Immediately insert the thermometer and stopper in position. Allow the apparatus to cool and take the temperature reading after 30 minutes. This will indicate the heat loss through the insulation.

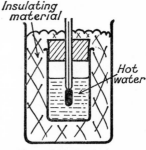

Figure 5.12. Insulation experiment

3. Investigate the hot-water system in your hairdressing salon and at your home. Find out if lagging or insulation has been used to insulate the hot-water system and the building.
4. Visit your local gas or electricity showroom and examine the various types of space heaters.
5. Set up an electric fire between a strong source of light (film-strip projector) and a screen. Switch on the fire and observe its shadow on the screen. The convection current can be easily seen.

QUESTIONS ON CHAPTER 5

1. Compare the methods of transference of heat by (a) conduction, (b) convection, and (c) radiation. Make a labelled sketch of any heating appliance and show how the heat from the heater travels into the room space.
2. What is meant by insulation of heat? Give a list of substances used as insulators, with examples of their use in a hairdressing establishment.

3. Explain the term *convection*. Describe a typical low-pressure hot-water system fitted with an electric immersion heater.
4. Explain the term *conduction*. Give an example of the application of conduction to hot machine or wireless permanent-waving equipment.
5. Write short notes on the following: (*a*) Radiant or infra-red heat; (*b*) lagging; (*c*) cavity walls; (*d*) hair as body-heat insulator; (*e*) radiators.
6. Describe the circulation of air in a room which has an electric radiant fire fitted on one wall and a sash window on the adjacent wall.
7. Explain what convection currents are and what causes them. Describe how convection currents can ventilate a room.

6 CHANGE OF PHYSICAL STATE AND HUMIDITY

All substances can be divided into three classes or physical states: solids, liquids, and gases.

Some substances can change their physical state by (*a*) adding heat to them or *heating*, (*b*) withdrawing heat from them or *cooling*. For example, water can exist as solid ice, liquid water, and gaseous steam.

The following diagram indicates the main changes of physical states, and also gives the names of the types of change:

	SOLIDIFICATION			CONDENSATION	
SOLID	←	→ LIQUID	←		→ GAS
	MELTING OR FUSION			BOILING OR EVAPORATION	

MELTING

Melting or fusion is the change from a solid to a liquid and takes place at a definite temperature called the *melting-point*.

Experiment

Take some crushed ice and place it in a filter-funnel, inserting a Celsius thermometer into the ice (Figure 6.1). While the ice melts the

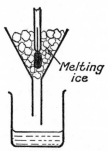

Figure 6.1. Melting-point of ice

temperature will remain steady at 0°C. The change from solid ice to liquid water has taken place at a steady temperature.

The melting-point is the temperature at which a solid changes into a liquid. The *freezing-point* is the temperature at which a liquid changes into a solid.

45

Experiment

To determine the melting-point of emulsifying wax (Figure 6.2):

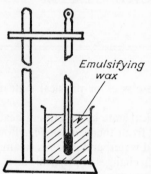

Figure 6.2. Melting-point apparatus

Take a beaker (100 cm³) and three-quarters fill it with the emulsifying wax used in cosmetic preparation. Heat the wax until it has completely melted, and insert a thermometer in the beaker, supporting it with a clamp, making sure that the thermometer is suspended freely in the liquid wax. Take thermometer readings every minute until the wax has solidified. The melting-point can be obtained from your results by noting the temperature readings that remain stationary over a period of about ten minutes.

All pure substances have definite melting-points, and the melting-point of a substance can therefore be used as an indication of its purity.

The melting-point of a pure substance can be lowered by adding another substance to it. For example, if two parts of crushed ice and one part of salt are mixed together the ice melts and freezes again at minus 18°C, that is, 18 degrees below the melting-point of pure ice.

APPLICATIONS OF MELTING

1. *Cosmetics* such as lipstick and solid brilliantines should melt easily by means of the natural body heat. The main ingredients of lipsticks are natural waxes that can be made to melt at body temperature by the addition of other ingredients to lower the wax melting-point. The same principle applies to solid brilliantine.

2. *Freezing-mixtures* of ice and salt can be used for making ice-cream and for cooling purposes in a laboratory.

3. *Wax depilatories* or hair-removers consist of a mixture of paraffin wax and beeswax. The wax mixture is melted and applied to the hair-removal site and allowed to solidify; the solid wax is then stripped off, pulling the hair out at the same time.

4. When allowed to cool, *brilliantine* and other semi-solid preparations show a *depression* or hollow in the surface. This is also seen in cooled paraffin wax. It is due to the fact that the molten liquids *contract* on cooling, the outer parts cooling quicker than the central part of the mixture.

BOILING

Boiling is the change from a liquid to a gas, the change taking place throughout the *body* of the liquid at a definite temperature: the *boiling-point*.

Insert a thermometer into a beaker of cold water and heat the water slowly. Observe how the temperature of the water rises steadily until the water boils, when the temperature remains steady at the boiling-point.

The thermometer does not indicate the heat required for the change from water to steam. This *invisible* heat is described as *latent heat*.

Latent heat is the heat required to change the state of a substance without raising its temperature.

PRESSURE AND THE BOILING-POINT

The effect of pressure on the boiling-point can be demonstrated as follows:

(a) Lowering the pressure

Boil the water in the round-bottomed flask (Figure 6.3), remove the bunsen burner and close the screw clip. It is seen that the water boils at 100°C. The temperature then falls and the boiling ceases. Cooling

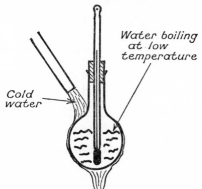

Figure 6.3. Water boiling under low pressure

the flask under a cold-water spray causes some steam to condense and the air pressure inside the flask becomes less. The water now boils again, although the temperature may be only 70°C.

Conclusion:

When the air pressure is lowered the boiling-point of water is lowered.

Applications

1. The boiling-point of water *decreases* the higher we go up in the air since the air pressure also decreases. Therefore water will boil at a lower temperature at the top of a mountain.
2. Condensed milk is made by boiling milk under low pressure in vacuum pans. If the excess water was removed by ordinary boiling it would result in the burning of the milk; therefore the process is carried out rapidly under low pressure without the subsequent 'burning'.
3. Many chemicals and perfumes decompose when heated strongly at their ordinary boiling-points. They are purified by distillation at low pressure and at a much lower boiling-point.

(b) Increasing the pressure

Water is boiled in the round-bottomed flask and the steam is led into the mercury container (Figure 6.4). The mercury imposes a high

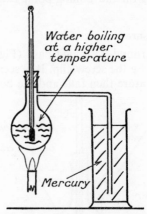

Water boiling at a higher temperature

Mercury

Figure 6.4. Water boiling under high pressure

pressure on the boiling water, and the water now boils at a temperature above 100°C.

Conclusion:

Increased air pressure raises the boiling-point of water.

Applications

Pressure-cookers, sterilizers, and autoclaves work on the principle that water at high pressures will boil at a higher temperature than normal.

1. Pressure-cookers will therefore cook foods quicker because their temperatures will be higher than the temperatures of open pan cookers.

4. Hot permanent-waving machine: the aluminium heater-clips are heated by conduction from the heater bars of the machine

3. Maximum and minimum thermometer

5. Apparatus used to determine the elasticity of hair and other fibres

6. Iron filings arrange themselves into a visible magnetic field when a current flows through a solenoid coil

7. Induction coil

2. Sterilizers are used to destroy bacteria that may be present on dressings and surgical instruments. Sterilization destroys *all* bacteria, plant or animal, beneficial or harmful. Sterilizers are similar to pressure cookers in that they produce a higher temperature under high pressure (Figure 6.5). The sterilizing cabinet used in hairdressing establishments is more correctly described as a *disinfecting* cabinet. Articles that have been in the cabinet are not completely free of bacteria or sterile.

Figure 6.5. Sterilizer or autoclave

STERILIZATION TEMPERATURES AND PRESSURES

Towels, gowns, and dressings	250°F	15 lb/in.²
China, glass, and rubber	230°F	7 lb/in.²

EVAPORATION

This is the change from a liquid to a gas and takes place from the *surface* of the liquid at *any* temperature.

Volatile liquids evaporate rapidly, e.g. methylated spirit and perfume.

Non-volatile liquids evaporate with difficulty, e.g. liquid paraffin.

The following conditions are important in assisting evaporation:

(1) Large surface area;
(2) Wind or moving air;
(3) Dry air or low humidity;
(4) High temperature.

Experiments

To illustrate the rate of evaporation of water under various conditions:

1. *Surface area*

Take three beakers (250 cm³) and measure 100 cm³ of water into each beaker. Cut two pieces of blotting-paper measuring 12 by 2 in. and 12 by ¼ in. respectively and place them in beakers as in Figure 6.6.

E

Put the beakers aside for one week and note the water loss. The greatest water loss is from the beaker having the piece of blotting-paper of large surface area, and the least from the beaker with no blotting-paper.

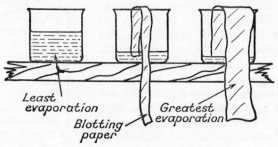

Figure 6.6. Evaporation and surface area

2. *Temperature and moving air*

Take three metal discs of equal size and paint water on to the surface of one. Put them aside and note the time it takes for the water to evaporate from the disc. Direct a stream of cold air from a hand hair-dryer on to another disc painted with water and note the time it takes for the water to evaporate. Repeat the experiment using another disc, but this time use a stream of warm air from the hair-dryer.

It is observed that evaporation is greatest from the disc using moving air and high temperature.

3. *Air humidity*

Place a beaker of water with a blotting-paper strip under a large bell-jar. Place a beaker with an equal amount of water and a blotting-paper strip of identical size on the bench alongside the bell-jar (Figure 6.7). After one week note the water loss from the beakers.

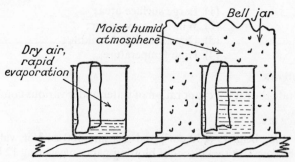

Figure 6.7. Evaporation and humidity

It is observed that the water loss is least under the bell-jar because the moist or humid air reduces the rate of evaporation.

APPLICATIONS OF EVAPORATION

1. Hair-drying is a process of evaporation that requires the conditions outlined, namely:

   (a) Warmth is provided by the hair-dryer heating unit.
   (b) Moving air or wind is provided by the hair-dryer fan.
   (c) Hair will dry quicker if the surrounding air is dry; this condition will exist inside the dryer hood.
   (d) If the hair is loose and free flowing it will dry rapidly, since it offers a larger surface area. When hair is wound into curlers the drying time is longer owing to the small surface area available.

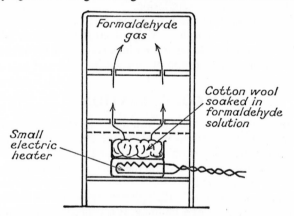

Figure 6.8. Disinfecting cabinet

2. Clothes drying is a process that will proceed rapidly on a warm, sunny, breezy, dry day, provided the clothes are hung out offering their maximum surface area.

3. Disinfecting cabinets produce a gas, *formaldehyde*, by the evaporation of formaldehyde solution from a small heater unit situated in a space below the cabinet (Figure 6.8). Formaldehyde is a useful disinfectant and is also used as a preservative for biological specimens.

COOLING EFFECT OF EVAPORATION

During the process of evaporation heat is absorbed from the surroundings, this heat being the latent heat of evaporation.

Experiments

To illustrate the cooling effect of evaporation:

1. Soak a piece of cotton wool in methylated spirit and squeeze some of the spirit on to your fore-arm. Repeat the experiment using ether, making sure that *all* naked lights are extinguished before using these highly inflammable liquids. You will experience a greater cooling effect using the ether than with the spirit.
2. Wrap cotton wool round the bulb of a thermometer and soak the cotton wool in ether. Suspend the thermometer from a stand along-side a plain thermometer. Note the rapid fall in the temperature as the ether evaporates. Also observe the formation of ice on the cotton wool surface.

Sweat or perspiration is the clear fluid secreted by *sudoriferous* or sweat glands in the skin that cools the body surface by evaporation. It is therefore a natural cooling lotion.

Cooling lotions such as after-shave lotion, eau-de-cologne, and friction preparations consist mainly of ethyl alcohol or methylated spirit suitably perfumed. Their cooling effect is due to the heat being drawn from the skin to evaporate the spirit.

CONDENSATION

This is the change from a gas or vapour to a liquid. Steam that issues from the spout of a kettle is visible to the eye as a mist, since it is a vapour made up of tiny drops of condensed water. If a sheet of glass is held near the spout of the kettle the emerging steam will soon form drops of condensed water.

Condensation dampness is the appearance of isolated damp patches on the cold outer walls of a building. It is caused by the condensation of the water vapour present in the air on the cold surface of a wall. It may be remedied by the application of an insulating material to the wall.

Display-window condensation is due to the atmospheric water vapour condensing on the cold glass surface of the window, thus causing 'steaming' of the glass. It can be overcome by fitting small tubular heaters along the inside of the window.

Both types of condensation in hairdressing salons can be overcome by efficient *ventilation* to remove the moist air.

DISTILLATION

Distillation is a process of purification and consists in boiling a substance and condensing the vapour in a *condenser*, the condensed vapour or distillate being collected in a receiver.

Figure 6.9 shows the apparatus used for the simple distillation of liquids and for the production of distilled water. The condenser is cooled by a constant stream of cold water.

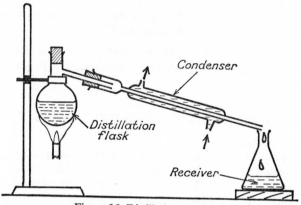

Figure 6.9. Distillation apparatus

Distilled water is water that is free from dissolved salts and air. It is very insipid to drink and is used mainly for making accumulator battery acid, for diluting hydrogen peroxide before use in hairdressing processes, and in cosmetic preparations.

Steam distillation is used for the distillation of perfumes from flowers and herbs with the apparatus shown in Figure 6.10.

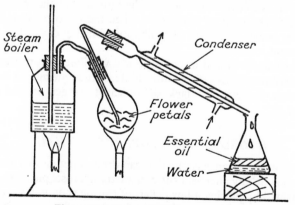

Figure 6.10. Steam-distillation apparatus

HUMIDITY

Humidity means the presence of water vapour in the air that has entered the air from the following main sources:

1. Evaporation of water from lakes, rivers, and seas.
2. Water produced by the respiration of animals and plants. One person produces approximately *two pints* of water a day during respiration.
3. Production of water vapour from numerous processes such as burning of coal, coal gas, and oil (see Chapter 13).

The presence of humidity in the atmosphere of a hairdressing establishment can be indicated by the condensation present on the room windows.

SOURCES OF HUMIDITY IN HAIRDRESSING ROOMS

1. Use of steamers.
2. Steam produced from hot water used during shampooing.
3. Evaporation of water from hair during the drying process.
4. Evaporation of water from the various aqueous hairdressing preparations such as cold-wave and setting lotion.
5. Respiration and perspiration of people in the room.

All these sources in addition to the natural humidity of the air result in a more than average atmospheric humidity in most hairdressing establishments.

EFFECT OF HUMIDITY ON THE HUMAN BODY

The body is sensitive to changes in the humidity of the air, since we are conscious of 'muggy' tiring days when the atmosphere is humid, and we are keenly conscious of exhilarating bracing days when the air is less humid.

The excessively humid air of a poorly ventilated room can cause general tiredness, bodily discomfort, and lassitude owing to a deficient perspiration process and lack of sufficient oxygen in the water-saturated air.

HYGROSCOPIC PROPERTY OF HAIR

A hygroscopic substance is one that can draw water vapour into itself from the air. Many chemical substances are hygroscopic. This can be demonstrated by placing a few pellets of caustic soda in a watch-glass and putting the specimen aside for a few days, after which it will be seen that the pellets have turned into a watery liquid. The hygroscopic nature of hair can be demonstrated by carefully weighing a dish of clean hair cuttings, followed by drying the hair in a *steam*-heated oven. After drying, it will be noted that a loss in weight has taken place.

If the dish of hair is allowed to stand in air and absorb more water by the hygroscopic process, further weighing will indicate a weight increase.

This remarkable hygroscopic property of hair is responsible for the condition of hair. Owing to its hygroscopic nature hair is never scientifically described as 'dry' unless the air is abnormally dry as in arid desert regions.

Although hair is an extremely absorbent and hygroscopic substance, it is also, by contrast, an extremely difficult fibre to wet with water. The former property of absorption of water depends on the *medulla* of the hair fibre, while the surface scaly *cuticle* layer of the hair is responsible for the water-repelling property.

MEASUREMENT OF HUMIDITY

The humidity of air is measured by means of an instrument called a *hygrometer*. The hygrometer indicates the relative humidity of the air expressed as a percentage and the term means: the ratio between the amount of water vapour that the air *could* hold and what it actually *does* hold at the same temperature.

$$\text{Relative humidity} = \frac{\text{Actual amount of water in the air}}{\substack{\text{Maximum amount the air could hold} \\ \text{at same temperature.}}}$$

The hair hygrometer incorporates a strand of 50 *degreased* human hairs connected by pulleys to a pointer. When the air is very humid the hairs *absorb* water and increase in length, this movement being transmitted through the pulley system to the pointer. When the humidity is *low* the hairs lose water to the air and they become *shorter*, this movement being again indicated by the pointer travelling over the humidity scale (Figure 6.11).

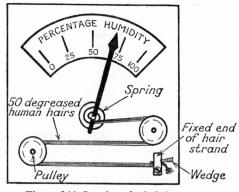

Figure 6.11. Interior of a hair hygrometer

The hair hygrometer is a useful instrument for hairdressing salons in order to provide a constant record of prevailing atmospheric humidity, the humidity being indicated as a percentage of humidity—normal humidity being between 60 and 70 per cent.

APPLICATIONS OF HUMIDITY

1. *Hair condition* or its lustre is partly dependent on atmospheric humidity, this being due to the hygroscopic property of hair. An arid desert climate will produce extremely dry hair of poor condition, whereas the moist temperate climate prevailing in the British Isles will keep hair in good condition. Similarly, good skin condition depends on a moist atmosphere to provide a supple healthy skin.

   Steamers (Figure 6.12) are appliances used to condition hair by

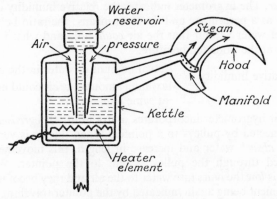

Figure 6.12. Steamer

   providing a humid atmosphere within the steamer hood. Steam is generated by means of an electrically heated kettle and led into the hood by way of a tubular manifold distribution system. In hard water districts it is advisable to fill the steamer with distilled water.

   Sea-water, and its dissolved *sodium chloride* salt, should be rinsed from the hair with fresh water. If salt water is allowed to dry on the hair it will change the condition of the hair, causing it to become sticky, owing to the hygroscopic property of the sodium chloride salt that coats the hair.

2. Wool, cotton, and linen are spun into thread in a controlled humid atmosphere, because dry air will cause the thread to snap.

   Woollen garments contain small amounts of water in the fibre owing to the hygroscopic nature of wool, which serves to absorb part of the body perspiration.

A woollen carpet and other woollen soft furnishings will help to *control* the humidity of a room by means of the hygroscopic property of wool.

3. Factory hygrometers are used to indicate the maximum limit of humidity allowed by the Factory Act in order to protect the health of the workers. Hygrometers are also used in meat and tobacco stores.

★ ★ ★

SUGGESTIONS FOR PRACTICAL WORK

Perform the experiments outlined in this chapter.

1. Using a hair hygrometer record the daily humidity of your salon.
2. Steam-distil some flower petals in a 1,000-cm³ flask of the steam-distillation apparatus described in this chapter. Rose petals when distilled will produce a pleasant-smelling rose water.
3. Prepare a cooling or friction lotion using the method described in Chapter 18.

QUESTIONS ON CHAPTER 6

1. What is meant by the humidity of air? How is humidity measured? Describe some important applications of humidity to hairdressing.
2. Explain the meaning of the following processes, giving examples in each case together with diagrams to illustrate your answer: (*a*) boiling; (*b*) evaporation; (*c*) condensation; (*d*) distillation.
3. Explain the term *evaporation*. What are the main conditions required for evaporation? How are they applied to hairdressing?
4. Write short notes on the following: (*a*) condensation damp; (*b*) cooling lotions; (*c*) hair condition; (*d*) melting; (*e*) sterilization.
5. Describe a sterilizer or autoclave and explain how it works. Compare this with a sterilizing cabinet used in a hairdressing salon. Illustrate your answer with diagrams.

7 ELECTRICITY, CIRCUITS, AND ELECTRICAL TERMS

Electricity is a form of energy that can be converted into heat, light, and power for the purpose of operating many different types of electrical appliances.

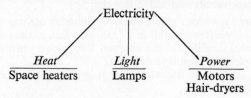

All matter is made of tiny particles of electricity of two main kinds:
(a) negative and very light *electrons*;
(b) positive and heavier *protons*.

The positive proton and negative electron join together and form the hydrogen *atom* or smallest particle of matter (Figure 7.1).

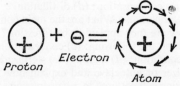

Figure 7.1. Electron and proton forming the hydrogen atom

An electric current flowing through a wire can be considered as a flow of very fast-moving electrons leaping from atom to atom in the wire (Figure 7.2).

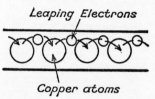

Figure 7.2. Electron flow or electric current

HOW ELECTRICITY IS MADE

(a) ELECTRICITY BY FRICTION

Electrons can be removed from atoms by friction or rubbing. For example, electrons can be drawn out of hair by vigorous brushing or combing. The hair transfers some of its electrons to the brush or comb, which becomes *negatively* charged or rich in electrons, while the hair becomes *positively* charged because of a shortage of electrons.

When the negatively charged brush is held over the positively charged hair it will be seen that the hair rises towards the brush or stands on end. When hair is combed after washing it is seen to stick to the comb owing to the transfer of electricity by friction.

Nylon and other artificial materials used in clothing tend to crackle when being removed. Dust is drawn towards furniture that has been rubbed during polishing owing to friction or static electricity.

Experiment

Tear up a 2-in. square of tissue paper into tiny pieces. Rub a comb or fountain-pen briskly along your sleeve; it will become negatively charged. Hold the electrified comb or pen over the pieces of tissue paper, when they will leap up and cling to it. This is because unlike charges of electricity are drawn towards each other (Figure 7.3).

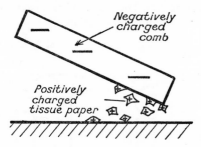

Figure 7.3. Frictional electricity

(b) ELECTRICITY FROM CHEMICAL CHANGES

A simple electric cell is made by dipping plates of copper and zinc into weak sulphuric acid. A torch bulb is connected to the plates using cotton-covered copper wire (Figure 7.4). When the different metals are immersed in the acid, the lamp lights up, showing that an electric current has been produced. The light now becomes dim and soon goes out, and at the same time it is seen that bubbles of hydrogen gas have covered the copper plate. If the copper plate is removed, washed in water, wiped clean, and replaced in the acid, the lamp will light up again.

Polarization is the process in which hydrogen bubbles collect on the metal plate and stop the flow of electricity.

Primary cells are cells that make electricity by chemical action. The simple cell and the following are examples of primary cells:

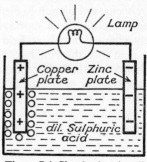

Figure 7.4. Simple electric cell

1. Leclanché wet cell

This consists of (*a*) a zinc rod, and (*b*) a carbon rod surrounded with a black depolarizing mixture (manganese dioxide and powdered carbon) that serves to prevent polarization and therefore supplies a steady electric current (Figure 7.5). The rods are immersed in a glass jar of sal ammoniac (ammonium chloride) solution.

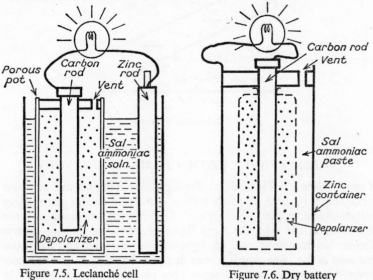

Figure 7.5. Leclanché cell   Figure 7.6. Dry battery

The depolarizer is contained in a porous, or unglazed, pot, which allows water to seep through it freely. Wet Leclanché electric cells are used mainly for the economic operation of electric bells but are being rapidly replaced by the more convenient dry Leclanché cell.

2. Dry Leclanché cell or dry battery

This (Figure 7.6) is similar to the wet cell described above, except that the solution of sal ammoniac is replaced with a paste of sal ammoniac and the porous pot by a muslin bag of depolarizing mixture. The zinc container replaces the rod and glass jar of the wet cell.

Dry Leclanché cells provide a portable supply of electricity, and are available for various voltages.

The main disadvantage of dry batteries is that once they are exhausted they must be discarded, for they cannot be recharged with electricity.

3. Secondary cells or accumulators

These are cells that can be filled or *charged* with electricity and emptied or *discharged*. Accumulators have the advantage over dry cells

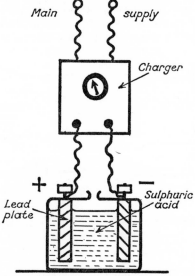

Figure 7.7. Accumulator

in that they can be recharged with electricity many times (Figure 7.7). The typical accumulator consists of a series of lead plates or grids separated by sheets of wood or glass. The plates are immersed in battery acid or weak sulphuric acid.

Care of accumulators: Accumulators should be charged according to the maker's instructions, using a battery charger that operates from the main electricity supply.

The specific gravity of the battery acid is found by using a hydrometer. When the accumulator is fully charged the specific gravity is 1·25. After use it must not be allowed to drop below 1·17, when recharging is necessary. Distilled water is used to 'top up', or replace water lost from the battery by evaporation.

Uses of accumulators: To supply cars, buses, and ships with electricity. Accumulators provide a stand-by supply of electricity useful in emergency when the main electricity supply breaks down. Hospitals and telephone exchanges have battery rooms for this purpose.

Note. The large-scale production of electricity from water, coal, oil, atomic energy, and wind will be considered in Chapter 10.

CIRCUITS

An electric circuit is the flow of electric current from the positive terminal to the negative terminal of an electric supply. The electric cell or power station acts like a *pump* to drive the electricity round the circuit. *Symbols* or shorthand signs are used to indicate the components of a circuit. Figure 7.8 shows some typical electric symbols.

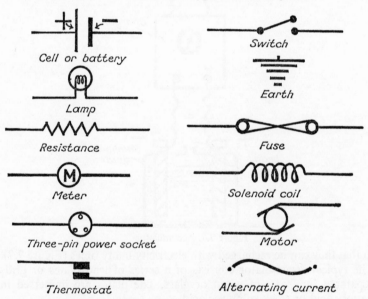

Figure 7.8. Electrical symbols

A *simple circuit* consisting of a dry battery, lamp, and a switch is drawn as in Figure 7.9. When the switch is open the circuit is said to

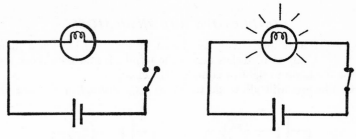

Figure 7.9. 'Broken' circuit   Figure 7.10. 'Complete' circuit

be *broken* and no electric current flows. When the switch is closed the current flows and the circuit is now *complete* (Figure 7.10). A *short circuit* is the touching together of two bare electric wires resulting in the breaking of the circuit (Figure 7.11).

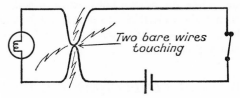

Figure 7.11. 'Short' circuit

LIVE AND NEUTRAL WIRES

The house electric circuit is supplied by feed, or *live*, wires and a return or *neutral* wire from the power station. The feed live wire is covered with red insulating material, and the neutral return wire is covered with black insulation (Figure 7.12). (Continental and other foreign flexible cables have differently coloured live and neutral wire insulation.)

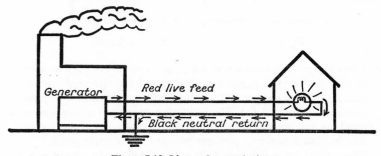

Figure 7.12. Live and neutral wires

CONDUCTORS AND INSULATORS

Construct a simple circuit as shown in Figure 7.13. Place many different kinds of materials across the terminals and note those that cause the lamp to light or complete the circuit.

Conductors will allow electricity to pass through and cause the

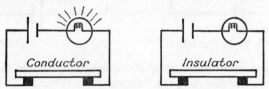

Figure 7.13. Conductor and insulator circuits

lamp to light. Examples are: copper, silver, iron, aluminium, brass, graphite carbon, water, the human body, earth or soil.

Insulators do not allow electricity to pass through them and therefore do not light the lamp. Examples are: wood, rubber, plastics, porcelain, waxed paper, hair, air.

APPLICATIONS OF CONDUCTORS AND INSULATORS

1. *Switches* are inserted in the live or feed wire of a circuit (Figure 7.14). The insulated plastic handle, or dolly, controls the off-on mechanism. Protection from electric shock is also afforded by the plastic cover and porcelain base. The conducting metal parts are of pure copper and silver, and the electric wires are fitted into brass terminals.

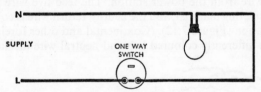

Figure 7.14. Circuit with switch in the live wire

2. *Cable and flexible cord* insulation consists mainly of plastic, rubber, cotton, and waxed paper wrapped round the stranded wire conductors of pure copper metal, which are coated with tin to prevent corrosion (Figure 7.15). The insulation prevents the live feed wire touching the neutral return wire, thus preventing a short circuit. The insulated covering protects people from electric shock.

Many *electrical appliances* such as hand hair-dryers, food mixers, have plastic bodywork. Similarly, the handles of many appliances and lampholders are made of plastics to protect the operator from electric shock.

4. *Thermostatic switches*, which automatically control the flow of

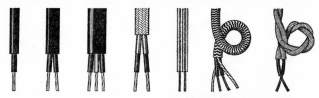

Figure 7.15. Samples of cables and flexible cords. *Left to right:* single-core, twin core, three-core, twin-core, figure-8 plastic flexible, non-kink flexible, twin-core flexible

electricity into a heating appliance, have silver contacts. This is because the electric sparking would burn copper but not silver.

5. *Electric plugs* and sockets are insulated with plastics and the terminal and pins are made of brass, a good conductor.

ELECTRIC SHOCK

Electric shock can result in severe burns, shock, and, in extreme cases, death.

It can be caused by touching a bare live wire (for example, through a frayed flexible cord) or by handling electrical appliances and fittings with wet hands. (For treatment of electric shock see page 280.)

SOME PRECAUTIONS AGAINST ELECTRIC SHOCK

1. Flexible electric cords should never be allowed to trail from an appliance.
2. Worn and frayed cords should be replaced immediately.
3. Always make certain that the correct size of cord is fitted to an appliance.
4. Never allow flexible cords to be placed under carpets, rugs, or linoleum.
5. Never handle electrical appliances with wet hands or near to water taps.

MEASUREMENT OF ELECTRICITY

THE VOLT

The volt (abbreviated V) is the unit used in measuring electric pressure; it is measured by a *voltmeter*.

As previously stated, the electric cell or mains supply acts like a

F

pump that drives the electricity through the circuit at a definite pressure or voltage.

VOLTAGES OF VARIOUS ELECTRICAL SUPPLIES

Electricity supply	Voltage
Simple cell	1·5
Single dry cell	1·5
Accumulator	2
Bicycle lamp battery	3
Transistor radio battery	9
Car-battery accumulator	12
Portable radio battery	30
Continental mains supply and ship's supply to cabins, etc.	110–120
Standard mains supply in Great Britain	240
Voltage in pylon cables	132,000

In Great Britain the voltage supply may vary from one part of the country to another between 210 and 250 V. It is therefore important to state the *voltage* of your supply when ordering new electrical equipment. The voltage of an electrical installation is stamped on the nameplate of the electricity meter. In France, Holland, and other European countries the voltage is 110 V. It is therefore important to check the voltages of continental electrical appliances before using them in this country. Travelling irons and electric shavers are made to operate on either 110 or 240 V.

THE AMPERE

The ampere is the unit of rate of flow of electric current; it is measured by means of an *ammeter*. Ampere is abbreviated to A, or sometimes amp. A vacuum cleaner takes about an ampere, whereas an electric cooker can take 30 A. This is an indication that more electricity flows into an electric cooker than into a vacuum cleaner.

The current (number of amperes) flowing into an appliance governs the size of the following:

(a) *switches*, which are available in 2, 5, 15, and 30 A sizes;

(b) *cables*, which are available in 2, 5, 10, 15, and 30 A sizes;

(c) *plugs* and *sockets*, which are available in 2, 5, 13, and 15 A sizes.

CURRENT REQUIRED BY DIFFERENT APPLIANCES

Appliance	Amperes
Radio, television Shaver Door chimes Lamp Vacuum cleaner Marcel iron heater	up to 2
Floor polisher Hair-dryer Steamer	5
Electric fire Immersion heater Washing-machine	13

THE OHM

The ohm is the unit of *resistance*. The abbreviation for ohm is the Greek letter Ω (omega).

Conductors such as copper and brass offer little resistance to the flow of electricity. Non-conductors or insulators have a high resistance and prevent the flow of electricity.

Experiment

Connect a 1·5 V lamp to a 1·5 V battery and it will burn brightly. If a long coil of thin nichrome wire is placed in this circuit the lamp burns less brightly (Figure 7.16). The coil of thin wire offers a resistance to

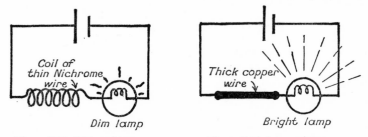

Figure 7.16. High resistance   Figure 7.17. Low resistance

the flow of current. If a thick copper wire is placed in the circuit the lamp burns brightly, because the thick wire is of low resistance (Figure 7.17).

Conclusion:

High resistors	*Low resistors*
Insulators, wood, plastic	Metals, copper and brass
Thin wires	Thick wires
Long wires	Short wires

Applications of resistance

1. Heater-unit elements are thin wires of *nichrome*. (Nichrome is an alloy of nickel and chromium metals.)
2. The volume control on a radio set is a *variable* resistance, consisting of a thin wire whose effective length may be altered to increase and reduce the flow of current.
3. Heat-control switches on wireless permanent-waving machines, hair-dryers, and convector heaters are variable resistances similar to the above.

OHM'S LAW

Ohm's Law gives the relationship between voltage, current, and resistance as follows:

$$\text{Volts} = \text{Amperes} \times \text{Ohms}$$

$$\text{Amperes} = \frac{\text{Volts}}{\text{Ohms}}$$

$$\text{Ohms} = \frac{\text{Volts}}{\text{Amperes}}$$

Ohm's law and its applications seldom enter into hairdressing calculations, but the following example will indicate its main application:

Example

An electric hair-dryer takes a current of 4·5 A at a pressure of 250 V. Calculate the resistance of the hair-dryer.

$$\text{From Ohm's law: Ohms} = \frac{\text{Volts}}{\text{Amperes}}$$

$$\text{Pressure} = 250 \text{ V}$$
$$\text{Current} = 4 \cdot 5 \text{ A}$$
$$\text{Resistance} = \frac{250}{4 \cdot 5} = 55 \cdot 5 \text{ ohms.}$$

★ ★ ★

SUGGESTIONS FOR PRACTICAL WORK

1. Draw up a list of all the electrical appliances used in your hairdressing salon.

2. Try to make the hair of a fellow pupil stand up by frictional electricity.
3. Notice the discharge of electric sparks from the hair and the electrode during electric high-frequency treatment.
4. Construct a simple electric cell, using the method outlined in this chapter.
5. Saw a dry battery in half using an engineer's hacksaw. Draw and describe its appearance.
6. Obtain an accumulator and determine the specific gravity of the battery acid using a battery-acid hydrometer.
7. Set up the simple circuit described in this chapter for finding the conductivities of various materials.
8. Dismantle a one-way wall switch, examine and draw its interior parts. *Two-way* switches are used to control lights in hall-ways so that they can be switched on or off from either of two positions; a bed-light can be similarly controlled by two switches.
9. Examine and draw stripped cables and flexes showing the insulation and conducting materials.
10. Dismantle a three-pin plug and draw its interior, indicating the insulating and conducting materials.

QUESTIONS ON CHAPTER 7

1. Explain the term *voltage* of an electric current, giving numerical examples of voltage values. What is electric shock? What treatment would you use for a case of electric shock? Illustrate your answer with diagrams.
2. Make a list of the electrical appliances found in a well-equipped hairdressing salon. Select *one* appliance and describe two different insulators and two different conductors that enter into the composition or make-up of the appliance.
3. What is meant by *insulation* of an electric current? Give a list of conductors and insulators with examples of their application in electrical appliances.
4. Write short notes on the following: (*a*) cables and flexible cords; (*b*) amperes; (*c*) resistors; (*d*) short circuit; (*e*) broken circuit.
5. What precautions should you observe in buying continental and foreign electrical appliances?
6. Describe how electricity is produced by: (*a*) friction; and (*b*) a Leclanché dry cell. Give examples of their application to hairdressing practice.
7. Describe a primary and a secondary electric cell. Give some applications of each and describe their advantages.

8 ELECTRICAL ENERGY, HEAT, AND ELECTROLYSIS

Electrical *power* is measured in units called *watts*.

The power, or the rate at which an electric appliance delivers its energy either in the form of heat or light, depends on the rate of flow of the current (amperes) and the electric pressure (volts). A bright, high-powered electric lamp will have electric current flowing through it at a fast rate, while a dim low-powered lamp will have electric current flowing at a slower rate.

The relationship between current flow and electric pressure or voltage is expressed as follows:

$$\text{Watts} = \text{Volts} \times \text{Amperes}$$

$$\text{Amperes} = \frac{\text{Watts}}{\text{Volts}}$$

$$\text{Volts} = \frac{\text{Watts}}{\text{Amperes}}$$

The watt (W) is the unit of electric power. The *kilowatt* (kW) is equal to 1,000 watts:

$$1 \text{ kW} = 1,000 \text{ W}$$

Loading, or *wattage*, is the term used to describe the rating or number of watts used by an electrical appliance. The loading of an appliance is usually marked on it by means of a small nameplate, on the back of the appliance (Figure 8.1). The accompanying table gives

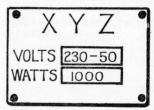

Figure 8.1. Nameplate showing wattage and voltage

the loading of some important appliances. It will be seen from the table that *small* wattage values indicate that the appliance will use *little* electricity whereas high wattage values indicate greater consumption of electricity.

70

LOADING OF SOME ELECTRICAL APPLIANCES

Appliance	Loading in watts
Dry shaver	8
Hair clippers	20
Ventilation fan	25
Radio	50
Towel rail	150
Vacuum cleaner	250
Floor polisher	250
Tubular window heater	60 per foot
Hand hair-dryer	500
Stand or salon hair-dryer	800
Marcel iron heater	250
Steamer	700
Fire, one bar	1,000 (1 kW)
Fire, two bar	2,000 (2 kW)
Convector heater	2,000 (2 kW)
Sink-water heater	2,000 (2 kW)
Wash-boiler	3,000 (3 kW)
Immersion heater	2,000 (2 kW)
Washing machine	3,000 (3 kW)

Experiment

To find the loading of an electric appliance:

Set up the circuit shown in Figure 8.2. The circuit consists of a 10-A ammeter, 0–250-V voltmeter and a standard 13-A socket. The electricity from the mains is controlled by a fused plug and wall

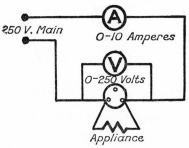

Figure 8.2. Circuit for finding wattage of an appliance

socket. It is convenient to set out the circuit on an old drawing-board and use single P.V.C. 3/029 cable for the wiring (Figure 8.3).

The appliance is plugged into the 13-A socket and the current switched on, preferably at a wall-switch source. The readings of the ammeter and voltmeter are noted. Switch off the current at the wall switch, and *then* remove the appliance.

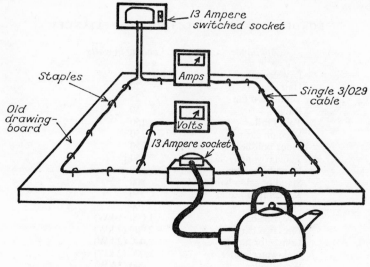

Figure 8.3. Experiment to determine wattage of an appliance

The wattage of the appliance can now be calculated from the formula:

$$\text{Watts} = \text{volts} \times \text{amperes}$$

Example

A salon hair-dryer is rated at 250 volts and takes a current of 2·12 amperes. Calculate the loading of the appliance.

Since Watts = Volts × Amperes

$$\text{Voltage} = 250$$
$$\text{Amperage} = 2\cdot12$$

Wattage of hair-dryer = $250 \times 2\cdot12 = 530$ W

UNITS OF ELECTRICITY

The unit of electrical energy is the *kilowatt-hour* (kWh). It is also called the *Board of Trade Unit* or 'unit' and is equal to 1,000 watts for 1 hour:

1 Kilowatt-hour or Electrical unit = 1 kW or 1,000 watts for *one* hour.

The number of electrical units or kilowatt-hours consumed by an electrical appliance is equal to the wattage or loading of the appliance divided by 1,000:

$$\text{Kilowatt-hours or units consumed per hour} = \frac{\text{Wattage or loading}}{1,000}$$

Example

How many units does a 2-kW electric fire consume per hour?

$$\text{Since units} = \frac{\text{Wattage}}{1,000} \quad \frac{2,000}{1,000} = 2 \text{ units.}$$

ELECTRICITY METER

The electricity meter records the number of kilowatt-hours or units of electricity consumed. The small dials should be ignored, since they are used only for testing the meter.

HOW TO READ THE ELECTRICITY METER

Read the larger dials from left to right. Each dial hand should always be read as indicating the figure it has last passed, and not the one it is nearest to. If the hand is between two figures write down the lower figure, with the exception of 0 and 9, when you should write down 9. A gas meter is read in the same way as an electricity meter. In rural areas when the consumer is often very remote from the central station, the consumer reads his own meter by using the easy-to-read *cyclometer* electric meter.

In order to determine the number of kilowatt hours or units of electricity consumed subtract the first meter reading from the second meter reading. For example, if the meter reading on 1 May is 2,960 units, and a later reading on 13 May is 2,999 units (Figure 8.4), the total number of units consumed is as follows:

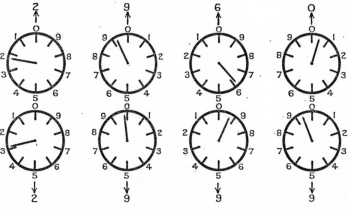

Figure 8.4. Meter reading

Second reading 13 May   2,999 units
First reading 1 May   2,960 units

Units consumed   39

Note. The meter nameplate has your mains supply voltage stamped on it.

COST OF ELECTRICITY

The cost of electricity varies from one part of the country to another. Tariffs or methods of charging for electricity also vary from area to area. The following are some of the tariffs in use:

1. *Flat-rate tariff.* The same rate of charge, e.g. 1*d.* or 1½*d.*, is applied to every unit used.
2. *Two-part tariff.* All current used is charged for at the same rate per unit, and a fixed quarterly charge is made whether electricity is used or not.
3. *Variable block tariff.* An initial block of units is charged for at a high rate of, say, 6*d.* per unit, and the remaining units are charged at one or more lower rates.
4. *Off-peak tariff.* For storage heaters.

Simple calculations of costs for operating electrical appliances can be made using the following formula:

COST OF OPERATING AN APPLIANCE

Cost of operating an electric appliance

$$= \frac{\text{Wattage}}{1,000} \times \text{Number of hours used} \times \text{Rate per unit}$$

Example 1

Calculate the cost of running an 800-watt steamer for 12 hours at 1*d.* per unit:

$$\text{Cost} = \frac{800}{1,000} \times 12 \times 1d.$$

$$\frac{9,600}{1,000} = 9 \cdot 6 \text{ pence.}$$

Example 2

A gentlemen's hairdressing salon uses the following electrical appliances for the times stated. Calculate the cost of electricity used at 1*d.* a unit:

Hair clippers   20 watts for 6 hours
Water-heater   2 kilowatts for 2 hours

Hair-dryer   500 watts for 1 hour
Lighting   300 watts for 8 hours
Towel-dryer   100 watts for 8 hours
Radio   50 watts for 8 hours.

Appliance	Calculation	Cost
Hair clippers	$\frac{20}{1,000} \times 6 \times 1d.$	0·12d.
Water-heater	$\frac{2,000}{1,000} \times 2 \times 1d.$	4·0d.
Hair-dryer	$\frac{500}{1,000} \times 1 \times 1d.$	0·5d.
Lighting	$\frac{300}{1,000} \times 8 \times 1d.$	2·4d.
Towel-dryer	$\frac{100}{1,000} \times 8 \times 1d.$	0·8d.
Radio	$\frac{50}{1,000} \times 8 \times 1d.$	0·4d.
	TOTAL COST	8·22 pence

Method of calculating the length of time an appliance can be used for the price of one unit:

$$\text{Operating time for } one \text{ unit} = \frac{1,000}{\text{wattage}}$$

Divide the wattage into one thousand.

Example

Calculate how long a 750-watt steamer can be used for one unit of electricity:

$$\text{Operating time for one unit} = \frac{1,000}{750} = 1·33 \text{ hours.}$$

OPERATING TIMES FOR VARIOUS ELECTRIC APPLIANCES
FOR ONE UNIT OF ELECTRICITY

Appliance	Operating time in hours for one unit
Hair clippers	50 hours
Hand hair-dryer	2 hours
Salon hair-dryer	1¼ hours
Towel-rail	7 hours
One-bar fire (1 kW)	1 hour
Two-bar fire (2 kW)	½ hour
Steamer	1¼ hours
Water-heater (2 kW)	½ hour

Horse-power (h.p.) or rate of working is a term applied mainly to electric motors or generators:

$$1 \text{ horse-power} = 746 \text{ watts}$$

The electric hair-dryer motor is of *fractional* horse-power using 30 to 40 watts, that is $\frac{1}{20}$ horse-power approximately.

HEATING EFFECT OF AN ELECTRIC CURRENT

Electrical energy can be converted into heat energy, which in turn can be used for many purposes in the home, industry, and hairdressing salon. Electric lamps, cookers, and radiant fires obtain their heat by the conversion of electrical energy into heat.

The following experiments will demonstrate the production of heat by an electric current and will show the important principles that govern the heating effect of an electric current.

Experiments

1. Attach a thin piece of wire (a strand removed from a flexible cord is suitable) between two brass screws fixed to a wooden board, as in Figure 8.5. Connect the board to a switch and variable trans-

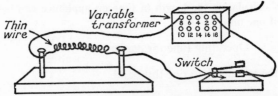

Figure 8.5. Experiment to show the heating of an electric current

former to provide a supply of low-voltage electricity at various voltages between 2 and 20 V. Adjust the voltage of the transformer to 2 V and press the switch; repeat the experiment at 4, 6, 8, and 10 V. As the voltage is stepped up, or increased, it is observed that the thin wire becomes hot and finally white-hot and burns away.

Replace the thin wire with a piece of 22 S.W.G. copper wire and repeat the experiment, stepping up the voltage to 20 V, when it will be seen that this thick copper wire remains cool.

Conclusion:

This experiment shows that the heating effect of an electric current depends on the *thickness* of the conducting wire and also on the current *voltage*.

2. Obtain an old electric fire heating element and cut off one-sixteenth of its total length with a pair of wire-cutters. Cut a sheet of tin from a tin can using tin shears. Fold the tin sheet as in Figure 8.6.

Attach the coil of heating element to the tin reflector and connect it to a low-voltage variable transformer using insulated wire. Make sure that the heating element does not touch the tin reflector. Step up the voltage until the miniature electric fire is radiating heat.

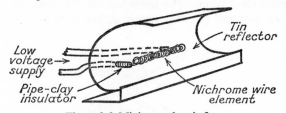

Figure 8.6. Miniature electric fire

Conclusion:

The electric fire element is made of a nickel-chromium alloy called nichrome, and is of a high resistance compared to the 22 S.W.G. copper wire. The heating effect of a current depends on the resistance of the conducting material.

Summary:

The heating effect of an electric current depends on:
(1) The resistance of the conductor.
(2) The voltage of the current.
(3) The thickness of the wire; that is, thin wire will offer a greater resistance than thick wire.

APPLICATIONS OF THE HEATING EFFECT OF AN ELECTRIC CURRENT

1. **Heater elements** fitted in electric appliances consist of coils of high-resistance wire such as nichrome alloy, either wrapped round a fireclay support, as in radiant heaters, or embedded in magnesium oxide as in kettle, immersion, and hot-plate heaters.

Marcel iron heaters consist of a nichrome wire wrapped round a sheet of mica round a copper tube as in Figure 8.7. Mica is a

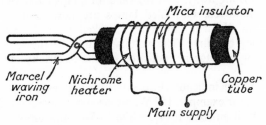

Figure 8.7. Heater element of a Marcel heater

non-conductor of electricity and will not burn. It is also used in electric iron elements.

Hair-dryer heaters are made of nichrome wire elements supported on a mica sheet frame. The revolving fan drives the air over the heater element and gives the stream of hot air (Figure 8.8).

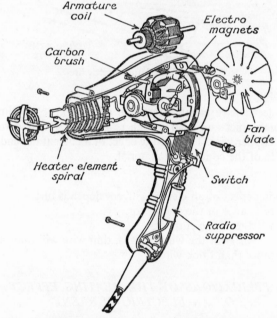

Figure 8.8. Hair-dryer: exploded view

2. **Electric filament lamps** have a hair-like filament of tungsten metal that becomes white-hot giving light. This is a further conversion of electrical energy into another form, namely, light energy.

Filament lamps can be of two kinds: (*a*) gas-filled to prevent the filament burning away, and (*b*) vacuum lamps from which all air has been removed. Gas-filled lamps are now used almost universally. All filament lamps are marked with the voltage and wattage they consume. The voltage should be the same as your mains supply voltage as indicated on the electricity meter nameplate.

Lamp wattage indicates the degree of brightness of a lamp. Large watt values, for example, 150 W, are used for centre-light illumination of a medium-sized room, while 15-W lamps are very dim and used for nursery night-lights.

Clear glass filament lamps produce a very bright dazzling light causing glare that is painful to the eyes. This type of lamp is fitted into closed lamp-shades, or used to illuminate window displays.

Opal or pearl glass filament lamps produce a softer light and are suitable for fitting into open-type lamp-shades and are best for home and salon lighting purposes.

Silica lamps give a softer or more diffused shadowless light. They are suitable for open shades and fittings and very suitable for salon illumination.

FUSES

A fuse is the *weakest* part of the house or salon circuit. If too much electricity is flowing through a circuit cable, the cable can get very hot and cause a fire, since circuit cables are laid under floor boards and near to wood that can easily burn. The fuse is therefore a safety device to protect the consumer from (*a*) fire, and (*b*) damage to electrical appliances.

A fuse consists of a thin piece of tinned copper wire, supported in a non-conducting holder. The melting or 'blowing' of fuse-wire can be demonstrated using the same apparatus as in Figure 8.5.

WHY A FUSE 'BLOWS'

When an appliance suddenly stops working or lights on one floor go out this is a good indication that a fuse has blown. The following are the main reasons:

1. The flex leading to an appliance has become frayed and a short circuit has occurred.
2. Too many appliances have been plugged into one power socket.
3. A light point has been overloaded by running appliances other than lamps from a lamp-holder socket. This is a very dangerous practice.
4. There is old or corroded fuse-wire in the fuse holder. The tin coating serves to prevent corrosion.
5. A faulty appliance has caused a short circuit.

Location of fuses:

1. The main fuse-box is usually in the hall, cellar, or pantry; or the space below the stairs.
2. Plugs are fitted with fuse links or cartridge fuses. Cooker switches and cookers may also have a fuse link.

TYPES OF FUSES

Rewireable fuses consist of a porcelain non-conducting holder with the fuse-wire held in position by brass screws. The holder fits into the porcelain fuse-carrier. Rewireable fuses are fitted in the old type fuse-box and also in the modern consumer unit fuse-box.

Cartridge or **link** fuses consist of a small cylinder or porcelain with metal caps at each end with the fuse-wire inside the cylinder. Cartridge fuses are fitted into the consumer unit fuse-box and also into plug tops and fused switches.

Fuse sizes are measured in amperes. Fuse-wire can be purchased in various sizes, fixed to cards.

Circuit or appliance	Fuse-wire size (A)
Lighting circuit	5
Power-point circuit	15
Immersion-heater circuit	15
Electric cooker circuit	30
Ring-circuit main fuse	30

Cartridge fuses are available in the following sizes: 2, 5, 10, 13, 30 A

HOW TO CALCULATE THE CORRECT SIZE OF FUSE FOR AN APPLIANCE

Apart from the fuse sizes suggested for circuits as given in the above table, it is useful to be able to calculate the correct size for a cartridge fuse to be fitted in an appliance plug. The following formula can be used for all fuse size calculations:

Since Watts = Amperes × Volts

therefore $\quad$ Amperes $= \dfrac{\text{Watts}}{\text{Volts}}$

Assume voltage is 250.

$$\text{Fuse size} = \frac{\text{Wattage of appliance}}{250}$$

Example 1

Calculate the correct size fuse for a 3-kW washing-machine fused plug operating from a 250-V main supply:

$$\text{Fuse size} = \frac{\text{Wattage}}{250}$$

Wattage of appliance = 3,000

$$\text{Fuse size} = \frac{3,000}{250} = 12 \text{ A}$$

The nearest standard size cartridge fuse is 13 A; this is the size recommended. The 10-A cartridge fuse would not be adequate to carry the current and would blow if used.

Example 2

Is it in order to operate three 800-W hair-dryers from a multipoint 13-A power socket?

$$\text{Fuse size} = \frac{\text{Wattage}}{250}$$

$$\text{Total wattage} = 3 \times 800 = 2,400$$

$$\text{Correct fuse size or socket loading} = \frac{2,400}{250} = 10 \text{ A approx.}$$

Therefore three 800-W hair-dryers can safely be operated from one 13-A power-point. Five such hair-dryers, total loading 4,000 W, i.e. 5×800, would require the following fuse size:

$$\frac{4,000}{250} = 16 \text{ A}$$

This would indicate considerable overloading of the 13-A power-point, resulting in the fuse being blown.

Appliance loading (W)	Cartridge fuse size (A)
450	2
450–1,000	5
1,000–2,000	10
2,000–3,000	13
Above 3,000	30

HOW TO REPLACE A FUSE

1. Switch off the main switch of your fuse-box.
2. Examine the appliance. If the appliance produced a spark or burning smell it indicates a fault in the appliance that should receive expert attention, or flexes should be replaced.
3. Remove the fuses from the fuse-carriers and examine each one for a broken fuse. The overloading of a power-point causes the re-wireable fuse to *part* in the middle. A short circuit causes the wire to *burn away* completely.

   Cartridge fuses do not show any visible signs of blowing, and must be tested using the circuit shown in Figure 8.9.
4. Rewire the fuse holder using the correct size fuse-wire. Wrap fuse-wire *clockwise* under the brass screw head and screw up tightly.
5. Replace the fuse and switch on the main switch.

a

82

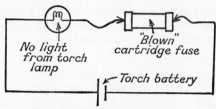

Figure 8.9. Testing a 'blown' fuse

Note. If your neighbours also have a power failure it may indicate a general failure. If there is no electricity supply to your house it may indicate a blown main fuse; in both cases contact your electricity board.

CIRCUIT-BREAKERS

Fuses have attendant difficulties of varying fuse sizes and their replacement. The circuit-breaker automatically disconnects any circuit containing a faulty appliance. The circuit can be restored by flicking the miniature circuit-breaker switch to the 'on' position. The circuit-breaker has a great advantage in a modern hairdressing salon in that there is no risk of prolonged interruption to any electrical hairdressing process such as hair-drying, the circuit breakdown being attended to by the *flick* of a miniature circuit-breaker switch. Circuit-breakers are simple to operate and safe to use. No special tools are needed to maintain them.

ELECTROLYSIS

This is the process of *decomposing* a chemical compound by means of an electric current.

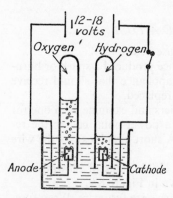

Figure 8.10. Electrolysis of acidulated water

Experiment

To demonstrate the process of electrolysis:

Partly fill a 250-cm³ beaker with water to which a trace of sulphuric acid has been added. Insert the conducting wires with their terminal sheets of platinum into the acid. Connect a 12-V accumulator and turn on the switch. After a while it will be seen that bubbles of gas begin to gather round the platinum terminals. This gas can be collected in inverted test-tubes, as shown in Figure 8.10.

If a lighted taper is inserted into the test-tube containing oxygen, the gas will cause the taper to burn brightly. The hydrogen in the other test-tube will burn with a slight 'pop'.

Conclusion:

The electric current has decomposed or broken down the water into two simple chemical elements, hydrogen and oxygen.

ELECTROLYTIC TERMS

Electrodes are the terminals of conducting wires made of platinum metal, which are used to lead electricity into a liquid or apply it to the body.

The *anode* is the positive terminal or electrode, which is connected to the positive terminal of the power supply or accumulator.

The *cathode* is the negative terminal or electrode, which is connected to the negative terminal of an electric supply.

Electrolytes are substances that can be decomposed by electricity.

APPLICATIONS OF ELECTROLYSIS

1. Many *industrial processes,* such as the purification of copper metal and the electroplating of silver and chromium ware, are performed by electrolysis.

2. *Medical applications.* The human body can conduct electricity because of the large amounts of water and salt that are contained in the body cells and tissues. Electric shock involves the electrolysis of the body fluids; it can result in destruction of cells and tissue with fatal results. Controlled electrolysis can be applied to the surgical ionization or removal of warts and growths from the skin. It can also be used for introducing chemical substances into the subdermal tissues.

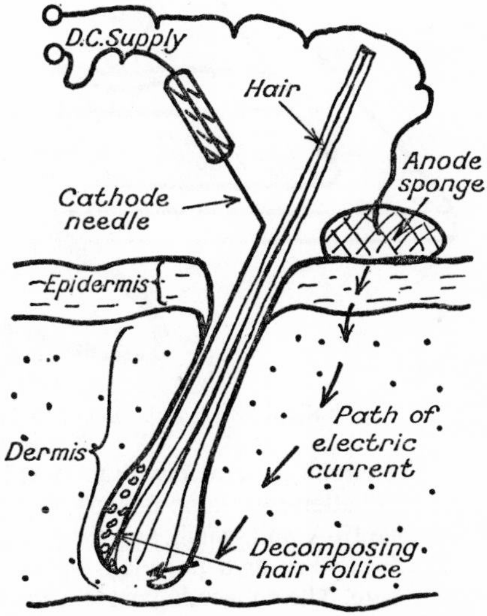

Figure 8.11. Electrolytic hair-removal

3. *Electrolytic hair removal* or *depilation* (Figure 8.11) involves the destruction of the *hair papilla* by electrolysis and is used for the removal of prominent facial and superfluous hair. A cathode or negative electrode needle is inserted into

the hair follicle, while a sponge soaked in salt solution forms the anode or positive electrode. The current flows through the skin towards the hair papilla and into the cathode needle, decomposing and destroying the hair-forming tissue at the base of the follicle.

★ ★ ★

SUGGESTIONS FOR PRACTICAL WORK

In addition to the experiments described in this chapter the following may be performed:

1. The following experiment demonstrates the overloading of a circuit and the function of a fuse or circuit-breaker (Figure 8.12).

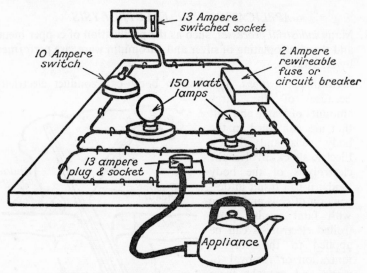

Figure 8.12. Experiment to show how a fuse blows

The circuit is permanently mounted on a wooden board and consists of two batten-type lamp-holders, one standard 13-A surface socket outlet, one 10-A wall switch, and either a Crabtree type C-50 2·5-A miniature circuit-breaker or a porcelain rewireable fuse-holder fitted with a 2-A fuse-wire. The connecting cable is insulated P.V.C. 3/027 cable.

Insert two 150-W filament lamps into the lamp-holders and switch on the current, when the lamps will light up. Switch off the current and connect an appliance with a watt rating of at least 750 W. Switch on the current and note how the lights appear for a short time when the fuse blows or the circuit-breaker switch flicks off.

2. Find out the situation of your main fuse-box or circuit-breaker unit. Note the position of the electricity board's fuse-box immediately below the meter. You must not interfere with either the meter or the board's fuse-box; these are the property of the electricity board or your electricity suppliers.

3. Make a list of the appliances in your salon that have standard fused plugs. Check the cartridge fuse size in the plugs and see if the correct size fuse is fitted. Many standard plugs are fitted with 13-A cartridge fuses where a 2- or 5-A fuse should be fitted.

4. Obtain some old porcelain fuse-holders and carriers and practise the re-wiring of the fuse. (Your local electricity board may be able to supply you with old fuse-boxes.)

5. Make a list of all the electrical appliances in your salon and insert their wattage values by reading the makers' name plate on the back of the appliance.

6. Read your electricity meter before the hairdressing salon begins work for the day and take the meter reading again last thing before closing. Determine the number of units of electricity used and the approximate cost at $1\frac{1}{2}d$. per unit. If a note is left in the meter cupboard of your reading, together with the date, you may obtain a record of the salon's annual consumption and cost if the meter is read again a year later.

7. Obtain some old discarded hairdressing appliances and, using a screw-driver, dismantle them and examine the heater units. Students must *not* in any circumstances tamper with appliances that are in working order.

QUESTIONS ON CHAPTER 8

1. Make a list of the electrical appliances you would expect to find in a modern hairdressing salon. Give an approximate value of the loading of each appliance. A salon convector heater is rated at 2 kW at 240 V. Calculate the correct size cartridge fuse required for the heater's standard fuse-plug.

2. Explain in a few words the meaning of the following electrical terms: (a) watt; (b) ampere; (c) kilowatt; (d) kilowatt-hour.

3. What is a fuse? How does a fuse blow? Give examples of two types of fuse.

4. Describe an experiment to show how you would find the watt rating of an appliance that has no label.

5. Write short notes on the following: (a) circuit-breakers; (b) filament lamps; (c) electric heaters and heater units.

6. Describe a simple experiment to show the heating effect of an electric current. Give some applications of this heating effect as used in hair-dressing appliances.

7. A salon proprietor has one steamer (75 W) and two hair-dryers (700 W). How many of these appliances can operate from a 13-A power socket, mains voltage 220 V?

8. Three 800-W hair-dryers, one 2-kW water-heater, and a 150-W towel-rail are in continuous operation for 8 hours. Calculate the number of units of electricity used and the cost of electricity at $1d$. per unit.

9. What is a fuse-box? Describe how you would repair a fuse. Compare the advantages and disadvantages of the circuit-breaker unit and a fuse-box unit.

10. Explain the terms *electrolysis*, *cathode*, and *electrode*. Give some applications of electrolysis.

9 EARTHING AND SALON CIRCUITS

EARTHING

Earthing is a method of safeguarding against electric shock in the event of a fault developing in an appliance or plug.

A thunder-cloud becomes charged with *static* electricity which is discharged at a great voltage towards the earth as lightning, the damp air conducting this terrific flow of current. The electricity is safely carried to earth through *copper* lightning conductors that serve to prevent damage to tall spires and towers. It is therefore apparent that all electricity will flow by the shortest path to earth (Figure 9.1).

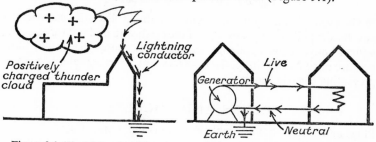

Figure 9.1. Electricity travelling towards the earth

Figure 9.2. Neutral return wire to earth

The mains electricity supply enters the house or salon at 240-V pressure through a *red* insulated *live* wire and returns to the power station or substation by way of the *black* insulated *neutral* wire, the end of which is connected to the *earth* (Figure 9.2). If a red insulated live wire were to break and make contact with the metal frame of the appliance, the frame would become 'live', giving an electric shock. The electricity would flow through the human body to the earth, since the

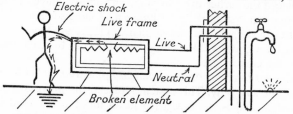

Figure 9.3. Electric shock from a non-earthed appliance

87

body offers a quicker route to earth than the black insulated neutral wire (Figure 9.3).

Earth wire is used to carry the electric current away from a live appliance to earth. It is a thick copper wire of low resistance and covered with *green* insulation (green fields and green earth!). Three-core cable and flexible cord consist of (*a*) red live wire, (*b*) black neutral wire, and (*c*) green earth wire. One end of the green earth wire is connected to the frame of the electric appliance, while the other end is connected to earth by way of a main cold-water pipe (Figure 9.4).

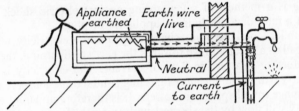

Figure 9.4. Earthed electric appliance

In the event of the appliance frame becoming 'live' the current will now flow rapidly to earth by way of the earth wire and not through the human body. A live appliance frame usually causes the fuse to blow because of short circuiting, the fuse acting as a further safety device in preventing electric shock.

PLUGS AND SOCKETS

Plugs and sockets are available in various types and sizes:

(*a*) *Two-pin* plugs have live and neutral connecting terminals *only* and are not provided with an earth terminal. They were used in early non-earthed electrical installations and are now rapidly becoming obsolete. It is strongly advised that a salon with two-pin plugs and sockets should change over to the three-pin system.

(*b*) *Three-pin* plugs and sockets are all provided with an earth terminal, which is the largest pin of the three.

   i. *Round* three-pin plugs and sockets are available in 2-, 5-, and 15-A sizes and are *not* fitted with fuses. This type of plug replaced the earlier two-pin plug. The disadvantage of the round three-pin system is that a house may have sockets of different sizes in each room, and appliance plugs may have to be fitted with long awkward trailing flexes in order to reach the socket of the correct size.

   ii. The *flat three-pin* or *fused standard* plug and socket is available in one size only. This system replaced the previous round-pin system and is the type used in all modern electrical installations or *ring* circuits (see below).

PROTECTIVE DEVICES FOR USERS OF ELECTRICITY

The main protective devices can be summarized as follows:

(*a*) *Insulation* (Chapter 7) protects the user of electricity from electric shock by means of non-conducting insulating material. Hand hair-dryers and mixers are *not* fitted with an earth wire since the bodies of these appliances are made of plastic insulating materials.

(*b*) *Fuses* (Chapter 8) protect the user from electric shock and fire by means of the thin easily melted fuse-wire, the weakest link in the circuit.

(*c*) *Earthing* protects the user from electric shock by means of the thick copper earth wire.

ELECTRICITY SAFETY PRECAUTIONS

1. Report any faulty appliance or switch, and replace frayed flexible cords.
2. All appliances should be fitted with three-pin plugs and should be earthed.
3. Never handle electrical appliances with *wet* hands or near to water and sinks.
4. Never pull out plugs by holding the flexible cord.
5. Always switch off the appliance at the wall switch before examining the appliance for faults.
6. Never overload an electric power-point. Always calculate the correct amperage needed for your appliance.
7. Never use portable appliances in the bathroom. All bathroom switches should be of the pendent cord type.
8. Broken switches and plugs should be replaced as soon as possible.
9. Never lay flexible cords under a carpet.
10. If in doubt call the electricity board.

SERIES AND PARALLEL CIRCUITS

The *series* circuit consists of appliances or resistances arranged one after the other in a circle; it is similar to a group of people joining hands in a ring (Figure 9.5).

Arrange six 1·5-V torch lamps in series as in Figure 9.6 and connect the circuit to a variable low-voltage supply. Note the voltage required to

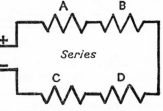

Figure 9.5. Series circuit

produce the normal lamp brightness. Remove one lamp from its holder and note how the circuit is broken.

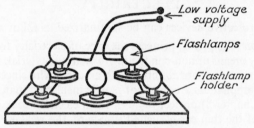

Figure 9.6. Lamps in series

It is seen that at least 9 volts are required to make the lamps burn brightly and the circuit is broken when a lamp is removed.

The joining of appliances or lamps in series calls for an *increased circuit voltage*, since the total resistance of the circuit equals the sum of each separate resistance. Series circuits are used in Christmas-tree and window-display lighting circuits.

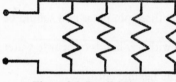

Figure 9.7. Parallel circuit

The *parallel* circuit arrangement of appliances or resistances is shown in Figure 9.7. It resembles a ladder or a row of people with their hands on each other's shoulders.

Arrange six 1·5-V torch lamps as in Figure 9.8 and connect the circuit to a 1·5-V accumulator. Remove one lamp and note how the remaining lamps continue to burn brightly. Insert a simple switch to control one lamp.

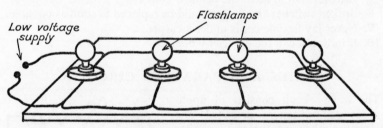

Figure 9.8. Lamps in parallel

When resistances are joined in parallel the total resistances of the appliances is *less* than each of the resistances separately, each lamp or appliance receiving the same amount of electricity. A lower voltage is required to operate the circuit. The parallel arrangement is used for all domestic electric circuits. Figure 9.9 shows electric lamps

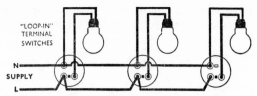

Figure 9.9. Lamps and switches in parallel

arranged in parallel; Figure 9.10 shows power-points arranged in parallel.

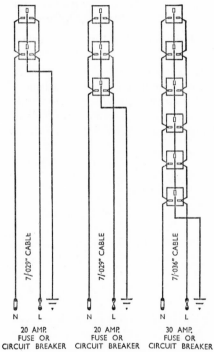

Figure 9.10. Power-points in parallel

APPLICATIONS OF A PARALLEL ARRANGEMENT

1. **The three-heat switch** with its low, medium, and high heat settings is used to control the heater unit of a hood hair-dryer. It consists of two resistances through which the current flows as follows: (*a*) *Low* heat or cool: the current flows through the two resistances in series; the amount of current to the heater unit is therefore *reduced* (Figure 9.11). (*b*) *Medium* heat: the current flows through one

resistance; therefore the amount of current reaching the heater unit is now *increased* (Figure 9.11). (*c*) *High* heat: the current flows

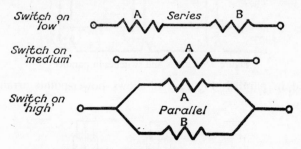

Figure 9.11. Three-heat switch circuit

through two resistances in parallel; the amount of current reaching the heater is now therefore considerably *greater* (Figure 9.11).

2. **Hairdressing salon circuits.** (i) *Old-type* distributive system (Figure 9.12). In this circuit a large fuse-box with its fuses of various sizes is situated next to a mains switch, meter, and electricity board's fuse.

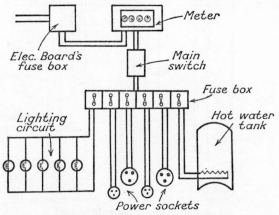

Figure 9.12. Old-type distributive circuit

The lights are supplied by a 5-A fused circuit with the lamps arranged in parallel. Each power socket has a separate length of cable to connect it to its own fuse. The power sockets of the older type installation may be of various sizes, 2, 5, and 15 A, and therefore non-interchangeable, without adaptors. They also require considerable lengths of expensive connecting cable and flexible cord.

(ii) *Modern ring circuit.* This circuit (Figure 9.13) consists of a compact consumer's fuse unit or circuit-breaker controlled by a mains switch. The lighting circuit is controlled by a 5-A fuse or 5-A miniature circuit-breaker. This is the fuse or miniature circuit-breaker to repair in the event of a breakdown in the lighting system. The electric immersion heater and cooker have separate 30-A fuses or 30-A circuit-breakers. The ring circuit consists of a cable that supplies all the power-points in your installation and is connected to one 30-A fuse or miniature circuit-breaker, the power-points being arranged in parallel (Figures 9.10 and 9.13).

The main *features* of the ring-main circuit (Figure 9.13) are:

1. All plugs and sockets are of the *same size*, namely 13-A standard

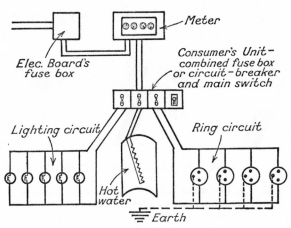

Figure 9.13. Modern ring circuit

plug and socket. The plugs of your appliance will therefore fit any other socket in your installation.
2. Each plug has its *own fuse*; this contributes to the safety of the system.
3. At least fifteen to twenty power-points can be included on one ring circuit, and this will allow one power socket for each appliance.
4. Considerably *less cable* is required to install the ring circuit compared with the old distributive circuit. This results in saving of cable and cuts down cost.
5. A faulty appliance will blow its own plug-top fuse and will not cause a general breakdown in the main circuit, with resulting inconvenience to all your clients.

Note. It is important to see that each of your plug tops is fitted with the correct size fuse for the appliance it is connected to.

★　★　★

SUGGESTIONS FOR PRACTICAL WORK

In addition to the experiments described in this chapter the following can be performed:

1. Obtain an old discarded electric fire or hairdressing appliance and dismantle it to see where the earth wire is connected to the frame of the appliance.
2. Find out what type of electricity circuit you have in your home and in your hairdressing salon.
3. Obtain 2-, 5- and 15-A round-pin plugs and compare their size and interior structure.
4. *How to wire a three-pin plug:*
    (*a*) Strip back, for about 2 in., the outer insulation of the flexible cord to expose the two current-carrying conductors (Figure 9.14).

Figure 9.14. Stages in wiring a three-pin standard fused plug

    (*b*) Cut off $\frac{1}{2}$ in. of the red live and black neutral conductor.
    (*c*) Strip off $\frac{1}{2}$ in. of insulation from all three wires.
    (*d*) Make a 'fishtail' end of the red live conductor as in Figure 9.14. Twist the bare wires of the black neutral and green earth to prevent splaying ends.
    (*e*) Connect up the wires as follows—RED wire to live pin *L*, BLACK wire to neutral pin *N*, GREEN wire to earth pin *E*.
        Fatal accidents may occur if the conducting wires are not connected correctly. If the flexible cord has a colour scheme other than red, black, and green **do not** attempt to connect it to a plug, but call in a qualified electrician. The red, black, and green colour code is used for all British cables and flexible cords. Continental and foreign cables use a different colour code of brown, yellow, etc. Do not use Continental flex without consulting a qualified electrician; it could be dangerous.
    (*f*) See that all stray strands of wire are cut away and that the rubber insulation reaches the terminals.
    (*g*) Tighten the screws of the cord grip to hold the cable or flexible cord firmly.
    (*h*) Replace the fuse of correct size and reassemble the plug top.
        The round-pin plug is connected in a similar manner. Do not attempt to connect a two-pin plug to any electrical appliance.
5. *How to wire a lamp-holder:*
    (*a*) Switch off the electricity supply at the main switch.

(b) Dismantle the lamp-holder and thread the flex through the cover.

(c) Insert the bare wires into the terminals and tighten the screws. Cut away any exposed bare wire.

(d) Hook the flex under the small lugs in order to take the weight of the lamp and its shade.

(e) Reassemble the lamp-holder and the shade.

   Note. Before cleaning lamps and shades, see that the main switch is off, then wipe over the lamp-shade with a damp soapy cloth.

A well-illustrated and informative booklet called *Design for Living*, describing the ring circuit in the home, can be obtained from J. A. Crabtree & Co. Ltd, Lincoln Works, Walsall, Staffs.

QUESTIONS ON CHAPTER 9

1. 'An efficiently operated electrical installation should never require fuse replacement, except for replacing old corroded fuses.' Comment on this statement and state how you would prevent fuses blowing.

2. Explain the term *watts*. Describe ways in which users of electrical appliances are protected against fire and shock. Illustrate your answer with simple diagrams.

3. Give one illustrated example of an electrical safety device. Make out a list of rules to observe when handling electrical appliances.

4. Explain the following terms: (a) simple electric circuit; (b) series arrangement; (c) parallel arrangement; (d) ring-main circuit; (e) short circuit.

5. Give an illustrated account of a typical modern electric installation for a hairdressing salon. Describe the advantages of such a circuit.

6. Draw and describe a standard universal fused plug. What size fuse is required for a plug fitted to a 1,500-W permanent-waving machine, operating from a 240-V mains supply?

7. Why has a power plug three pins? Give a brief account of the different types of plugs and sockets that you may encounter in an electric installation.

8. Give reasons for the failure of a hair-dryer to operate when switched on from a wall switch.

9. A person touches a live electric-fire frame and receives a severe electric shock. Describe how you would render first aid to this person.

10 ELECTROMAGNETISM

We have seen that electrical energy can be converted into heat and light. In this chapter we are to consider how an electric current can produce magnetism or *electromagnetism*. This is of considerable importance in connexion with its application to electric motors and other hairdressing appliances.

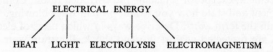

MAGNETISM

Magnetism is found in a natural mineral called *lodestone*. This mineral has the power of drawing iron filings towards itself; it is therefore magnetic.

PROPERTIES OF MAGNETS

1. Dip a bar magnet into iron filings and note how the iron filings gather in clusters at the ends or poles of the magnet.
2. Obtain a magnetic compass. This consists of a needle magnet, suspended over a compass card. Note how the compass needle, or magnet, always comes to rest in the same position. The magnetic pole that points to the north is called the north-seeking magnetic pole.
3. Using the apparatus shown in Figure 10.1, arrange the magnets

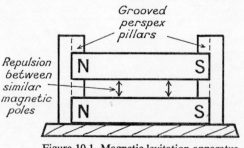

Figure 10.1. Magnetic levitation apparatus

96

with their north poles parallel to each other. It will be seen that one magnet floats above the other, owing to magnetic *repulsion* between similar magnetic poles. Arrange the magnets with opposite poles, north and south, parallel to each other and observe how they are strongly drawn towards each other:

> Like poles *repel* each other.
> Unlike poles *attract* each other.

4. Place a piece of paper over a bar magnet and carefully sprinkle iron filings on to the paper from a pepper-pot. Gently tap the paper with a pencil and note how the iron filings arrange themselves into a definite pattern showing the *magnetic field* of the magnet (Figure 10.2).

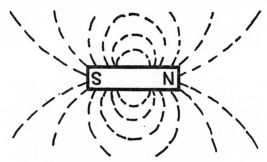

Figure 10.2. Magnetic field of a magnet

MAKING MAGNETS

Certain metals such as iron, steel, and nickel are magnetic, that is, they are drawn towards a magnet. These metals are also used to make magnets. *Soft iron* is used to make horse-shoes and nails. It magnetizes easily but soon loses its magnetism and is called a temporary magnetic substance. Permanent magnets are made from *hard steel*, which is difficult to magnetize but keeps its magnetism longer than soft iron.

The **single-touch** method of magnetization consists in stroking a piece of metal, such as a 6-in. nail or an old clock-spring, with a permanent magnet. The stroking must always be in the same direction, as shown in Figure 10.3.

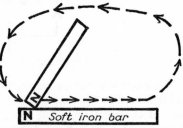

Figure 10.3. Single-touch method of making a magnet

H

The **electromagnet** consists of a coil of cotton insulated copper or a *solenoid* wrapped round a 6-in. nail, the coil being connected to a battery and switch as in Figure 10.4. A dish of tacks or iron filings is held below the 6-in. nail and the current switched on. It will be seen that the iron filings or tacks are drawn towards the nail that has now become a strong electromagnet. When the current is switched off the iron filings fall back into the dish.

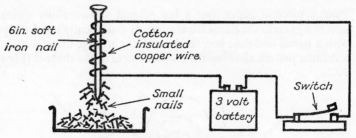

Figure 10.4. Simple electromagnet

If a greater number of coils is wound on to the solenoid it will be seen that more iron filings can be picked up because the electro-magnetism has now been increased. Increasing the flow of electric current by using more batteries will result in greater electromagnetism. Plate 6 illustrates an apparatus used to show the magnetic field that is produced when a current flows through a solenoid coil. The iron filings arrange themselves into a visible magnetic field. This apparatus has terminals which, when connected to the current, produce a stronger magnetic effect owing to the increased number of coils in the solenoid.

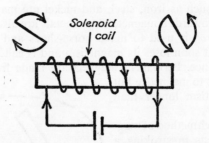

Figure 10.5. Polarity of a solenoid coil

The electromagnet has *magnetic poles* similar to a bar magnet; they are indicated in Figure 10.5. The south pole shows a *clockwise* direction of current flow, while the north pole shows an *anti-clockwise* direction of current flow. Applications of electromagnets are to be seen in powerful electromagnet cranes used in scrap-iron yards.

The miniature *circuit-breaker* (see Chapter 8) operates by a spring-loaded electromagnetic mechanism that comes into operation when too much current flows through the switch as in overloading of appliances.

The simple *electric bell* (Figure 10.6) consists of a solenoid that attracts a piece of soft iron causing the hammer to strike the bell and at the same time break the circuit. The spring-operated soft iron moves

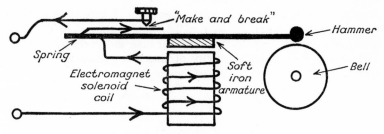

Figure 10.6. Electric bell circuit

back to its original position in turn, switching on the current and causing the hammer to strike the bell, owing to the electromagnetic attraction produced by the solenoid coil.

Electromagnets are used in hospitals to remove tiny pieces of metal that have entered the eye accidentally.

INDUCED ELECTRIC CURRENTS

Obtain a solenoid coil of many turns of cotton insulated wire and connect it to a *galvanometer*, which is a very sensitive current-detecting device.

Push a strong bar magnet into the solenoid coil and note the deflection of the galvanometer needle. Withdraw the magnet and again

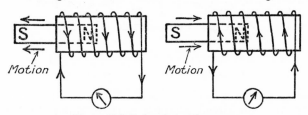

Figure 10.7. Induced electric current

note the deflexion of the galvanometer. An induced electric current (see Figure 10.7) has been made by moving a bar magnet and a stationary solenoid coil. *Motion* or mechanical energy has been converted into *electrical* energy. The direction of flow of the induced electric current alters as the magnet enters and leaves the solenoid coil. Such a current is described as an *alternating current* (*a.c.*). Repeat the experiment keeping the bar magnet stationary and move the coil over the magnet.

Note. In the electromagnet circuit, electricity flowing in one direction or *direct current* (*d.c.*) is used to produce magnetism.

DYNAMOS OR ELECTRIC GENERATORS

An electric dynamo or direct current generator (Figure 10.8) makes a direct current of electricity by rapidly spinning the solenoid coil or *armature* between the poles of strong bar magnets or electromagnets. The alternating current electricity produced is picked up from the *split-ring commutator* by means of the graphite *brushes*.

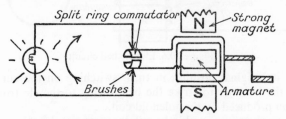

Figure 10.8. Direct current: dynamo or generator

Obtain an old G.P.O. telephone hand-generator as fitted in the older-type telephone switch-boards and mount it on a wooden board as in Figure 10.9. A 150-V voltmeter and 110-V filament lamp are fitted into the circuit. Turn the handle of the generator, first slowly, and then faster, when it will be seen that the lamp burns brightly as the current generated is increased. Remove the lamp and operate

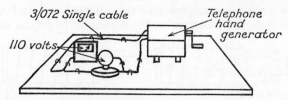

Figure 10.9. Telephone hand-generator

the dynamo generator again, when it will be noticed that removing the lamp from the circuit makes it easier to rotate the handle of the dynamo generator. (*Note.* Do not touch the bare terminals of the dynamo generator, for a severe electric shock (110 volts) will be experienced.) Dismantle the dynamo generator and notice the two large permanent magnets and coiled armature. The *alternator generator* is similar to a dynamo in having a coil or armature rotating between stationary magnet poles (Figure 10.10). The alternating current pro-

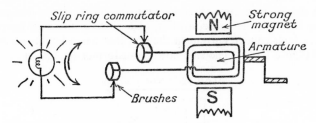

Figure 10.10. Alternating current

duced is picked up from the *slip rings* by means of the graphite brushes. This is the type of generator used for the large-scale production of electricity.

ALTERNATING AND DIRECT ELECTRIC CURRENTS

Direct current, or d.c., flows in one direction only. It is obtained from chemical dry batteries, accumulators, battery-chargers, and dynamo generators and is used in cars, ships, and bicycle lights.

Alternating current, or a.c., is obtained from alternator generators and transformers and is the type of current generated on a large scale for use in consumers' appliances. If the direction of flow of an alternating current alters 50 times per second, its *frequency* is described as 50 cycles. *High frequency* will mean the current alters more than 50 times a second. Approximately 90 per cent of all electricity consumers have a.c. supplies; the remainder use d.c., some of it from small private generators. Most appliances are made to operate on a.c. or d.c. supplies, but this must be checked when ordering new equipment.

The a.c. mains-operated battery-charger converts or *rectifies* a.c. into d.c. Accumulators cannot be charged by means of alternating current.

TRANSFORMERS

The transformer is an apparatus for changing the voltage of an electric current (a.c.). There are two main types of transformer: step-up transformers, and step-down transformers. Step-up transformers convert current from a *low* voltage to a *higher* voltage. Such transformers are found in a power station, where the voltage is stepped up from 11,000 V to 132,000 V.

Step-down transformers convert from a *high* to a *lower* voltage. For example, radio and television sets have step-down transformers converting the mains voltage from 240 V to 12 V a.c.

The transformer consists of two insulated copper coils wrapped round a soft iron core. Step-up transformers take in low-voltage current through the coil consisting of a small number of turns and produce high-voltage current in the coil that has a larger number of turns (Figure 10.11). The step-down transformer operates in reverse.

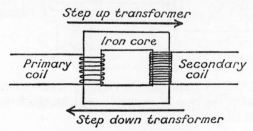

Figure 10.11. Transformer structure

INDUCTION COILS

The induction coil is an apparatus (see Plate 7) used to produce a *high-voltage* direct current from a *low-voltage* direct current supply. The high-voltage direct current produced flows intermittently, that is, the current stops or 'breaks', which is followed by starting or 'making'.

The induction coil consists of two coils: (*a*) the *primary coil* of thick insulated copper wire wrapped round a core of soft iron rods; (*b*) the

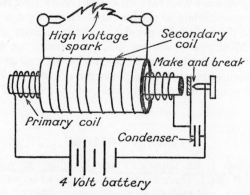

Figure 10.12. Induction coil structure

secondary coil, consisting of thin insulated wire several miles long, wrapped around the primary coil as in Figure 10.12. When the current is switched on, sparks of electricity at a high voltage will discharge across the gap between the terminals. A neon gas *discharge tube* can be fitted into the circuit showing the typical 'neon light' appearance as the electricity discharges through the tube.

Note. High voltages between 1,000 V and 300,000 V can be produced in an induction coil. Such apparatus should be used only under expert supervision.

APPLICATION OF THE INDUCTION COIL

1. Sparking-plugs in motor-car engines operate from a high-voltage induction coil.
2. X-ray and ultra-violet lamps (see Chapter 11).
3. Street lighting and neon signs.
4. High-frequency hairdressing treatment involves the use of an induction coil. The apparatus produces a *high-voltage* current of *very low strength* or *amperage* that discharges from the glass electrode into the skin surface, stimulating the *arrector pili* muscles of the hair. The high-voltage low-amperage current obtained from this induction coil is *intermittent* and *alternating*. This means the current flow stops and changes its direction of flow very frequently. The main effect of high-frequency current is to stimulate nerves and muscle fibres into activity and to dilate the blood capillaries present in the *dermis* layer of the skin.

    When the glass electrode is held near the skin a distinct smell is noticed as the high-voltage current discharges through the air. This is due to a gas, *ozone*. Ozone is formed in the vicinity of electrical machines that produce electric sparks. The smell of ozone can be detected near turbine generators and X-ray machines (and also near to ultra-violet ray lamps). In medicine the gas is used as an antiseptic and air-purifier. During high-frequency treatment the ozone produced also exerts a disinfecting action on the hair and skin.

    Note. Ozone is highly poisonous in large concentration.

Summary:

1. The step-up transformer produces a high-voltage alternating current of *considerable strength* or high amperage. An electric shock from such a transformer would have fatal results.
2. The high-frequency induction coil produces a high-voltage alternating current of *low strength* or *negligible amperage*; there is therefore not sufficient power to give a fatal electric shock.

ELECTRIC MOTORS

The action of an electric motor is the reverse to that of a dynamo. That is, electrical energy is converted into motion or mechanical energy:

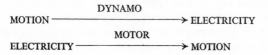

The electric motor (Figure 10.13) consists of an *armature* coil rotating between strong electromagnets. The current flowing through the armature coil is picked up from the *split-ring commutator* by way of the carbon graphite brushes. This is the type of motor fitted into most

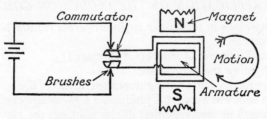

Figure 10.13. The electric motor

electrically driven appliances of *fractional* horse-power rating; that is, motors that use small amounts of electricity (one horse-power = 746 watts). Fractional horse-power motors are also called *universal* motors, being designed to operate on a.c. or d.c. supplies. If an electric hair-

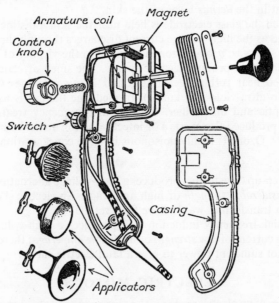

Figure 10.14. Vibrator massage machine: exploded view

dryer consumes say, 800 W, 750 W is used by the heater while only 50 W is used to drive the motor (see Figure 8.8).

The vibrator massage machine (Figure 10.14) does not operate by means of a universal motor but must have either an a.c. or d.c.

supply. Always check whether the motor-driven appliances you are about to purchase operate from an a.c. or d.c. supply.

LARGE-SCALE GENERATION OF ELECTRICITY

Large power stations produce electricity in alternator generators similar to that previously described.

The mechanical energy required to spin the armature or rotor is obtained from the following sources:

(*a*) water power or hydro-electric power;
(*b*) steam obtained by heating water in a boiler by burning coal or fuel oil, or from atomic energy;
(*c*) oil- or gas-driven engines.

Water or steam jets are directed on to the blades of the *turbine wheel*, which is thus made to spin rapidly. In turn it causes the generator rotor to spin, and electricity is produced.

Transmission and distribution of electricity to the consumer is by means of step-up transformers that send the electricity into the overhead cables of the 'grid' system to all parts of the country, and step-down transformers that reduce the voltage to the 240 V required for domestic purposes.

★ ★ ★

SUGGESTIONS FOR PRACTICAL WORK

1. Obtain a number of magnets and study their magnetic properties using the method described in this chapter.
2. Examine an electric bell. Using a dry battery, connecting wire, and a bell-push, set up the electric bell circuit.

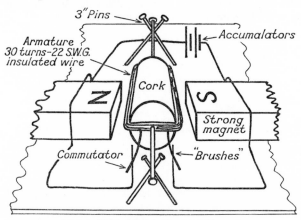

Figure 10.15. Model of an electric motor

3. Obtain a G.P.O. telephone hand-generator from surplus government material stockists. Set up the generator as shown in this chapter.
4. Obtain an old discarded high-frequency apparatus, dismantle it, and examine the circuit coils and the 'make-and-break' mechanism.
5. Construct the simple electric motor shown in Figure 10.15. Wrap at least 30 turns of 0·22 S.W.G. cotton insulated wire round a large cork. The coil may be kept in position with 'Sellotape'. Use 3-in. pins to support the coil. The remaining part of the motor consists of two strong bar magnets placed on either side of the coil. Use a 2-V accumulator to supply current to the motor. Note the effect of using more than one accumulator.

QUESTIONS ON CHAPTER 10

1. Describe high-frequency equipment. What precautions are necessary in its use?
2. What is meant by *voltage*? Describe two methods of producing high voltages. State the method used in a hairdressing treatment.
3. Describe an experiment to show how you would make a simple electro-magnet. How would you increase the electromagnetic effect of your apparatus? Give two examples of the application of electromagnetism.
4. What is an induced electric current? Describe how an induced current can be produced. Explain the terms *alternating* and *direct current*.
5. Draw and describe an induction coil. Give two applications of this apparatus.
6. Give a brief account of the large-scale method of generating and dis-tributing electricity.
7. Describe a simple electric motor. Explain the terms *motor horse-power* and *fractional horse-power motors*. What kind of motor would you find in electrical appliances?
8. Write short notes on the following: (*a*) turbines; (*b*) frequency; (*c*) alter-nating and direct current; (*d*) ozone; (*e*) magnets.
9. An electric meter nameplate is stamped: 230 volts, 50 cycles a.c. Total amperes = 60. Explain briefly the meaning of these terms.

11 LIGHT AND COLOUR

Light is a form of *energy* that is produced by, for example:

(*a*) the sun,
(*b*) atomic energy: the atom bomb produces a blinding light,
(*c*) electricity,
(*d*) burning fuels.

All light travels in *straight lines*. This can be demonstrated by means of the ray box (Plate 10). A further example is given when a beam of sunlight streams through a small opening in the curtains of a darkened room. The straight edges of the light beam are easily seen.

Transparent materials such as glass and 'Perspex' allow light rays to pass through them.

Opaque materials such as wood and iron prevent light rays from passing through them.

Translucent materials, for example, frosted glass, plastic lampshades and greaseproof paper, allow some light rays to pass through them. Hair is regarded as a translucent material in that it allows some light to pass through it and therefore produces the attractive so-called 'highlights' clearly seen in fair hair.

REFLECTION OF LIGHT

When a beam of light strikes a surface three things can happen to it, according to the nature of the surface (Figure 11.1).

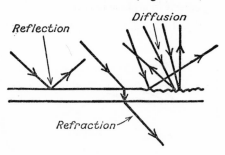

Figure 11.1. Reflection, refraction, and diffusion of light

1. The beam of light can be *reflected* from a polished surface.
2. The beam of light can penetrate into and through the material if it is transparent—*refraction*.
3. The beam of light can be scattered or *diffused* if the surface of the material is rough. The individual surface scales of the hair fibre diffuse the light, producing an attractive lustre.

Light striking the smooth oiled surface of hair is partly reflected and partly refracted. Scattering of the light by diffusion shows up dry hair in poor condition. The rough surface of paper makes the paper appear white by diffusion of light rays.

The *law of reflection* (shown in Figure 11.2) is given as follows:

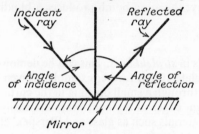

Figure 11.2. Law of reflection of light

The angle formed by the incident ray equals the angle formed by the reflected ray.

MIRRORS

Mirrors are made of very thin highly polished sheets of glass that are coated with a reflecting layer of silver metal or an *amalgam* of tin and mercury metals. Sheets of highly polished stainless steel may also be used as mirrors, but their surface is liable to damage by scratches.

Note. Lacquer deposits on salon mirrors are easily removed with a cloth damped with methylated spirit.

How you can see yourself in a plane mirror

Consider a small object placed in front of a mirror. This object will

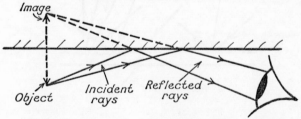

Figure 11.3. Formation of an image in a plane mirror

give out light rays that will travel towards the mirror and be reflected in accordance with the law of reflection (see Figure 11.3). The reflected rays will now enter the eye, where an image of the object is seen as if it were coming from the back of the mirror.

Lateral inversion

This is the term used to describe how the right side of the *object* appears as the left side of the *image*. Figure 11.4 shows the lateral inversion of letters or side-to-side turning of the mirror image.

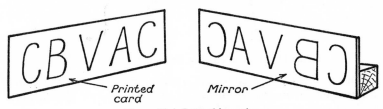

Figure 11.4. Lateral inversion

Figure 11.5 illustrates the arrangement of mirrors used to view the back of a person's head, showing the light-ray paths.

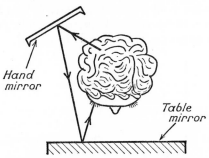

Figure 11.5. Reflection in a hand-mirror

Two or more inclined mirrors can be used to produce a large number of images, as shown in Plate 9. This type of mirror arrangement is used to display articles for exhibition purposes and for wall mirrors used in salon decor.

Curved mirrors

Curved mirrors are of two kinds: (*a*) concave mirrors, the reflecting surface curves *inwardly*; (*b*) convex mirrors, the reflecting surface curves *outwardly*.

The concave mirror is used to *magnify* the size of the object and is used for this purpose in shaving and cosmetic compact mirrors. When a concave mirror is used for the purposes described, the face must be brought close up to the mirror. Figure 11.6 shows the use of a concave mirror as a shaving or compact mirror.

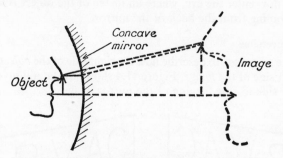

Figure 11.6. Formation of an image in a concave mirror

Convex mirrors are used to give smaller images than the object and are used mostly in driving mirrors of cars. This mirror gives a wider angle of view of traffic behind the car.

THE SPECTRUM: DISPERSION OF LIGHT

Obtain a glass *prism*, hold it towards a source of light and observe the rainbow colours of the *spectrum*. A spectrum can be projected on to a screen using the apparatus arranged in Figure 11.7.

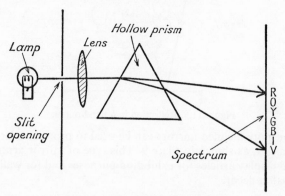

Figure 11.7. Formation of a spectrum

The lamphouse is fitted with a slit opening, so that the light rays pass through the lens as a parallel beam of light. The *hollow* glass prism is filled with *carbon disulphide* (inflammable and unpleasant-smelling) and placed in the path of the white light, when a spectrum will be projected on to the screen. This experiment shows that white light can be split up into a mixture of colours, or the component colours of white light can be separated or dispersed by means of a prism:

$$\text{White light} = \text{Spectrum (ROYGBIV)} \begin{cases} \text{Red} \\ \text{Orange} \\ \text{Yellow} \\ \text{Green} \\ \text{Blue} \\ \text{Indigo} \\ \text{Violet} \end{cases}$$

A rainbow is an example of the production of a spectrum by the dispersion of sunlight through water droplets of rain.

White light can be re-formed from its components by rapidly spinning a card painted with the seven colours of the spectrum. The coloured card is fixed to the whirling table and made to turn rapidly when it appears to be nearly white, showing the re-formation of white light from the spectrum (Plate 8).

INFRA-RED, ULTRA-VIOLET, AND X-RAYS

Sunlight energy travels towards the earth partly as visible white light and partly as invisible *electromagnetic rays*, such as ultra-violet, infra-red, and X-rays. The sun may be considered as a great atomic bomb or radioactive substance that is undergoing continuous decomposition or *fission*, during which it gives out heat, light, and other rays, which travel towards the earth.

Instead of the term *rays* we can also use the alternative term— *waves*. Waves can be classified according to their wavelengths into short, medium, and long waves. The wavelength is the distance between the crests of two waves (Figure 11.8).

Figure 11.8. Wavelength

The following shows the electromagnetic waves that are contained in sunlight:

RADIO WAVES	INFRA-RED	VISIBLE SPECTRUM (ROYGBIV)	ULTRA-VIOLET RAYS	X-RAYS

All the electromagnetic waves of sunlight reach the earth except the harmful short-wave X-rays.

ULTRA-VIOLET RAYS

Ultra-violet rays are those beyond the violet end of the spectrum. They are present in sunlight and will travel through clean air towards the earth. Smoke-laden air will *prevent* the rays reaching the earth. Ultra-violet rays are beneficial to the human body, since they can produce *vitamin D* in the skin. The rays have important *disinfecting* powers and are used to disinfect wounds, water, and air. Ultra-violet ray therapy is useful for treating certain skin complaints such as boils and spots.

Artificial sunlight or ultra-violet ray treatment can be provided by the *mercury vapour* lamp or the *carbon-arc* lamp. In the carbon-arc lamp (Figure 11.9) a high-voltage current is struck between carbon-

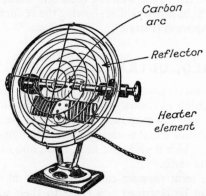

Figure 11.9. Carbon-arc ultra-violet ray lamp

rod electrodes. The mercury-vapour lamp is used in the artificial sun-lamp of the type shown in Plate 12.

It is essential to wear dark-coloured spectacles when receiving ultra-violet ray treatment, since the rays are harmful to the naked eye.

Ultra-violet ray lamps are used by skin specialists to diagnose ring-worm of the scalp; when exposed to the rays the infected hairs give off a yellow-green light or fluorescence.

X-RAYS

X-rays are produced in special X-ray tubes, by the discharge of a high-voltage current through the tube. X-rays are *harmful* in large doses, since they destroy cells and tissues. For this reason X-rays are given in carefully controlled doses to destroy ringworm and cancerous growths. The use of X-rays for locating bone fractures and faults in metal castings is among the more notable applications.

INFRA-RED RAYS

Infra-red rays are those rays that lie beyond the red end of visible spectrum, and are present in sunlight. All heated matter gives off infra-red rays. Infra-red rays are used mostly in radiant heat-treatment for the relief of pain in muscles and joints. The applied heat improves the circulation of the blood in these organs. Combined ultra-violet and infra-red lamps are available for use in the home.

Note. Electromedical and radiant treatment in any form should not be given to a person without the prior approval of a physician or surgeon. Physiotherapists normally administer the treatment under medical supervision.

COLOURS

Red, green, and blue are called *primary* colours, because *any* colour can be obtained by mixing them. White can also be formed as shown in the whirling disc experiment. This colour mixing effect applies to coloured lights as used for stage illumination.

PRIMARY COLOURS $\begin{cases} \text{RED} & + \text{ GREEN} = \text{YELLOW} \\ \text{RED} & + \text{ BLUE} \ = \text{MAGENTA} \\ \text{BLUE} & + \text{ GREEN} = \text{PEACOCK} \end{cases}$

RED   +   BLUE   +   GREEN = WHITE

The colour of a solid object such as a red rose is due to all the colours of white light being *absorbed* (OYGBIV) except the red colour which is *reflected.* White objects reflect *all* the colours of the spectrum (ROYGBIV) and none is absorbed. Black objects *absorb all* the colours of the spectrum (ROYGBIV); none is reflected. Black hair is therefore the result of the hair pigment absorbing all the colours of the spectrum. White hair is due to the reflection of the spectrum colours by the *air* bubbles trapped within the hair shaft. Skin and hair pigmentation is caused by a substance called *melanin.*

Artificial light produced by electric filament lamps is yellowish-red in colour, being deficient in the blue and green colours of the spectrum; this makes colour-matching difficult by artificial light. Fluorescent light provides the nearest approach to natural daylight. Fluorescent lamps are mercury-vapour lamps generating ultra-violet radiation which is absorbed by the fluorescent lining of the tube and reflected as white light.

I

LIGHTING AND LAMPS

The lighting installation of a hairdressing establishment should provide sufficient illumination to allow people to work free from eyestrain which may be caused by *glare* or *poor light*.

The rate of flow of light is *measured* in units called *lumens*. Illumination is measured in *lumens per square foot*, or the amount of light falling on an area of one square foot per second. Sunlight is equivalent to 10,000 lumens per square foot; daylight indoors by a window to 200 lumens per square foot.

GLARE

Glare is discomfort caused by dazzling bright light entering the eyes. The main causes of glare are:

(*a*) reflection from *polished* or *shiny* surfaces such as mirrors, glass, painted walls, ceilings, and highly polished furniture;

(*b*) *unshaded* lamps with *clear glass* filament lamps fitted in them.

Glare can be prevented by the following methods involving illumination by *diffused light*:

(*a*) Walls, ceilings, and furniture should have a roughened or matt finish in order to *diffuse* the light.

(*b*) Warm-coloured paints in *matt* finish should be used.

(*c*) Opal or pearl lamps should be used in open lampshades. Clear glass lamps should be fitted with *translucent* shades.

(*d*) Fluorescent lighting gives a soft white diffused light with very little glare.

(*e*) Mirror lights should shine on the client's face and not on the mirror itself. Small pearl tubular lamps can be arranged on either side of the mirror, or small wall-lamps fitted with diffusing shades can be used.

Plate 11 illustrates a hairdressing salon in which glare is eliminated by diffused lighting.

★   ★   ★

SUGGESTIONS FOR PRACTICAL WORK

1. Experiment to prove the law of reflection: support a strip of plane mirror on a sheet of drawing paper (Figure 11.10). Mark the position of the mirror on the paper. Place two pins in the positions *A* and *B*. Place two more pins *C* and *D* in front of the mirror and in line with the images of *A* and *B*. Remove the mirror and the pins, draw the lines *AB* and *CD* and

construct line *EF* perpendicular to the mirror surface By measurement the angle *AEF* should prove equal to the angle *CEF*.

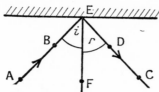

Figure 11.10. Experiment to prove law of reflection of light

2. Obtain a ray-box and use the apparatus to demonstrate reflection of light rays from (i) plane, and (ii) curved mirrors. A similar ray-box can be obtained for mixing the three primary colours.
3. Examine your hairdressing salon illumination system as follows:

   (*a*) wall and ceiling surfaces;
   (*b*) colour scheme used for decor;
   (*c*) mirror illumination;
   (*d*) type of lamps and shades used;
   (*e*) reflecting power of furniture, fittings, and floor surface.

   The ideal salon should have a complete absence of dazzling light and glare. Does this apply to your salon?
4. Arrange a visit to the physiotherapy unit of your local hospital to observe the correct use of the various electro-medical appliances.

QUESTIONS ON CHAPTER 11

1. Explain the term *dispersion of light*. Describe an experiment to illustrate how you would obtain a spectrum. Give a brief account of the importance of infra-red and ultra-violet rays.
2. Explain the terms *reflection* and *diffusion* of light rays. Draw ray diagrams showing how (*a*) an image is formed in a plane mirror, and (*b*) how a client can be shown the hair arrangement at the back of her head.
3. What is the cause of light glare? Why is diffused light important in hairdressing salons?
4. Give a short illustrated account of radiant or ray treatments and their applications.
5. Write short notes on the following: (*a*) lateral inversion; (*b*) concave mirrors; (*c*) primary colours; (*d*) fluorescent tube lighting.
6. Write a short essay on 'light'.
7. Give an account of the main factors that contribute to the condition or healthy appearance of hair.
8. Draw a diagram showing the position of the electromagnetic waves in relation to the visible spectrum. Describe how one of the short-wave radiations is produced and its main uses.

PART II
Chemistry

12 CHEMISTRY AND CHEMICAL TERMS

Chemistry is the study of the behaviour and composition of matter, or the study of what matter is made of. Chemistry is important to hairdressers in so far as it shows the composition and properties of the substances used in various hairdressing processes.

Chemistry is providing hairdressers with a wide range of preparations that have resulted in new shampoos, cold-waving lotions, dyes, rinses, and a variety of cosmetics, each preparation carefully prepared and developed through painstaking research work. It is therefore vital for trained hairdressers to have a sound knowledge of chemical science in order to understand thoroughly the appliances and chemical preparations they use.

CLASSIFICATION AND PROPERTIES

Classification and orderly arrangement of knowledge is the basis of scientific study; in other words, the scientist tries to sort out all his facts in a similar manner to the postman who sorts or classifies all

COMPARISON OF THE PROPERTIES OF METHYLATED SPIRIT AND WATER, INDICATING HOW THESE TWO LIQUIDS ARE CLASSIFIED OR 'SORTED'

Substance	Water	Methylated spirit
Chemical name:	Hydrogen monoxide	Ethyl alcohol
Physical properties:		
State	Clear colourless liquid	Blue-coloured liquid
Smell	None	Yeast-like
Taste	None	Burning taste
Specific gravity	1·0	0·80 (lighter than water)
Boiling-point	100°C	80°C
	Non-volatile	Volatile
	Slow to evaporate	Evaporates easily
Chemical properties	Does not burn	Burns easily with a blue flame
Chemical test	Turns white anhydrous copper sulphate blue	No action on anhydrous copper sulphate

letters and parcels. *Properties* are the first stage in sorting scientific knowledge of a substance. This means a substance is classified according to (*a*) physical properties, appearances, etc., and (*b*) chemical properties.

Physical properties include the general appearance of the substance and such *measurable* properties as its specific gravity and electrical conductivity.

Chemical properties indicate the *behaviour* of the substance when burnt or treated with other chemical substances.

CHEMICAL AND PHYSICAL CHANGES

Chemical and physical changes are terms used to describe the classification of the *changes* that matter can undergo.

Experiment

Mix together iron filings and powdered sulphur; divide the mixture into two equal parts and treat them as follows:

Part *A*: Heat the mixture gently in a hard glass test-tube. Note how the contents glow. Withdraw the heat and observe the miniature volcano effect. When the tube is cool, break it and examine the appearance and other properties of the contents. Add a little dilute hydrochloric acid to some of the solid and note what happens. Try the effect of a magnet on the solid.

Part *B*: Push a magnet into the mixture. Add a little dilute hydrochloric acid to the mixture and note what happens.

DIFFERENCES BETWEEN CHEMICAL AND PHYSICAL CHANGES

Chemical change	*Physical change*
Change in composition	*Change of state*
New substance formed, e.g., action of hydrogen peroxide on natural hair colour	No new substance formed, e.g., heating Marcel waving irons.
Heat given out, e.g., permanent-waving sachet, i.e., exothermic reaction	No heat given out, e.g., dissolving salt in water.
Difficult to reverse, e.g., it is impossible to change bleached hair back to its *natural* colour	Easily reversed, e.g., turn water into steam, and vice versa.

When the mixture of iron filings and sulphur is heated it undergoes a *chemical change*, because: (*a*) a *new* (black) substance is formed, (*b*) considerable *heat* is produced by the chemical change, (*c*) the new substance formed *differs* from the original mixture in being non-magnetic and has a different reaction with hydrochloric acid.

The following are some important physical changes: boiling, melting, evaporation, condensation, distillation, heating, magnetic and lighting effect of electric current. All these changes are temporary and easily reversed.

ELEMENTS, COMPOUNDS, AND MIXTURES

Elements, compounds, and mixtures are terms used in the classification of matter and chemical substances. All chemical substances are sorted or classified into one of the following classes.

ELEMENTS

Elements are the *simplest* forms of matter, and are the simple substances that combine to make all compounds and mixtures.

There are about a hundred different chemical elements that go to make up all the forms of matter on this earth.

SOME OF THE MORE IMPORTANT ELEMENTS THAT ENTER INTO HAIRDRESSING CHEMISTRY

Metals			*Non-metals*		
Name	*Symbol*	*Physical Property*	*Name*	*Symbol*	*Physical Property*
Aluminium	Al	Grey solid	Bromine	Br	Brown liquid
Antimony	Sb	Grey solid	Carbon	C	Black solid
Arsenic	As	Grey solid	Chlorine	Cl	Greenish-yellow gas
Calcium	Ca	Silver solid			
Chromium	Cr	Bright solid silver	Fluorine	F	Colourless gas
			Helium	He	Colourless gas
Copper	Cu	Brown, red solid	Hydrogen	H	Colourless gas
			Iodine	I	Black solid
Gold	Au	Yellow solid	Neon	Ne	Colourless gas
Iron	Fe	Grey solid	Nitrogen	N	Colourless gas
Lead (*Plumbum*)	Pb	Grey solid	Oxygen	O	Colourless gas
Magnesium	Mg	Grey solid	Phosphorus	P	White solid
Manganese	Mn	Black solid	Silicon	Si	Brown solid
Mercury (*Hydrargyrum*)	Hg	Silver liquid	Sulphur	S	Yellow solid
			Xenon	Xe	Colourless gas
Nickel	Ni	Grey solid			
Platinum	Pt	Silver solid			
Potassium (*Kalium*)	K	Soft silvery solid			
Silver (*Argentum*)	Ag	Silver solid			
Sodium (*Natrium*)	Na	Silver solid			
Tin (*Stannum*)	Sn	Grey solid			
Zinc	Zn	Grey solid			

The *symbol* written alongside the name of the chemical element is the chemist's shorthand system for showing *one atom* of the element.

The symbol is usually the first letter of the name of the element, e.g., H for hydrogen; O for oxygen; or it may consist of two letters, e.g., Ca for calcium.

Note. The first letter of a symbol is always a capital letter.

Some symbols for elements have been derived from the Latin name since early scientists and doctors used the Latin language in speech and writing. Iron, Fe (from the latin *ferrum*); copper, Cu (*cuprum*); sodium, Na (*natrium*); gold, Au (*aurum*).

Some uses of various elements

1. Aluminium, antimony, copper, and carbon are used in eye-shadow and eyebrow preparations.
2. Chromium-plated iron is used for many hairdressing appliances.
3. Sulphur in ointment form is used for skin diseases and as a lotion for scalp treatment.
4. Mercury is used in ointment form for skin diseases.
5. Magnesium is used in the photographic flash-bulb.
6. Aluminium, copper, nickel, and iron are used in a variety of metal appliances too numerous to mention.

Metals and non-metals

All chemical elements are divided into two sub-classes, namely metals and non-metals as shown in the preceding table.

TYPICAL PROPERTIES OF METALS AND NON-METALS

Metals	*Non-metals*
Have a metallic lustre	No metallic lustre
Good conductors of heat and electricity (see list of conductors [Chapters 5 & 7])	Poor conductors, or insulators (except graphite carbon, used for electric motor brushes)
Can be hammered and drawn	Brittle
High densities, e.g., mercury 13·6 gm/cm³	Low densities, e.g., hydrogen
Travel to the cathode during electrolysis	Travel to the anode during electrolysis (except hydrogen, which goes to the cathode)

COMPOUNDS

Compounds are substances formed by the chemical union of two or more elements:

$$Element + Element = Compound$$

For example, when the elements iron and sulphur are heated together, a chemical change takes place, and a chemical *compound*, iron sulphide, is formed.

$$\frac{\text{Iron}}{\text{element}} + \frac{\text{Sulphur}}{\text{element}} = \frac{\text{Iron sulphide}}{\text{compound}}$$

The component elements of iron sulphide cannot be separated by means of a magnet.

MIXTURES

Mixtures are made up of two or more substances, elements or compounds, that are present in different amounts and can be easily separated:

$$\text{Element iron} + \text{Element sulphur} = \frac{\text{Mixture of iron}}{\text{and sulphur}}$$

$$\frac{\text{Compound}}{\text{iron sulphide}} + \text{Element sulphur} = \frac{\text{Mixture of iron}}{\text{sulphide and sulphur}}$$

The iron filings can be easily removed from the mixture by means of a magnet.

SOME COMPOUNDS AND MIXTURES IMPORTANT IN HAIRDRESSING

		Chemical name of substance	*Composition*
Compounds	Hair—keratin	C, H, O, S, and N	
	Hydrogen peroxide	H and O	
	Soap—sodium palmitate	Na, C, O, and H	
	Ammonia—ammonium hydroxide solution	N, H, and O	
	Cold wave—reagent ammonium thioglycollate	N, H, S, C, and O	
Mixtures	Air	O and N	
	White henna	Mg, C, O, N, and H	
	Mascara	C and H	
	Calamine lotion	$ZnCO_3$ and H_2O	

Hair is a compound of the following elements: carbon (51%), hydrogen (7%), oxygen (19%), sulphur (5%), and nitrogen (18%). All these elements are joined together *chemically* and cannot be separated. Hair cannot be made by mixing these elements together in the proportions indicated.

Synthesis is the term used to describe the *building up* of a compound from its elements. For example, many hairdressing preparations are made synthetically from simpler substances, e.g., synthetic perfumes. *Analysis* is the process of *breaking down* a compound into its component elements. Hair has been analysed by chemists and found to have the composition described above. The analysis of a product indicates what it is made of. This information is useful in order to know what precautions to take when handling it.

CHEMICAL FORMULAE AND EQUATIONS

All matter consists of tiny particles called *atoms*. The various elements are made up of their own kind of atoms; for example, atoms of sulphur are different from atoms of iron in size and weight. The lightest atom is that of hydrogen. The *atomic weight* of an element is the ratio of the weight of its atom compared with that of the hydrogen atom.

ATOMIC WEIGHTS OF SOME ELEMENTS

Element	Symbol	Atomic weight
Hydrogen	H	1
Carbon	C	12
Oxygen	O	16
Sulphur	S	32
Iron	Fe	56
Curium (the heaviest)	Cm	242

Atoms do not usually exist on their own in the *free state*. They tend to join together into a more permanent relationship in the form of *molecules*. A molecule can be looked upon as the smallest part of a compound or element that can exist in the free state. Many atoms prefer each other's company to being on their own!

Atom + Atom = Molecule = Compound

Hair compound = millions of hair molecules

Radicals are groups of atoms that do not normally exist on their own in the free state; they often maintain their identity throughout chemical changes that affect the rest of the molecule of which they are a part.

FORMULAE

Formulae are the chemist's shorthand system for describing the *composition* of molecules of a compound or element. For example, a molecule of hydrogen is written as H_2; a molecule of water as H_2O. These formulae show that hydrogen consists of one element only, whereas water consists of two different elements: hydrogen and oxygen, present in the proportion of two parts of hydrogen and one part of oxygen:

$$H + H = H_2$$
molecule of hydrogen

$$H + O + H = H_2O$$
molecule of water

VALENCY

VALENCIES OR COMBINING POWERS OF IMPORTANT ELEMENTS AND RADICALS

Valency	*Element or radical*
('One-armed') *univalent*	Elements: H, O, Na, K Radicals: —OH hydroxyl; HCO_3 bicarbonate; —NO_3 nitrate
('Two-armed') *bivalent*	Elements: O, S, Ca, Mg, Zn Radicals: =CO_3 carbonate; =SO_4 sulphate; SO_3 sulphite
('Three-armed') *trivalent*	Elements: N, Al Radical: ≡PO_4 phosphate
('Four-armed') *quadrivalent*	C, Si

Ammonia is made up of the elements nitrogen and hydrogen. Its formula is not NH but NH_3. The reason for this is that different elements have different *combining powers*. One could think of them as having more than one 'arm'; for example, nitrogen has three 'arms' for combining purposes or is *trivalent*, hydrogen has only one arm or *univalent*.

The following symbols:

$$—N—\qquad\qquad H—$$
$$|$$

show the 'arms' or combining powers. Each arm must be connected to another arm; it is not allowed to hang free: Each nitrogen arm joins with a hydrogen arm, and forms NH_3.

$$H—N—H = NH_3$$
$$|$$
$$H$$

Water is H_2O, since the oxygen is *bivalent* (two-armed), and the hydrogen one-armed or *univalent*:

$$H—O—H = H_2O$$

Hydrogen peroxide is H_2O_2. This time the arrangement is as follows, with the two oxygen arms overlapping:

$$H—O—O—H = H_2O_2$$

HOW TO WRITE THE FORMULA OF A COMPOUND

Always write the symbol of the *metal* first, followed by the symbol of the *non-metal* or *radical*.

Examples

Formula = Metal + Radical

1. Calcium carbonate is $CaCO_3$. The calcium atom (Ca) is bivalent ('two-armed'), the carbonate CO_3 radical is also 'two-armed', therefore we write:

$$Ca===CO_3, CaCO_3$$

2. Magnesium sulphate is $MgSO_4$. The magnesium atom (Mg) is bivalent and the sulphate radical (SO_4) is also bivalent, therefore:

$$Mg===SO_4, MgSO_4$$

3. Sodium carbonate is Na_2CO_3. The sodium is univalent, and therefore *two* sodium atoms are required to hang on to the carbonate CO_3 radical's two 'arms':

$$Na—CO_3—Na, Na_2CO_3$$

4. Sodium bicarbonate is $NaHCO_3$. The univalent sodium joins with a univalent bicarbonate radical HCO_3:

$$Na—HCO_3, NaHCO_3$$

Note. You will come across some more chemical formulae in the following chapters on hairdressing chemistry. Try to remember as many of them as you can. Formulae of the more complicated chemical compounds will not be given, but it is important for you to remember the names of chemical compounds mentioned in this book. You can learn to remember the names of chemical compounds in the same way that you can remember the names of your clients, by using such memory aids as initials, etc. For example, T.E.L.S.: triethanolamine lauryl sulphate.

EQUATIONS

Equations are useful for showing chemical changes in shorthand form. They can involve the use of formulae or words, for example:

$$Fe + S = FeS$$

means that iron joins with sulphur to form iron sulphide.

$$MgSO_4 + \frac{Sodium}{soap} = Na_2SO_4 + \frac{Magnesium}{soap}$$

This is a mixed formula and word equation stating that when sodium soap is added to magnesium sulphate there is a chemical change in which sodium sulphate and magnesium soap are formed. We have used twenty-two words in this sentence to state what the equation gives in a much shorter form.

All chemical changes should be remembered as word equations, or in simpler cases as formula equations.

SUGGESTIONS FOR PRACTICAL WORK

1. Refer (in your local library) to the publication *Which?* and read the scientific test reports on the following products featured in past issues: cosmetics, soap and detergents, hair-dryers, hair-colour restorers, hair shampoos, insulation materials, electric razors, sun-lamps, and clinical thermometers.

2. Perform the experiment with iron filings and sulphur described in this chapter.

3. Examine the labels of various hairdressing preparations and note how many give the chemical names of the components of the preparation.

   Note. Trade names of proprietary hairdressing preparations should not be mentioned in examination answers.

QUESTIONS ON CHAPTER 12

1. Classify the following processes into chemical and physical changes. Give your reasons in each case: (*a*) hair bleaching, (*b*) hair drying, (*c*) steaming hair, (*d*) hair dyeing, (*e*) cold waving, (*f*) friction treatment, (*g*) electrolytic hair-removal, (*h*) perfume evaporation, (*i*) switching on the electric fire, (*j*) haircutting.

2. Give examples of three metallic and three non-metallic elements. Give an indication of their main uses. What are the main differences between metals and non-metals?

3. Write the formulae for the following substances: potassium carbonate; sodium sulphate; magnesium bicarbonate; calcium sulphate; calcium bicarbonate; zinc carbonate.

4. Write the full chemical names of the following: H_2O_2; NH_3; $NaOH$; Na_2CO_3; $Ca(HCO_3)_2$; $Ca(OH)_2$.

5. Explain the following terms giving examples in each case: (*a*) metals and non-metals, (*b*) element, (*c*) mixtures, (*d*) compounds, (*e*) symbols and formulae.

13 OXYGEN, AIR, AND HYDROGEN PEROXIDE

OXYGEN

Oxygen (formula O_2) is one of the most abundant elements on the earth and forms 50 per cent of the earth's rocks, water, and air.

PREPARATION

Oxygen may be prepared by either of the following methods:

1. By heating 'oxygen mixture'. This is a mixture of oxygen-rich substances, namely potassium chlorate and manganese dioxide. It is the potassium chlorate that produces the oxygen. The manganese dioxide is a *catalyst* that serves to speed up the chemical change.

Experiment

Partly fill a hard glass test-tube with 'oxygen mixture'. Set up the apparatus shown in Figure 13.1. Note that the oxygen gas is

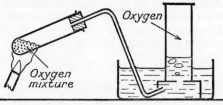

Figure 13.1. Laboratory preparations of oxygen from oxygen mixture

collected in gas-jars over water, in which it does not dissolve. Gently heat the mixture until the gas is collecting at a steady rate in the gas-jars.

2. Hydrogen peroxide (H_2O_2) is rich in oxygen, which can be released by means of manganese dioxide:

$$\text{Hydrogen peroxide} = \text{water} + \text{oxygen}$$
$$2H_2O_2 = 2H_2O + O_2$$

Experiment

Set up the apparatus shown in Figure 13.2. Carefully allow the

8. Re-formation of white light from a spectrum-coloured card

9. (Above) Two inclined mirrors: several images are produced from this arrangement

10. (Below) Light travelling in straight lines from a ray-box

11. A typical hairdressing salon with diffused lighting and absence of glare

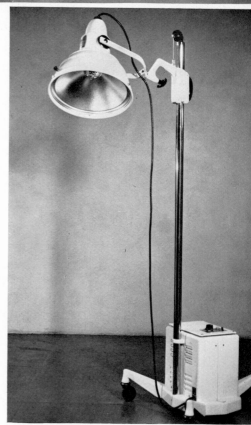

12. Mercury-vapour ultra-violet ray lamp

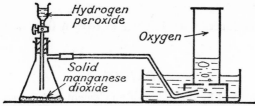

Figure 13.2. Laboratory preparation of oxygen from hydrogen peroxide

20-volume hydrogen peroxide (H_2O_2) to fall drop by drop on to the powdered manganese dioxide in the flask. The large-scale preparation of oxygen is from liquid air.

PROPERTIES

Oxygen is a colourless gas with no smell or taste.

If a glowing piece of wood is plunged into a gas-jar or tube of oxygen it will re-light and burn very brightly in the gas. This test was used to show the formation of oxygen during the electrolysis of water (Chapter 8).

Experiment

(This experiment should be performed by your instructor.)

Obtain the following non-metals: carbon, sulphur, and phosphorus, and the following metals: sodium, magnesium, and calcium. Gently heat a small portion of each in a deflagrating spoon and plunge it into a gas-jar of oxygen. Test the contents of the gas-jar with neutral litmus paper to which a little water has been added.

EFFECT OF BURNING THE VARIOUS ELEMENTS IN OXYGEN

	Element	Effect	Litmus
Non-metals	Carbon	Burns with a bright white light	Red
	Sulphur	Burns with a bright blue flame	Red
	Phosphorus	Burns with a blinding white light	Red
Metals	Sodium	Burns with a yellow flame	Blue
	Calcium	Burns with a red flame	Blue
	Magnesium	Burns with a brilliant white flame (Photographic flash-bulb)	Blue

K

Conclusion:

All the substances burn brighter in oxygen than in air, forming oxides.

OXIDES

Oxides are formed by the union of an element with oxygen; this process is also called *oxidation*. There are two main types of oxides: *acid* and *basic*, classified as follows, according to their action with water and litmus indicator.

ACID AND BASIC OXIDES

Oxidation
Element + Oxygen = Element oxide

Acid Oxides	*Basic Oxides*
Formed from non-metals, e.g. C, S, and P.	Formed from metals, e.g. Na, Ca, and Mg.
Carbon dioxide CO_2	Sodium oxide
Sulphur dioxide SO_2	Calcium oxide
Phosphorus oxides	Magnesium oxide

Acids	*Bases*
Formed from acid oxides with water and turn litmus RED.	Formed from basic oxides with water and turn litmus BLUE.
Carbonic acid H_2CO_3	Sodium hydroxide NaOH
Sulphuric acid H_2SO_4	Calcium hydroxide $Ca(OH)_2$
Phosphoric acid H_3PO_4	Magnesium hydroxide $Mg(OH)_2$

Conclusion:

Metal + oxygen = Basic (metal) oxide
Non-metal + oxygen = Acidic (non-metal) oxide.

Peroxides

Peroxides, such as hydrogen peroxide, lose their oxygen on heating.

Neutral oxides

Neutral oxides do not change the colour of neutral litmus indicator and are therefore neither acid nor basic, e.g., water or hydrogen oxide, H_2O.

OXIDATION

Oxidation is the process of *addition of oxygen* to an element or compound. The table shows some of the more important oxidation processes and their meanings. Oxidation processes are used during cold-waving and hair-dyeing treatments. They are sometimes misleadingly called 'neutralization' processes.

OXIDATION PROCESSES

Oxidation Process	Definition	Example
Combustion	Process in which substances join with oxygen, forming oxides, heat, and light	Combustion of wood, coal, petrol, and paper
Explosion	A process of very rapid combustion	Coal gas and gunpowder
Aerobic respiration	Process of liberating energy from food by means of oxygen, with the formation of carbon dioxide and water vapour	Plant and animal respiration
Bleaching	Process of adding oxygen to a coloured chemical compound and changing it into a colourless chemical compound	Hair and linen bleaching
Rusting	The slow process of adding oxygen to iron	Iron and steel

USES OF OXYGEN

1. Oxy-acetylene high-temperature metal cutters;
2. Used in hospital oxygen tents and by dentists;
3. Purifying water or aerating water;
4. For skin-divers and climbers;
5. Certain toothpastes contain a peroxide compound that liberates oxygen when brushed on the teeth.

NITROGEN

Nitrogen (N_2) is an important component of air, being present to the extent of four-fifths ($\frac{4}{5}$ths).

PREPARATION

Nitrogen gas is prepared by gently heating a solution of ammonium chloride and sodium nitrite (Figure 13.3). The large-scale preparation of nitrogen is from liquid air.

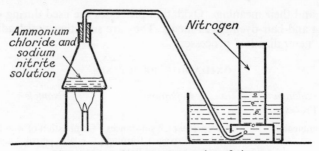

Figure 13.3. Laboratory preparation of nitrogen

PROPERTIES

Nitrogen is a colourless gas with no taste or smell.

Nitrogen is chemically lazy or *inert*. It does not allow things to burn in it, with the exception of magnesium metal. The gas has no action on litmus indicator and is therefore neutral.

Experiment

Collect a few jars of nitrogen and try the effect of burning different materials, including magnesium, in them.

USES

Nitrogen forms important chemical compounds such as ammonia and nitric acid, used for fertilizer manufacture.

THE AIR

In Chapter 2 reference was made to the pressure caused by the layer of air, many miles high, surrounding the earth. We shall now consider the chemical composition of air.

Experiments

1. Sprinkle a few iron filings inside a long graduated glass tube, plug the tube lightly with cotton-wool, and invert the tube in a jar of water. Put the apparatus aside for a week, allowing the iron filings to rust (oxidation). As the rusting occurs, oxygen is used up and the level of the water rises inside the tube by one-fifth (Figure 13.4).
2. Place a lighted candle in a dish and float it in a trough of water (Figure 13.5). Cover with a bell-jar and note how the level of the water rises inside the bell-jar owing to the removal of oxygen from the air by combustion (oxidation).

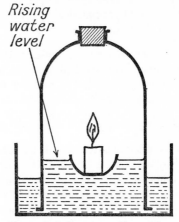

Figure 13.4. Demonstration of
the composition of air using
iron filings

Figure 13.5. Demonstration of the
composition of air using a
burning candle

Conclusion:

The two experiments show that approximately one-fifth of the air is
oxygen. This is used up during rusting and combustion. The remaining
four-fifths is nitrogen, which does not enable combustion or rusting to
take place.

AIR IS A MIXTURE

The composition of air is:

	per cent
Nitrogen	78
Oxygen	21
Inert gases	1

Plus:

Water vapour	0 to 4
Carbon dioxide	0·03
also, dust, bacteria,	
and chemical waste.	

Chemists consider air to be a mixture because its composition
varies from time to time, and each component can be *separated* by
simple methods. The oxygen present in the air allows all oxidation
processes, breathing, combustion, etc., to take place. Oxygen therefore
controls life on this earth.

Nitrogen serves to slow down the rate of all oxidation processes, or acts as a 'damper'. Life would proceed too rapidly if the air were pure oxygen. Coal fires, for example, would burn away rapidly, and human beings would continually eat food to satisfy the rapid rate of respiration of the body.

Inert gases. A group of gases with no chemical properties are also found in air: namely, helium, neon, argon, and krypton. They are used for filling electric lamps and for coloured discharge tubes used in advertising signs.

Water vapour is present in the air, giving it humidity (Chapter 6).

Carbon dioxide enters the air by the respiration of plants and animals and by the combustion of fuels. The amount of carbon dioxide in the air remains fairly steady, since living plants use it as a raw material in their feeding process called *photosynthesis*. In addition, some of the gas dissolves in rain, river, and sea-water.

Dust, soot, and ash are present in the industrial air of towns and cities and enter the air from smoky chimneys of factories, houses, ships, and railway engines. Approximately 250 tons of atmospheric dirt falls on each square mile of the large towns per year; this is equal to twenty-five lorry-loads of a mixture of dust, soot, and ash.

Chemical waste gases, mainly unpleasant-smelling sulphur compounds from the chimneys of factories and chemical industries, may also be present in the air in extremely small amounts.

Bacteria and **viruses** are continually present in the air and cause infectious diseases such as whooping-cough, influenza, poliomyelitis, and tuberculosis.

HYDROGEN

Hydrogen (H_2) is a comparatively abundant element in the form of its compounds, which include water, coal, oil, and other organic materials.

PREPARATION

Hydrogen gas is prepared in the laboratory by adding dilute hydrochloric acid to zinc metal using the apparatus shown in Figure 13.6.

Zinc + hydrochloric acid = hydrogen + zinc chloride

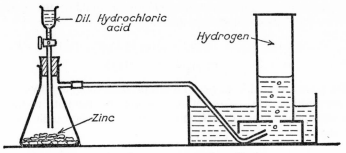

Figure 13.6. Laboratory preparation of hydrogen

PROPERTIES

Hydrogen is a colourless gas with no smell or taste, extremely light, of low density. It is used for filling balloons.

Experiments

1. Pass a stream of hydrogen gas through a clay pipe dipped into a shampoo solution. The light shampoo bubbles of hydrogen will rise to the ceiling.
2. Collect half a large test-tube full of hydrogen, light the gas in the test-tube, and note how the hydrogen burns with a 'pop'. This is used as a test for hydrogen (see also electrolysis of water, Chapter 8).
3. Hydrogen means 'water maker'. This property can be shown by the following experiment (Figure 13.7). Pass hydrogen or coal gas,

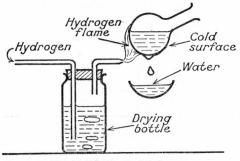

Figure 13.7. Synthesis of water

which is rich in hydrogen, through a gas-drying bottle containing concentrated sulphuric acid. The gas is then lit and the flame allowed to impinge on the cold surface of the flask. Droplets of water collect in the small dish. To prove that this liquid is water, its boiling-point is determined and found to be 100°C. This experiment demonstrates the *synthesis* or building up of water from its elements, hydrogen and oxygen:

Hydrogen + oxygen from the air = hydrogen oxide or water

$$2 H_2 + O_2 = 2H_2O$$

Fuels such as coal, coal gas, and oils produce water as a by-product of combustion. This is, therefore, a source of humidity in the air. Paraffin and gas fires will *add* moisture to the air, whereas electric fires dry the air.

REDUCTION

This is the process of *removal* of oxygen from a compound, and is the direct opposite of oxidation. The process of applying cold-wave reagent to the hair is a reduction process insofar as hydrogen is added to the hair compound, this being followed by an oxidation process (not a 'neutralization' process), using hydrogen peroxide.

Experiment

Place black copper oxide (basic oxide) in the apparatus shown in Figure 13.8. Pass a stream of coal gas over the heated copper oxide.

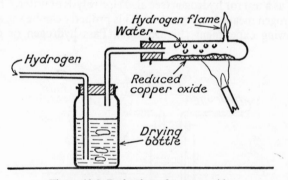

Figure 13.8. Reduction of copper oxide

Note how red copper metal appears after the oxygen has been removed; also, droplets of *water* appear in the cooler parts of the tube.

Conclusion:

$$\text{Copper oxide} + \text{Hydrogen} = \text{Copper} + \text{Water}$$
$$CuO + H_2 = Cu + H_2O$$

USES OF HYDROGEN

1. Filling balloons.
2. Manufacture of margarine and cooking fats from animal and vegetable oils.
3. As a raw material in the manufacture of ammonia, NH_3.
4. Manufacture of plastics, nylon, etc.

WATER (HYDROGEN OXIDE)

Water (H_2O) is a compound of hydrogen and oxygen. This has already been shown by (a) the *synthesis* of water experiment described above, and (b) the *analysis* or breaking down of water into its elements using the method of electrolysis described in Chapter 8.

PROPERTIES OF WATER

Pure water is a clear, colourless, tasteless liquid with no smell. Drinking-water derives its slight taste from the air and salts dissolved in it. Pure water boils at 100°C or 212°F and freezes at 0°C or 32°F.

WATER OF CRYSTALLIZATION

Obtain some blue crystals of copper sulphate and gently heat them in a test-tube. It will be seen that the blue crystals break down into a white powder and also produce steam that condenses on the cooler parts of the tube.

Crystals that produce water vapour on heating are said to be *hydrated*, that is, contain *water of crystallization*. The residue is said to be *anhydrous* or without water. If a little water is added to the white anhydrous copper sulphate it turns blue. This is useful as a chemical test for water.

Hydrated	HEAT	Anhydrous
Copper sulphate crystals	=	Copper sulphate powder
BLUE		WHITE

Hydrated washing soda crystals contain 63 per cent of water, while *anhydrous* washing soda powder is free from water. Similarly hydrated Glauber's salt contains 50 per cent water. These two substances are ingredients of various cosmetic preparations. It is therefore important to read the label on the bottle to see if the compound is *hydrated* or *anhydrous* in order that the right weight of material is used.

HYGROSCOPIC SUBSTANCES

Hygroscopic substances have the power of drawing water into themselves, e.g. hair, common salt, caustic soda and many other chemical compounds. It is therefore important to replace the cap or stopper of a bottle containing any hairdressing preparation in order to prevent damage to the product through the hygroscopic property of any of its components. The dry powder contained in a bottle can often be changed into a syrupy, useless mess by leaving off the stopper and allowing the hygroscopic ingredient to exercise its effect.

Experiment

Place small amounts of the following substances on watch-glasses and record the weights in each case: (a) washing soda crystals, (b) caustic soda pellets, (c) anhydrous sodium sulphate. Leave the watch-glasses and their contents aside for about a week and then weigh them again, noting any increase or decrease in weight.

HYDROGEN PEROXIDE

Hydrogen peroxide (H_2O_2) is an important chemical reagent used in many hairdressing processes.

PREPARATION

Hydrogen peroxide is manufactured on a large scale by the electrolysis of sulphuric acid. It is also produced by the reduction and oxidation of *anthraquinol*.

In the laboratory, a weak solution of hydrogen peroxide can be obtained by adding *barium peroxide* to ice-cold *dilute* sulphuric acid. The barium peroxide is added a little at a time until the solution is just acid to litmus indicator. The solution is then filtered. Test the solution by the chemical test described on page 139.

PURE HYDROGEN PEROXIDE

Pure 100 per cent hydrogen peroxide is a colourless syrupy liquid with a peculiar smell. It explodes violently when boiled or when finely powdered metals are added to it. This strong hydrogen peroxide is used mostly for space rockets and in atomic submarines.

Ordinary hydrogen peroxide as used in laboratories and hairdressing salons is available in strengths from 3 to 30 per cent. The description of the properties of hydrogen peroxide that follows applies to the ordinary form.

CHEMICAL TEST FOR HYDROGEN PEROXIDE

Add hydrogen peroxide to a solution of potassium iodide containing dilute sulphuric acid. The formation of a brown colour due to iodine indicates that the substance is hydrogen peroxide.

PROPERTIES OF ORDINARY HYDROGEN PEROXIDE

1. The decomposition or breakdown of hydrogen peroxide into water and oxygen gas

$$\text{Hydrogen peroxide} = \text{water} + \text{oxygen}$$
$$2H_2O_2 = 2H_2O_2 + O_2$$

can be achieved by any of the following methods:

   (a) Alkalis such as *ammonium hydroxide* or salts such as *sodium acetate* when added to hydrogen peroxide will release the oxygen for oxidizing purposes.
   (b) Heat from radiators or sunlight will decompose hydrogen peroxide; it is therefore advisable to store it in a *cool dark* place, preferably in *brown* bottles.
   (c) *Dust* entering the bottle will decompose hydrogen peroxide; stoppers should therefore be replaced immediately after use.

Experiment

Half-fill a test-tube with weak hydrogen peroxide and add a pinch of manganese dioxide. Note the evolution of oxygen gas. See if it will relight a glowing splint of wood.

2. *Stablizers* are used to prevent the decomposition of hydrogen peroxide while in store. All hydrogen peroxide sold for general use contains a stabilizer such as glycerine, ethyl alcohol, or small amounts (0·05–0·2 per cent) of sulphuric or phosphoric acids.
3. The *bleaching power* of hydrogen peroxide is entirely due to the oxygen it releases in order to oxidize the coloured compound. A trace of ammonium hydroxide or sodium acetate is added to the hydrogen peroxide. This *neutralizes* the acid stabilizer and releases the oxygen. Hydrogen peroxide is a valuable bleach for hair, silk, wool, feathers, and other delicate materials.

Experiment

Obtain some dark hair and insert small amounts into four test-tubes. To test-tube *A* add pure water; this is called the 'blank', or standard. To test-tube *B* add 20-volume hydrogen peroxide and a trace of ammonium hydroxide. To test-tube *C* add the same volume of 20-volume hydrogen peroxide and a pinch of sodium acetate. To test-tube

D add ordinary stabilized 20-volume hydrogen peroxide. Place the test-tubes in a rack and set them aside for a few days, then examine the bleaching effect in each test-tube.

Bleaching paste or 'white henna' is a mixture of magnesium carbonate and sodium acetate or ammonium carbonate, which is mixed to a smooth paste with 20-volume hydrogen peroxide and applied to the hair for bleaching purposes.

4. The *antiseptic* properties of hydrogen peroxide make it useful for treating infected wounds. Many bacteria cannot live in the presence of oxygen and are therefore called *anaerobes*. Oxygen in large amounts is provided by air or hydrogen peroxide, hindering the growth of these harmful bacteria. It is also used as a mouthwash after or during dental treatment.

Note. Strong hydrogen peroxide will cause white skin burns.

VOLUME STRENGTH OF HYDROGEN PEROXIDE

Volume strength means the *number of volumes* of oxygen gas formed from *one volume* of hydrogen peroxide. The term is used to describe the strength of hydrogen peroxide for example, and the strength at which it is used for various hairdressing processes.

Experiment

To find the approximate volume strength of a solution of hydrogen peroxide, set up the apparatus shown in Figure 13.9 which consists of a small burette (5 cm^3) containing the hydrogen peroxide under test and a graduated gas measuring-tube inverted in a dish of water. Allow 1 cm^3 of the hydrogen peroxide to drop slowly on to the manganese dioxide in the flask (100 cm^3). It will be seen that each drop decomposes and produces oxygen. The volume of the oxygen collected in the measuring-tube is an *approximate* indication of the volume strength of the hydrogen peroxide:

One cm^3 of 20-volume hydrogen peroxide gives 20 cm^3 of oxygen, or one pint of 20-volume hydrogen peroxide gives 20 pints of oxygen.

One cm^3 of 40-volume hydrogen peroxide gives 40 cm^3 of oxygen, or one pint of 40-volume hydrogen peroxide gives 40 pints of oxygen.

Hydrogen peroxide can be purchased at the following volume strengths: 10, 20, 30, 40, and 100 volumes. For a more accurate determination of volume strength, the volume of hydrogen peroxide added from the burette should be *subtracted* from the volume of oxygen collected in the measuring tube.

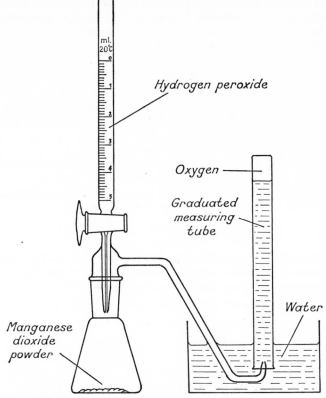

Figure 13.9. Apparatus for testing volume strength of hydrogen peroxide

DILUTION OF HYDROGEN PEROXIDE

In order to prepare hydrogen peroxide of weaker volume strength from a stronger solution it is advisable to use distilled or de-ionized water (softened water). The following dilution ratios are used for diluting 40-volume hydrogen peroxide:

(1) Twenty-volume strength can be prepared from *one part* water and *one part* 40-volume hydrogen peroxide.

(2) Ten-volume strength can be prepared from *three parts* water and one part 40-volume hydrogen peroxide.

APPLICATIONS OF HYDROGEN PEROXIDE IN HAIRDRESSING

1. The *bleaching of hair* is one of the main applications, and for this purpose hydrogen peroxide is used at 20-volume strength with a

trace of added ammonium hydroxide. Certain proprietary bleaching preparations are available that contain magnesium peroxide and sodium perborate. These are strong oxidizing or bleaching chemicals, which may be applied as a cream or lotion by mixing with water.

2. Cold-wave lotions *reduce* the hair to a soft condition. This action is stopped by the use of an *oxidizing* agent, such as 20-volume hydrogen peroxide, sodium bromate, or sodium perborate. The last two substances are white solids that need to be dissolved in distilled or de-ionized water before use.

   Note. The process is *not* neutralization.

3. The dyeing of hair using the oxidation-type of permanent dye that contains *phenylene-diamine* compounds. The application of 20-volume hydrogen peroxide results in the *coloured* dye appearing by oxidation of the *colourless* phenylene-diamine base.

$$\begin{matrix} \text{Colourless} \\ \text{dye base} \end{matrix} + \begin{matrix} \text{hydrogen} \\ \text{peroxide} \end{matrix} = \begin{matrix} \text{Coloured dye} \\ \text{compound} \end{matrix}$$

4. *Lightening dyed hair* that is too dark can be achieved by using a solution of hydrogen peroxide and ammonia or a bleaching paste or cream of the composition described above in (1).

$$\begin{matrix} \text{Coloured dye} \\ \text{compound} \end{matrix} + \begin{matrix} \text{hydrogen} \\ \text{peroxide} \end{matrix} = \begin{matrix} \text{Colourless} \\ \text{dye base} \end{matrix}$$

This is a bleaching process.

YELLOWING OF BLEACHED HAIR

The gradual yellowing of bleached hair is a process similar to the yellowing of wool. The following are suggested as the main causes of yellowing:

1. The ultra-violet rays present in sunlight can cause yellowing on prolonged exposure of the hair or wool fibre to sunlight. The ultra-violet rays can destroy the cuticle surface scales of the hair and cause it to feel harsher.

2. Washing the hair with alkaline soap shampoo may be a contributory cause of yellowing of bleached hair. Strong alkalis cause yellowing in wool, which is intensified on exposure to sunlight.

3. Hair-conditioning preparations containing olive oil can cause yellowing by the olive oil being changed by oxidation into coloured substances which are absorbed by the hair.

★ ★ ★

SUGGESTIONS FOR PRACTICAL WORK

Perform the experiments described in this chapter.

1. Obtain some hanks of over-dyed hair and note the effect of immersing the hair in a solution of 20-volume hydrogen peroxide containing ammonium hydroxide.
2. Obtain a small weft of hair and apply a hydrogen peroxide paste bleach. Allow it to over-bleach. Examine the hair after washing it in clean water and note its slimy feel, which is due to overbleaching. Mount some of the hair on a microscope slide and view its condition through a projection microscope.
3. Obtain the following: (a) some coloured silk and wool, (b) hair coloured with a colour rinse, (c) some naturally coloured feathers. Place them in four beakers and note the bleaching effect of ammoniacal hydrogen peroxide.

QUESTIONS ON CHAPTER 13

1. What is meant by the term *oxidation*? Give examples of this process. What are oxides? Give examples of (a) an acidic oxide, (b) a basic oxide, (c) a peroxide, and (d) a neutral oxide. What are the main uses of hydrogen peroxide in hairdressing practice?
2. What does bleaching mean? Give a brief account of the chemical composition of bleaching preparations and their main applications.
3. Name two peroxides and their use in hairdressing. What is meant by *volume strength* of hydrogen peroxide? Explain the purpose of stabilizers and the use of ammonium hydroxide with hydrogen peroxide.
4. Describe an experiment showing how you would demonstrate the composition of air. What is the normal composition of air? Describe how you would measure the amount of water vapour in the air.
5. Hydrogen means 'water former'. Explain how you can show this by experiment. Explain the following terms, giving examples in each case: (a) hydrated substance, (b) anhydrous substance, (c) hygroscopic.
6. Write short notes on the following chemical compounds: (a) oxygen, (b) magnesium oxide, (c) magnesium peroxide, (d) nitrogen, (e) sodium bromate and sodium perborate.
7. Explain the terms *oxidation* and *reduction*. Give examples of their use in hairdressing practice.
8. Explain why it is important to keep hairdressing reagents in a cool dark place, and why you should always replace the cap or stopper of a bottle.
9. Describe the preparation of oxygen gas. What happens when sulphur and magnesium are burnt in the gas? Explain what is meant by an acidic oxide and a basic oxide. Give examples of each.
10. Write a brief account of two of the following: (a) air pressure, (b) chemical composition of air, (c) humidity of air.

14 ACIDS, BASES, SALTS, AND ALCOHOLS

ORGANIC AND INORGANIC COMPOUNDS

All chemical compounds are divided into two main groups, namely, *organic* compounds and *inorganic* compounds. Organic compounds are the compounds of carbon, or the chemical compounds obtained from living things, i.e. plants or animals. Inorganic compounds are obtained from non-living things such as rocks and minerals.

Organic compounds	*Inorganic compounds*
From plants and animals	From rocks and minerals
e.g. sugar from sugar-beet, hair, methylated spirit	e.g. salt, sand, and iron
Char easily on heating	Do not char on heating
Contain the element carbon	
Melt easily at low temperatures	High melting-points

Our further study of chemistry will include both inorganic and organic substances together.

FURTHER CLASSIFICATION OF CHEMICAL COMPOUNDS

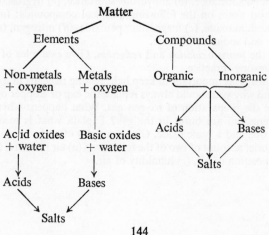

144

13. Cotton seed

14. Ground-nuts

15. 'Formulating a perfume': the perfumery research bench or 'organ'

16. Coconut seed

The chart on page 144 gives a summary of the classification of matter. It shows that compounds are divided into acids, bases, and salts. The third group is a new group that will be considered in greater detail together with the acids and bases.

ACIDS

All acids contain hydrogen that can be exchanged with a metal to form a salt.

Example

Hydrogen gas is made by adding dilute hydrochloric acid (HCl) to the metal zinc (Zn). The hydrogen of the hydrochloric acid is replaced by the zinc metal to form the salt zinc chloride, $ZnCl_2$.

$$Zn + 2HCl = ZnCl_2 + H_2$$

Zinc + hydrochloric acid = zinc chloride + hydrogen

Examples of inorganic acids are hydrochloric acid, HCl, nitric acid, HNO_3, and sulphuric acid, H_2SO_4, obtained from rock salt, saltpetre, and sulphur *minerals* respectively. Typical organic acids are acetic, citric, and lactic acid, obtained from vinegar, lemon, and milk respectively.

PROPERTIES OF ACIDS

1. All acids have a *sour* taste, e.g. sour milk (lactic acid), lemons (citric acid).
2. All acids will turn litmus indicator, a vegetable dye, *red*.
3. Acids are corrosive; they will rot cloth and flesh. Organic acids are *weak acids* and are not very corrosive; the inorganic acids are *strong acids* with correspondingly strong corrosive powers. All organic acids have a COOH acidic group.
4. Acids will *neutralize* bases and alkalis to form salts and water. If ammonium hydroxide is added to hydrochloric acid containing red litmus, the colour of the indicator will gradually change to pale blue or neutral as the salt ammonium chloride and water are formed.

Acid + base = salt + water

$$\text{Hydrochloric Acid} + \text{ammonium hydroxide} = \text{ammonium chloride} + \text{water}$$

5. When acids are added to sodium bicarbonate, bubbles of carbon dioxide gas are produced. (This is similar to a foam bath.) Mix together small amounts of sodium bicarbonate and citric acid powder and stir them into warm water containing shampoo. Note the rapid production of bubbles or *effervescence*.

IMPORTANT ACIDS AND THEIR USES

Acids	Appearance and properties	Uses
Hydrochloric, HCl	Colourless liquid, strong smell	Making other chemical compounds
Nitric, HNO_3	Yellow liquid, strong smell	Dyes, fertilizers, and explosives
Sulphuric, H_2SO_4	Oily liquid, no smell	Fertilizers, battery acid, and artificial fibres
Phosphoric, H_3PO_4	Syrupy liquid	Fertilizers and medicines
Acetic (from vinegar)	Strong-smelling liquid. Pure form is called 'glacial acetic acid'	Acid hair rinse, smelling-salts
Citric acid (from citrus fruits—oranges and lemons)	White crystals with sour taste	Acid hair rinse, lemonade powder
Lactic acid (from sour milk or buttermilk)	Clear syrupy liquid	Skin lotions and cordial flavour
Salicylic acid (from oil of wintergreen)	White crystals	Antiseptic, dandruff, skin, and corn-remover. Aspirin, cosmetic cream, preservative
Benzoic acid	White plate-like crystals	Cosmetic cream, preservative, and antiseptic
Butyric acid (in butter, cheese, and sweat)	Unpleasant smelling liquid	None
Oxalic acid (from rhubarb leaves)	White crystals—poisonous	Iron-stain remover
Thioglycollic acid $\begin{array}{c} COOH \\ | \\ CH_2HS \end{array}$ (from vine leaves by chemical treatment with *sulphur* compounds)	Colourless, unpleasant-smelling liquid	Cold-wave lotion and hair-remover; used for putting permanent pleats in suits and dresses.

Acids	Appearance and properties	Uses
Stearic acid (from beef fat)	White waxy solid	Cosmetic creams and lotions, candles, and soaps
Palmitic acid (from beef fat)	White waxy solid	Cosmetic creams, candles, polishes, and soaps
Oleic acid (from olive oil)	Oily liquid	Soaps and waterproofing agent

ACID HAIR RINSES

Acid hair rinses are weak solutions of acetic acid and citric acid used for: (a) removing hard water deposits or calcium soaps from the hair; (b) neutralizing the remaining alkali of the soap; (c) counteracting the effect of over-bleached hair with its jelly-like coating.

Temporary colour rinses also contain citric acid. Hair-conditioners contain citric acid and may also contain sour milk, lemon juice, and sour beer (i.e. lactic, citric, and acetic acids).

BASES

Bases are the oxides or hydroxides of metals.

Example

Calcium metal when burnt in oxygen gas forms white calcium oxide, a base that partly dissolves in water forming calcium hydroxide:

Calcium + oxygen = calcium oxide
Calcium oxide + water = calcium hydroxide

ALKALIS

Alkalis are bases that *dissolve readily in water*, e.g. caustic soda or sodium hydroxide, NaOH, and caustic potash or potassium hydroxide, KOH.

PROPERTIES OF BASES AND ALKALIS

1. All have a bitter taste similar to that of soap.
2. They are soapy to touch.
3. They turn litmus indicator blue.
4. Will neutralize acids to form salts and water (see Properties of Acids [4]).
5. Bases and alkalis are corrosive. They will rot cloth, hair, and flesh.
6. They form soaps with plant and animal oils or fats (see Chapter 16).

BASES AND ALKALIS

Base or alkali	Properties	Uses
Ammonium hydroxide, NH_4OH	Ammonia (NH_3) is a gas that dissolves readily in water forming ammonium hydroxide (NH_4OH): $NH_3 + H_2O = NH_4OH$ Ammonia plus water gives ammonium hydroxide The strongest solution of ammonium hydroxide has a specific gravity of 0·880 Always handle it with care	(1) Hydrogen peroxide bleaching process (2) With thioglycollic acid in cold-wave lotion (3) Alkaline hair rinse (4) Ammonia cosmetic creams (5) Smelling-salts (6) Fertilizers
Sodium hydroxide or caustic soda, $NaOH$	White solid that rapidly absorbs water from the air (hygroscopic)	(1) Soap manufacture (2) Grease-remover for sinks and drains (3) Vanishing-creams
Potassium hydroxide or caustic potash, KOH	White solid, very hygroscopic	(1) Soft soap manufacture (2) Grease-remover (3) Vanishing-creams (4) Cuticle-remover
Calcium oxide, CaO or 'burnt lime'	White solid that combines with water giving out considerable heat (exothermic reaction), forming calcium hydroxide $Ca(OH)_2$, 'slaked lime', $CaO + H_2O$ $= Ca(OH)_2 + Heat$	(1) Moistened with water, CaO is used in chemical exothermic permanent-waving pads or sachets (2) A hair-remover for animal hides (3) Large-scale water softener
Calcium hydroxide or lime-water $Ca(OH)_2$, 'slaked lime'	Clear liquid that turns cloudy in air	Lime hairdressing creams, now obsolete

ALKALINE HAIR RINSES

Alkaline hair rinses consist of ammonium hydroxide and borax, which has a weak alkaline action. The alkaline rinse serves to remove greasy sebum from the hair.

BASIC ORGANIC COMPOUNDS, OR AMINES

The organic compounds with properties similar to inorganic bases are called *amines*. They are related to ammonia, NH_3

$$
\begin{array}{c}
H \\
| \\
\end{array}
$$

Ammonia: $H{-}N{-}H$

$$
\begin{array}{c}
CH_3 \\
| \\
\end{array}
$$

Amines, e.g.: $H{-}N{-}H$ Methylamine

$$
\begin{array}{c}
CH_2CH_2OH \\
| \\
\end{array}
$$

Triethanolamine, e.g.: $CH_2CH_2OH{-}N{-}CH_2CH_2OH$

The hydrogen atoms of the ammonia have been exchanged with other radicals.

PROPERTIES OF AMINES

1. Turn litmus blue;
2. Soapy to touch;
3. Will neutralize acids to form salts;
4. Some amines have a fishy smell.

IMPORTANT AMINES

Triethanolamine or tri-ethan-ol-amine is a valuable amine used for making soapless detergents and shampoos, vanishing-creams, and cosmetic creams. Amines are valuable disinfectants, either as salts with coconut oil acids or as quaternary ammonium salts used in medicine. Certain amines are used as reagents in steam-waving of hair by the falling heat method (see page 198).

The permanent oxidation dye compounds are more complex amines of the diamine type (see Chapter 17).

Note. It is important to learn the long-sounding names given in this book in order to become familiar with the chemical composition of all the materials you use in hairdressing.

NEUTRALIZATION

This process is the interaction of an *acid* and a *base* to form a salt and water

neutralization

Acid + base   =   salt + water

Experiment

Place 25 cm³ of bench dilute hydrochloric acid in a beaker together with litmus indicator. Fill a burette with bench dilute sodium hydroxide and add it to the acid until the red colour of the litmus indicator just turns blue. When this occurs you will have a neutral solution.

$$\text{Hydrochloric acid} + \frac{\text{sodium}}{\text{hydroxide}} = \frac{\text{sodium}}{\text{chloride}} + \text{water}$$
$$\text{salt}$$

APPLICATIONS OF NEUTRALIZATION IN HAIRDRESSING

1. Acid hair rinses containing acetic and citric acids are used to partly neutralize the alkali that is present on the hair originating from the soap.
2. Ammonium hydroxide is used to neutralize the sulphuric or phosphoric stabilizers present in hydrogen peroxide and also to liberate the oxygen.
3. $\text{Ammonium hydroxide} + \dfrac{\text{thioglycollic}}{\text{acid}} = \dfrac{\text{ammonium}}{\text{thioglycollate}} + \text{water}$

Ammonium hydroxide is added to thioglycollic acid in order to form ammonium thioglycollate, this salt being the main *active* ingredient of 'cold-wave' lotion.

Note. It is incorrect and misleading to describe hydrogen peroxide as a 'neutralizer' used in the cold-wave or permanent dyeing processes. In both cases it is an 'oxidizer' or oxidation reagent.

HYDROGEN ION CONCENTRATION OR pH

When an acid is added to water it splits up into two parts: (*a*) hydrogen ions, and (*b*) the acid radical ions.

$$HCl = H^+ + Cl^-$$

hydrochloric   hydrogen   chloride
acid   ion   ion
(acid radical)

The symbol pH (small p, capital H) is used to describe the quantity of hydrogen ions present, or the acidity of a solution. The pH system is a scale used to measure acidity and alkalinity.

```
         ACID        |       ALKALINE
   1  ←——————————    7  ————————————→  14
  Very            Neutral              Very
 strong              |                strong
  acid               |                alkali
```

The pH scale

Pure water is pH 7 or neutral. Acidity is found between pH 1 and pH 7. Alkalinity is found between pH 7 and pH 14. A solution of pH 9 would be weakly alkaline while a solution of pH 5 would be weakly acid.

The pH value of a solution can be determined by: (*a*) the colorimetric indicator method using coloured indicators that give different colours at different pH values; (*b*) the electrometric pH apparatus, which gives a direct reading of the pH of the solution.

APPLICATION OF pH

The pH of ammonium thioglycollate used for cold-wave lotions is about pH 9, i.e., slightly alkaline, owing to the presence of ammonium hydroxide.

The pH of soapless detergent shampoo is pH 7, i.e., *neutral*, while soap has a pH value of 9, or *slightly alkaline*. This accounts for its stinging sensation in the eye, compared to the neutral action of shampoo.

Substance	pH	
0·4 per cent Hydrochloric acid	1	⎫
0·01 per cent Acetic acid	4	⎬ Acid
Citric acid	5	⎭
Soda water	7 −	⎫
Pure water	7	⎬ Neutral
Soapless detergent	7 +	⎭
Soap	9 to 10	⎫ Alkaline
1 per cent Sodium hydroxide	13	⎬

Experiment

The following formula for cold-waving lotion is reproduced with acknowledgement to A. Boake Roberts & Co. Ltd (Technical Information sheet 237a).

Part A	Thioglycollic acid 98 per cent	7 g
	Ammonia (S.G. 0·88)	20–22 cm³
	Water	30 cm³
Part B	'Emulsene' 1220	2·5 g
	Water	40 cm³

Procedure:

Mix together the Emulsene 1220 and water (part *B*) and heat to approximately 78°C. Disperse by stirring and continue to stir until cool. Add part *A* while stirring. Add the perfume (Abrac Thiomask). Finally adjust the pH value and stir until homogeneous.

Note. Adjust the pH to 9 using the colorimetric pH outfit or pH meter.

The effect of the cold-wave lotion that you have prepared can now be tested on specimen pieces of hair *not* attached to a human head.

Oxidation mixture:

Sodium lauryl sulphate	1 g
Sodium perborate monohydrate	80 g
Citric acid	6 g
Sodium bromate	13 g

Use 14 g of this mixture dissolved in $1\frac{1}{2}$ pints of de-ionized or distilled water.

This mixture contains the oxidizing chemical reagents, namely, sodium perborate and sodium bromate.

SALTS

Salts are produced when the hydrogen of an acid is replaced by a metal or the ammonium radical (NH_4). All salts consist of two parts: (*a*) the metal or ammonium radical, and (*b*) the acid radical.

$$\text{Salt} = \genfrac{}{}{0pt}{}{\text{metal}}{\genfrac{}{}{0pt}{}{\text{or}}{\genfrac{}{}{0pt}{}{\text{ammonium}}{\text{radical}}}} + \genfrac{}{}{0pt}{}{\text{acid}}{\text{radical}}$$

A list of metals and acid radicals is given in Chapter 12.

Experiment

To prepare copper sulphate salt:

Place 50 cm³ of dilute sulphuric acid in a 100 cm³ beaker. Carefully add black copper oxide and stir the mixture with a glass rod. Gently warm the mixture and add more copper oxide until a little remains undissolved. Filter, and set the liquid aside to cool, when blue crystals of copper sulphate will appear. Pour away the liquid and dry the crystals on sheets of filter paper.

$$\genfrac{}{}{0pt}{}{\text{Copper}}{\text{oxide}} + \genfrac{}{}{0pt}{}{\text{sulphuric}}{\text{acid}} = \genfrac{}{}{0pt}{}{\text{copper}}{\text{sulphate}} + \text{water}$$

Copper sulphate is an important ingredient of compound henna or sulphide dyes.

SOME IMPORTANT SALTS AND THEIR USES

Salt	Appearance and properties	Uses
Ammonium thioglycollate	Unpleasant-smelling liquid	Hair-remover; cold-wave lotion; permanent creases in suits and dresses
Potassium aluminium sulphate, or alum	White crystalline solid	Styptic to stop bleeding; astringent or skin tightener to close the pores of the skin
Borax	White powder, mild alkali	Water-softener, alkaline hair rinse, vanishing-cream
Cadmium sulphate	White solid	Sulphide dye
Copper sulphate	Blue crystals	Sulphide dye
Cobalt sulphate	Red crystals	Sulphide dye
Calcium carbonate or chalk, $CaCO_3$	White powder	Talcum powder
Magnesium carbonate, $MgCO_3$	White powder	Talcum powder; white henna bleaching paste
Mercury salts	White crystals—very poisonous	Sulphide dyes, antiseptics
Sodium acetate	White solid	Weak alkali, used instead of ammonium hydroxide to release oxygen from hydrogen peroxide
Sodium bromate Sodium perborate Magnesium Peroxide	White solids	All are oxidizing agents and are used in bleaching pastes
Sodium carbonate, Na_2CO_3	White solid. Feather crystals are sodium sesquicarbonate	Water-softener and bath salts
Sodium sulphite, Na_2SO_3	White solid	Reagent used in steam waving
Potassium permanganate, or 'Condy's fluid'	Dark red crystals	Main ingredient of chemical exothermic heat perm sachet; hair dyes; strong oxidizing agent, useful for disinfecting drains
Zinc carbonate, 'Calamine'	White powder	Talcum powder and calamine lotion
Zinc sulphate	White crystals	Skin and eye lotion

ALCOHOLS

The alcohols are organic compounds containing the elements carbon, hydrogen, and oxygen. They are similar to the alkalis in containing the OH *hydroxyl* group:

H—OH water or hydrogen hydroxide
Na—OH sodium hydroxide
CH_3—OH methyl alcohol
C_2H_5—OH ethyl alcohol

PROPERTIES OF ALCOHOLS

1. Do not affect litmus;
2. Inflammable;
3. Form salts or esters with acids.

Alcohol + acid = ester + water

Ethyl alcohol or ethanol, C_2H_5OH, is produced by the fermentation of sugar or starch using live yeast as the fermenting agent. The sugar or starch is first changed into glucose by the action of the yeast, the glucose being converted into ethyl alcohol and carbon dioxide.

$$\text{Glucose} \quad \xrightarrow{\text{Yeast}} \quad \text{ethyl alcohol} \quad + \quad \text{carbon dioxide}$$
$$C_6H_{12}O_6 \quad\quad\quad\quad C_2H_5OH \quad\quad\quad\quad CO_2$$

Experiment

Dissolve 5 g of glucose in 100 cm^3 of water in a 1-litre flask. Add 2 g of yeast and stir the mixture gently. Set up the apparatus shown in Fig. 14.1 and place the flask in a warm room or near to a radiator.

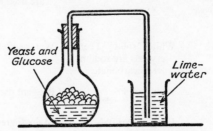

Figure 14.1. Preparation of ethyl alcohol

After a while it will be seen that the mixture begins to froth owing to the formation of carbon dioxide gas. Leave the mixture for five days, then filter. Distil the liquid and note the smell of ethyl alcohol in the first distillate.

Note. It is strictly illegal to distil alcohol, even in small quantities, without the permission of the Customs and Excise authorities. Permission is usually readily given for the use of alcohol for experimental purposes, if no other spirit is suitable.

Beer, wines, and spirits all contain ethyl alcohol and are prepared by the fermentation process. The sparkle or froth in alcoholic beverages is due to the carbon dioxide.

METHYLATED OR DENATURED SPIRIT

Ethyl alcohol for industrial and general use is rendered unfit for human consumption by the addition of the following denaturants: methyl alcohol, pyridine, and naphtha. A blue or red dye may also be included. **Surgical** spirit is a clear liquid containing methyl salicylate (oil of wintergreen) and formaldehyde as additional denaturants.

Industrial spirit is a clear liquid containing special denaturants that

SOME IMPORTANT ALCOHOLS AND THEIR USES

Alcohol	Appearance and properties	Uses
Methyl alcohol or methanol, CH_3OH, from distillation of wood	Clear colourless liquid, highly poisonous and inflammable	Denaturization of ethyl alcohol, perfumes, varnishes, and manufacture of formaldehyde
Ethyl alcohol or ethanol, C_2H_5OH, from fermentation of glucose	Clear colourless liquid, poisonous in large quantities, highly inflammable; antiseptic	Alcoholic beverages, solvent for lacquer and varnish; manufacture of dyes, lotions and cosmetics; medicinal tinctures and essences; perfumes
Isopropyl alcohol	Clear colourless liquid; antiseptic	Hair setting lotions. Useful for cleaning mirrors and windows
Cetyl alcohol, from spermaceti	White, waxy solid; melting-point 47°C	Cosmetic creams, ointments, and soaps; soapless detergents
Stearyl alcohol, from beef fat	White waxy solid	Cosmetic creams, ointments, and lotions
Lauryl alcohol, from coconut oil	Pale yellow liquid	Manufacture of soapless detergent and shampoo
Glycerine, or glycerol; by-product of soap manufacture	Sweet, syrupy liquid, very hygroscopic, absorbing moisture from the air	Cosmetics, soaps, skin creams, and lotions; for keeping tobacco and preserved fruits moist; manufacture of dynamite

allow it to be used for the preparation of cosmetics and other products where methylated mineralized spirit would be unsuitable.

Methylated mineralized or denatured spirit is coloured blue or red and contains some of the above denaturants. It is used for domestic purposes and can be purchased without a Customs and Excise permit. Customs and Excise permits are required for the purchase of *clear industrial spirit*. A permit will be supplied provided that the industrial spirit is used for (*a*) manufacturing purposes and the product is suitably denatured, or (*b*) for experimental use in schools and colleges.

Pure unadulterated ethyl alcohol costs approximately £4 a pint duty paid, while denatured spirit costs approximately 1s. 4d. a pint duty free.

ESTERS

Esters are the 'salts' that are formed when organic acids react with organic alcohols.

Organic acid + alcohol = ester + water

Acetic acid + ethyl alcohol = ethyl acetate + water

SOME IMPORTANT ESTERS

Ester	Appearance and properties	Uses
Ethyl acetate	Pleasant-smelling liquid	Fruit essence, nail-varnish solvent
Amyl acetate	Liquid smelling of pear-drops	Pear-drops essence, nail-varnish solvent
Dimethyl phthalate	Oily liquid with slight pleasant smell	Insect-repellent; denaturant for alcoholic preparations
Glycerol monostearate	White, waxy solid	Deodorant, bleaching, and antiperspirant creams
Isopropyl myristate	Pale yellow liquid	Cosmetic creams and lotions
Methyl salicylate	Oily liquid	Oil of wintergreen
Bornyl acetate	Oily liquid	Bath essence

Experiment

Take 5 cm³ of ethyl alcohol and 3 cm³ of glacial acetic acid, and add a few drops of concentrated sulphuric acid. Warm the mixture on a water-bath for 5 to 10 minutes, then pour the contents of the test-tube into a large beaker of cold water. Note the pleasant smell of the ethyl acetate ester that you have prepared.

PROPERTIES OF ESTERS

Esters are mainly neutral liquids with pleasant fruity smells. The oils, fats, and waxes of plants and animals are also esters. They will be dealt with in greater detail in the next chapter.

OTHER ORGANIC COMPOUNDS

FORMALDEHYDE

H.CHO is a gas with a strong smell. It is sold as a 40 per cent solution in water. Formaldehyde is used in disinfecting-cabinets as a 5 per cent solution, and it is also employed for preserving biological material.

ACETONE

CH_3COCH_3 is a highly inflammable solvent for lacquer, resin, and nail-varnish remover.

★　★　★

SUGGESTIONS FOR PRACTICAL WORK

Prepare the following cosmetic preparations described in Chapter 18 Notice the appearance and properties of the ingredients, and make frequent reference to this chapter for further details of the materials.
1. Calamine lotion.
2. Nail-varnish remover.
3. Cuticle softener.
4. Friction or cooling lotion.
5. Triethanolamine cream, e.g. hair cream, or vanishing-cream.
6. Acid hair rinse.
7. Hair-conditioning cream.
8. Permanent-wave lotion described in this chapter.
9. Astringent lotion.

QUESTIONS ON CHAPTER 14

1. Give examples of (*a*) two acids, and (*b*) two bases that are used in hair-dressing. What is the difference between a base and an alkali? Give named examples in each case. Explain the term *neutralization*.
2. Give the names of two acidic and two basic oxides. What are acids and bases? Give examples of some acids and bases used in hairdressing preparations.

3. What are the most important properties of acids? Give the names of some important acids and their uses. What is meant by the term pH? Give a brief account of its use.

4. Explain the following terms, giving examples in each case: (a) neutralization; (b) acid hair rinse; (c) alkaline hair rinse; (d) salts; (e) alcohols.

5. Explain the following terms: alcohol, acid, ester, salt, and base. To which class do the following substances belong: citric acid, calcium oxide, sulphur, triethanolamine, sodium hydroxide, amyl acetate, coconut oil, and ethanol?

6. What are alcohols? Describe the preparation of ethyl alcohol and give a brief account of its more important uses. What is denatured spirit?

7. Explain the terms *acidity*, *alkalinity*, and *neutral*. Describe how they can be measured.

8. Write short notes on the following substances indicating their uses in hairdressing practice: (a) acetic acid; (b) ammonium thioglycollate; (c) ammonium hydroxide; (d) triethanolamine; (e) sodium sulphite; (f) potassium permanganate.

9. What are the main applications of neutralization in hairdressing? Why is it incorrect to describe hydrogen peroxide as a cold-wave solution 'neutralizer'?

10. Describe briefly the main chemical ingredients of the following preparations: (a) alkaline hair rinse; (b) cold-wave lotion; (c) bath salts; (d) exothermic permanent-waving pads; (e) calamine lotion; (f) nail-varnish remover; (g) vinegar; (h) cosmetic creams.

11. Explain why (a) soapless detergent shampoo does not sting the eyes as much as soap; (b) lemon juice does not burn holes in cloth; (c) hydrochloric acid will rapidly corrode cloth.

12. Describe the main properties of bases and alkalis. What are the main applications of ammonium hydroxide in hairdressing? What is 0·880 ammonium hydroxide?

15 OILS, FATS, WAXES, RESINS, AND GUMS

CLASSIFICATION

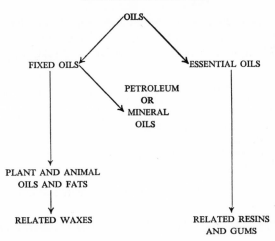

FIXED OILS

Fixed oils are plant and animal oils, together with petroleum oils that do not evaporate easily.

ESSENTIAL OILS

Essential oils are volatile oils, e.g. lavender oil.

PLANT AND ANIMAL OILS AND FATS

OCCURRENCE

These are oils or fats obtained from plants or animal sources (see Plates 13, 14, 16, and 18).

Vegetable or plant oils	*Animal oils or fats*
Groundnut or peanut oil	Whale oil
Cotton seed oil	Lard or pork fat
Almond oil	Tallow
Olive oil	Suet fat, butter
Coconut oil	Halibut oil ⎫
Castor oil	Herring oil ⎭ fish oils
Soya bean oil	
Linseed oil	
Cocoa butter fat	

Oils are usually *liquid* at ordinary room temperature (e.g. olive oil) but coconut oil is a white *solid*; in the tropics it is a liquid oil. Fats are usually *solids* at room temperature (e.g. lard and suet fat).

EXTRACTIONS OF OILS AND FATS

1. Crushing, e.g. peanuts and almonds.
2. Boiling or rendering with hot water, followed by skimming off the oil, e.g. fish oils.
3. Solvents are used to dissolve out the fats.
4. Melting, e.g. suet.

The residue left after extraction is used for cattle food or fertilizer.

CHEMICAL COMPOSITION OF OILS AND FATS

All animal and plant oils and fats are made of the elements hydrogen, carbon, and oxygen, and consist of two main ingredients: (1) fatty acids and (2) glycerine. Oils and fats may be regarded as salts, or more correctly esters, of fatty acids and glycerine.

OILS AND FATS	=	FATTY ACID AND GLYCERINE
PALM OIL/GLYCERYL PALMITATE	=	PALMITIC ACID + GLYCERINE
COCONUT OIL/GLYCERYL LAURATE	=	LAURIC ACID + GLYCERINE
BEEF FAT/GLYCERYL STEARATE	=	STEARIC ACID + GLYCERINE
OLIVE OIL/GLYCERYL OLEATE	=	OLEIC ACID + GLYCERINE
CASTOR OIL/GLYCERYL RICINOLEATE	=	RICINOLEIC ACID + GLYCERINE
BUTTER/GLYCERYL BUTYRATE	=	BUTYRIC ACID + GLYCERINE

CHOLESTEROL

Cholesterol is a white solid insoluble in water but soluble in oils. It is an important ingredient of animal oils, blood, and nerves, but is not found in plant oils. Cholesterol is an ingredient of some hair-restoring lotions. It is now considered that cholesterol can cause blockage of the arteries of the heart resulting in coronary thrombosis or heart failure.

GENERAL USES OF OILS AND FATS

1. Important food—margarine, butter, lard, and cooking oil;
2. Manufacture of soap and soapless detergents;
3. Cosmetic manufacture;
4. Linoleum, made from linseed oil and a sacking back.

OILS AND FATS USED IN HAIRDRESSING PREPARATIONS

Oil or fat	Appearance and properties	Uses
Almond oil	Clear liquid, slight smell	Brilliantines and skin creams
Castor oil	Clear liquid, high density, soluble in alcohol	Turkey-red oil, brilliantines, hair creams, nail-varnish, and lipstick
Coconut oil	Solid white fat with characteristic smell	Soaps and soapless detergents
Cocoa butter	Yellowish solid, from cocoa beans —melts easily	Skin creams
Lard, hog fat	Soft, white fat that melts easily	Skin creams and hair pomades
Linseed oil	Yellow liquid with a characteristic smell	Soap and soapless detergent
Olive oil	Yellow-greenish liquid with faint smell	Skin creams, hair creams, massage oil, soaps, and soapless detergents
Palm oil	Orange fat	Soaps
Peanut or Arachis oil	Pale yellow liquid	Brilliantine, soaps, and hair creams
Tallow	Hard, white solid	Soaps
Turtle oil	Colourless liquid	Skin cream

WAXES

Waxes are obtained from either plant or animal sources, e.g. beeswax or honeycomb and carnauba wax from Brazilian palm oil. Waxes are hard non-greasy solids that do not form grease-marks on paper.

M

CHEMICAL COMPOSITION OF WAXES

Waxes do not contain glycerine. All waxes are made up of two main parts, (1) fatty acids, (2) fatty alcohols:

$$\text{WAXES} = \text{FATTY ACIDS} + \text{FATTY ALCOHOLS}$$

They are described as *esters*.

$$\text{Spermaceti or cetyl laurate} = \text{lauric acid} + \text{cetyl alcohol}$$

$$\text{Beeswax or myricyl palmitate} = \text{palmitic acid} + \text{myricyl alcohol}$$

WAXES USED IN HAIRDRESSING PREPARATIONS

Wax	Appearance and properties	Uses
Lanolin	Yellow, sticky solid, with slight smell; mixes with water to form a cream or emulsion	Because of its resemblance to sebum, it is an important ingredient of: (1) Skin cream (2) Hair-conditioners (3) Ointments (4) Soap and soapless detergents
Sebum	Yellow solid	Natural skin secretion (1) Waterproofs the hair and skin (2) Keeps the skin supple and moist
Beeswax	White waxy solid	Waxing, thread, and silk for boardwork; skin creams
Spermaceti, whale wax	White waxy solid	Skin creams, ointments, candles, hair pomades
Carnauba wax	Yellow waxy solid	Candles, lacquer, and polishes
Candililla	White solid	Lipstick

LANETTE WAX

Lanette wax is an artificially prepared or synthetic wax. It is used in the preparation of skin creams and hair-conditioning creams.

$$\text{Lanette wax} = \text{stearyl alcohol} + \text{cetyl alcohol}$$
$$\text{Lanette wax SX} = \text{steamyl} + \text{cetyl alcohols (10\% sulphated)}$$

LANOLIN

Lanolin is an important wax for many hairdressing preparations. It is a yellow, sticky solid with a characteristic smell, and is the secretion that coats sheep's wool. Lanolin is obtained as a by-product of the woollen industry from the process of fleece washing to remove the grease.

$$\text{Lanolin} = \frac{\text{fatty}}{\text{acids}} + \frac{\text{fatty}}{\text{alcohol}} + \text{cholesterol}$$

MINERAL OILS

Petroleum or rock oil is the main source of mineral oils. Petroleum is found underground in many parts of the world and was originally formed millions of years ago from the remains of tiny organisms. Petroleum is therefore an organic substance.

COMPOSITION OF MINERAL OILS

All the mineral oils and gases from petroleum are composed of the elements *hydrogen* and *carbon* and are called *paraffin hydrocarbons*.

USES OF MINERAL OILS AND GASES

Mineral oil	Appearance	Uses
Petroleum gases	Colourless gases	(1) Bottled gas for cooking (2) Alkane compounds for making soapless detergents
Petrol	Pleasant-smelling inflammable liquid	(1) Motor-cars (2) Cleaning wigs; an excellent grease solvent
Paraffin or kerosene	Liquid	Heater and lamp fuel
Liquid paraffin	Clear, colourless liquid with no smell	(1) Brilliantines (2) Skin creams (3) Hair creams Excellent skin lubricant
Diesel oil	Liquid	Diesel engines of trains, buses, and ships
Petroleum jelly ('Vaseline'), soft paraffin	Yellow or white greasy solid	(1) Skin creams (2) Brilliantines (3) Ointments (4) Pomades
Paraffin 'wax' (not a true wax)	White waxy solid	(1) Creams (2) Wax hair-removers

EXTRACTION

Petroleum is carefully distilled at various refineries throughout the world, yielding the following main products.

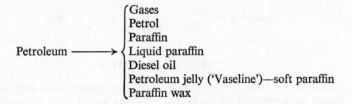

Petroleum ⟶ {
Gases
Petrol
Paraffin
Liquid paraffin
Diesel oil
Petroleum jelly ('Vaseline')—soft paraffin
Paraffin wax
}

PITCH

Pitch, the residue remaining after the distillation of petroleum, is used mainly for waterproofing roofing-felts and damp-proof courses.

ESSENTIAL OILS

These oils, obtained from plants, are *pleasant* smelling and can evaporate easily or are *volatile* liquids. They are produced in the plant by means of glands that are found in various parts of the plant as shown in Figure 15.1.

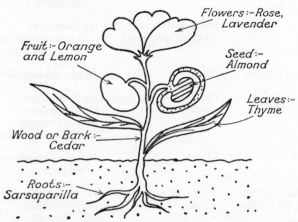

Figure 15.1. Distribution of essential oils in the flowering plant

EXTRACTION OF ESSENTIAL OILS

1. *Steam distillation* or boiling with steam (Figure 15.2). This method is used for the extraction of oils from lavender, rosemary, peppermint, eucalyptus, witch hazel, and lemon-grass plants. The steam carries the volatile oils into the condenser and the essential oil separates from the condensed water in the receiver.

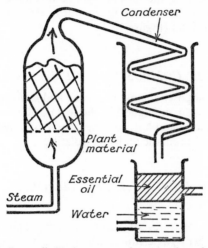

Figure 15.2. Steam-distillation process for extraction of essential oils

2. *Cold fat extraction* or *enfleurage*. Flower petals are placed on sheets of glass covered with very pure lard. The essential oils pass into the lard, which becomes a pleasant-smelling 'pomade'. The pomade may be used as such or the essential oils may be extracted with

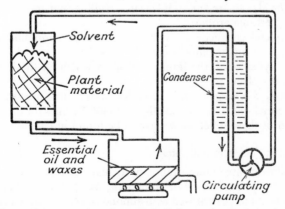

Figure 15.3. Extraction of essential oils by means of a hot solvent

alcohol, which does not dissolve the lard because fats are insoluble in alcohol.

3. *Crushing* or squeezing out the oils from fruit skins or rinds. This method is used for obtaining orange oils and related citrus oils.

4. *Solvent* extraction using petrol ether (obtained from petroleum). During this process the plant material is flooded with the solvent, which extracts the essential oil and wax. The solvent is then evaporated, leaving the oil and wax as a residue. The oil can be separated from the wax by using warm alcohol, leaving the insoluble wax behind (Figure 15.3).

CHEMICAL COMPOSITION OF ESSENTIAL OILS

These oils are composed mainly of *carbon* and *hydrogen* and may also include some oxygen, combined in the form of chemical compounds known as terpenes, camphor, and benzene derivatives. They are all liquids, pleasantly aromatic and very volatile.

USES OF ESSENTIAL OILS

1. Perfumes

Perfumes are mixtures of scent-producing substances carefully blended together by a perfumer, who relies entirely on his own sense of smell coupled with a knowledge of the chemistry of his perfume's raw materials (Plate 15). The raw materials used in perfume production are:

i Essential oils.

ii Animal products such as ambergris, musk, and civet cat secretions. These are very unpleasant smelling, but serve to prolong the perfume aroma.

iii Artificial chemicals or synthetic chemical compounds, mainly the pleasant-smelling esters.

iv Methyl alcohol, the liquid solvent in which all the ingredients are dissolved.

   Eau-de-Cologne and lavender water are preparations of essential oils dissolved in ethyl alcohol. Recipes for the preparation of these toilet waters are to be found in Chapter 18.

2. Flavouring essences and spices

The following are of importance, particularly in confectionery:
   Oil of peppermint; oil of cinnamon; oil of cloves; oil of almond (this is not to be confused with almond oil); oil of anise in aniseed; vanilla; and ginger.

3. Medicinal uses

Many essential oils have medical uses. In particular the essential oils are valuable antiseptics for internal and external use, and are ingredients of medicated shampoos. Oil of bay is an important ingredient of bay rum, which has medicinal properties in cooling the skin and also as an antiseptic. Oil of camomile is a useful tonic and stimulant.

USES OF SOME IMPORTANT ESSENTIAL OILS IN HAIRDRESSING

Essential oil	Preparation and properties	Uses
Almond	Distillation of almond seeds; contains small amounts of prussic acid poison	Flavour in almond paste
Bay	Distillation of bay leaves	Bay rum hair tonic
Bergamot	Crushing citrus rind	Eau-de-Cologne and soap perfume
Camomile	Distillation of camomile flowers	Tonic and stimulant for shampoos and hair preparations
Camphor	Distillation of camphor wood; white crystalline solid	Cold remedies, liniments, perfumes, and insecticides
Citrus oils	Crushing lemon, orange, mandarin, and bergamot rinds	Eau-de-Cologne, perfumes, and flavours
Cedarwood	Distillation of cedar wood	Perfumes and polishes
Cinnamon	Distillation of cinnamon bark	Perfumes and flavours
Clove	Distillation of clove flower buds	Flavour, disinfectant, mouth-wash, and perfumes
Jasmine	Enfleurage of flowers	Perfumes
Lavender	Distillation of flowers	Lavender water, soaps, and insect-repellents
Neroli	Distillation of orange flowers	Eau-de-Cologne
Rose or otto of roses	Enfleurage of rose petals	Perfume; rose-water is a by-product
Peppermint or menthol	Distillation of mint flowers; white crystals	Dental creams, antiseptic, cooling lotion, snuff, and confectionery

cont. overleaf

Essential oil	Preparation and properties	Uses
Rosemary	Distillation of flowers	Perfumes, soaps, and hair-washes
Sarsaparilla	Roots	Herbal beverage
Thyme	Distillation of leaves	Soaps, perfumes, and flavours
Violet	Solvent extraction of violet flowers	Perfumes
Witch hazel	Distillation of twigs of American witch hazel	Skin tonic, astringent, and antiseptic
Ylang-Ylang	Distillation of Cananga flowers	Expensive perfumes

RESINS

These are secretions from insects and the bark of trees that produce cones, called *conifers*, such as the pine tree. Resins are mixtures of essential oils and resin, and are also called oleo-resins.

SOME IMPORTANT RESINS

Turpentine is the secretion of the pine tree. When the turpentine gum is distilled, oil of turpentine is obtained and the residue is yellow. Rosin or resin is used in the manufacture of soap. Oil of turpentine is used for paint and varnish manufacture. Balsam of Peru is used in soap and perfume manufacture.

Lac is the resin produced by an insect found in India from which *shellac* is obtained. Dissolved in alcohol it is used as hair lacquer or french polish.

GUMS

Gums do not contain oils and are treated in this chapter because of their close relationship to resins, in that they are secretions of plants found on leaves, roots, and barks, or in seaweeds. Chemically, gums are mixtures of sugars or carbohydrates and are composed of carbon, hydrogen, and oxygen.

USE OF GUMS IN HAIRDRESSING PREPARATIONS

1. Gums swell in the presence of water and therefore mix with water, forming mucilages.
2. Preparations containing gums tend to go mouldy and therefore should contain a preservative, e.g. formaldehyde or essential oil of pine.

3. Gums form a plastic coating to hair and are used in hair lotions, fixatives, and wave-setting lotions.

4. These gums are edible and are used in artificial creams, salad creams, and ice-creams.

ORIGIN AND USES OF GUMS

Gum	Origin and uses
Tragacanth	Forms as a wound on the bark of a shrub in Turkey. It is picked off by hand. With water it swells up to form a slimy mucilage. Used as a hair fixative, setting-lotion, hand cream, salad cream.
Karaya	Indian gum, similar to gum tragacanth but much cheaper. Used as a hair fixative, setting-lotion, and hand cream
Agar	Gum or jelly-like substance from seaweed. Used in brushless shaving creams

COMPARISON OF OILS, FATS, WAXES, AND MINERAL AND ESSENTIAL OILS

Oils, fats, and waxes	Mineral oils	Essential oils
Vegetable: olive and peanut	Liquid paraffin	Lavender
Animal: lard and whale oil	Petroleum jelly	Cinnamon
Wax: lanolin, beeswax	Paraffin wax	Peppermint
Contain carbon hydrogen oxygen	Contain hydrogen carbon	Contain hydrogen, carbon, and some oxygen
$\text{Oils and fats} = \dfrac{\text{fatty}}{\text{acids}} + \text{glycerine}$ $\text{Wax} = \dfrac{\text{fatty}}{\text{acid}} + \dfrac{\text{fatty}}{\text{alcohols}}$	Paraffin hydrocarbons	$\dfrac{\text{Terpenes}}{\text{or camphor}} = \dfrac{\text{essential}}{\text{oils}}$
Form soap with caustic soda	No soap formed	No soap formed
Insoluble in alcohol (except castor oil)	Some soluble in alcohol	All soluble in alcohol
Non-volatile, i.e. fixed oils	Partly volatile: e.g. petrol Non-volatile: e.g. liquid paraffin	All volatile
Edible	Inedible	Partly edible, partly inedible
Skin creams and hair-conditioners	Brilliantines and creams	Perfumes, flavours, and medicinal uses

★ ★ ★

SUGGESTIONS FOR PRACTICAL WORK

Prepare the following cosmetic preparations using the recipes and formulae given in Chapter 18. Carefully notice the appearance and smell of the ingredients, referring to the relevant portions of this chapter for further details of the materials:

1. Hair-conditioning cream.
2. Solid brilliantine.
3. Gum tragacanth hair cream.
4. Gum tragacanth hair-setting lotion.
5. After-shave lotion.
6. Astringent lotion.
7. Eau-de-Cologne.
8. Lavender water.
9. Vanishing-cream.
10. Cold cream.

QUESTIONS ON CHAPTER 15

1. Write short notes on three of the following groups of substances giving named examples in each case and the use of the substance in hairdressing practice: (1) essential oils, (2) gums, (3) oils and fats, (4) mineral oils.
2. Write a short account of each of the following substances used in hairdressing preparations, under the headings of (a) appearance and properties, (b) uses: (1) gum tragacanth, (2) lanolin, (3) witch hazel, (4) liquid paraffin.
3. Give the names of (a) a vegetable oil, (b) a mineral oil, and (c) an essential oil. Give one important use of each in hairdressing practice and state why they are used.
4. By means of a table compare oils and fats, and mineral and essential oils.
5. Write brief notes on the following: (1) medicated shampoos, (2) setting lotions, (3) perfumes, (4) waxes.
6. What do you know of the following types of chemical compounds? Give named examples in each case and their use in the craft: (1) glycerides of fatty acids, (2) terpenes and camphors, (3) hydrocarbons, (4) resins.
7. Mention the main active ingredients used in the preparation of: (1) any hand cream, (2) any brilliantine, (3) Eau-de-Cologne.

16 CARBON, SULPHUR, WATER, AND DETERGENTS

CARBON AND ITS COMPOUNDS

We have previously referred to organic chemistry as being the study of carbon compounds. We shall now consider the chemistry of the element carbon. The element carbon is found in different physical forms called *allotropes*, namely, diamond, graphite, and non-crystalline carbon.

Diamonds as jewellery are well known, but their uses as glass -and rock-cutters are less familiar.

Graphite: this form of carbon feels greasy when rubbed between the fingers. It is used mainly for electric motor brushes, lubricants, and the 'lead' of pencils.

Non-crystalline forms of carbon are charcoal, coke, and lamp-black. Lamp-black is obtained by burning hydrocarbon paraffin oils in a short supply of air. Lamp-black is the main ingredient of black mascara and black boot-polish. The printed words that you are now reading are made from lamp-black used in the printer's ink. Mascara can be prepared as follows: mix 10 g of best quality lamp-black carbon with 90 g of soft soap, add a little water, and grind the mixture to the consistency of a thick paste, using a mortar and pestel.

CARBON MONOXIDE

Carbon monoxide (CO) is a highly poisonous gas with no colour or smell; it therefore gives no warning of its presence.

Properties

1. Carbon monoxide forms a compound with the haemoglobin of the blood called carboxy-haemoglobin. This results in death from oxygen shortage or carbon monoxide poisoning.
2. Carbon monoxide burns with a blue flame. It is one of the main components of coal gas.

Formation of carbon monoxide

Carbon monoxide will be formed when a carbon fuel such as paraffin or coal burns in an insufficient supply of oxygen or air. It is produced as follows:

1. Exhaust fumes from motor-cars. (It is dangerous to run a car engine in a garage with closed doors.)
2. Coal, coal gas, and paraffin-oil appliances burning with inefficient flue chimneys can produce carbon monoxide.
3. The practice of sealing off all draught inlets to a room and using gas or oil-burning appliances will result in carbon monoxide formation through lack of air for the appliance. An efficient ventilation or flue is essential where coal gas or oil appliances are used.

CARBON DIOXIDE

Carbon dioxide (CO_2) is present in the air in variable amounts between 0·05 and 0·3 per cent. The carbon dioxide present in the air is derived from (a) combustion of carbon-containing fuels, and (b) respiration of plants and animals.

The quantity of gas in the air remains fairly *constant* because it is used as a raw material during the process of food manufacture in plants, namely photosynthesis. Also a certain amount dissolves in rain-water.

Preparation of carbon dioxide in the laboratory

Place a few pieces of marble chips or calcium carbonate in a flask and add dilute hydrochloric acid (Figure 16.1). Collect a few gas-jars of the

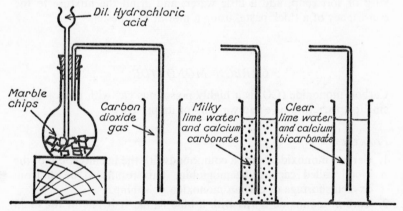

Figure 16.1. Laboratory preparation of carbon dioxide and action of the gas on lime-water

gas. Insert a burning taper into a gas-jar of carbon dioxide and note how the gas extinguishes the flame. Carbon dioxide will not allow things to burn in it. For this reason it is formed in fire-extinguishers by the action of acids on washing soda or sodium carbonate.

Lime-water test

Half-fill a large test-tube with clear lime-water, or calcium hydroxide $Ca(OH)_2$. Bubble in the carbon dioxide gas and note how the lime-water turns milky; this is due to the formation of insoluble calcium carbonate.

Calcium hydroxide + carbon dioxide = insoluble calcium carbonate and water

$$Ca(OH)_2 \quad + \quad CO_2 \quad = \quad CaCO_3 + H_2O$$

If more carbon dioxide gas is bubbled through the milky-coloured liquid it will gradually turn *clear*, owing to the formation of *soluble calcium bicarbonate* (Figure 16.1).

Calcium carbonate and water + carbon dioxide = soluble calcium bicarbonate

$$CaCO_3 \quad + \quad CO_2 + H_2O \quad = \quad Ca(HCO_3)_2$$

The gas produced during the fermentation of sugar can be tested in the above manner (see Chapter 14).

Note. It is advisable to learn these two equations at this stage, for they will be of some importance when we study the causes of hardness in water.

Carbonates

Carbonates are the salts of carbonic acid. Sodium carbonate, Na_2CO_3, or washing soda is available in feathery crystals called sodium sesqui-carbonate, used for bath salts. Calcium carbonate, $CaCO_3$, or chalk, is used in talcum powder. Magnesium carbonate, $MgCO_3$, is an ingredient of talcum powder and bleaching paste.

Uses of carbon dioxide

1. Mineral water and soda water have a slight acid taste owing to the weak acid carbonic acid, H_2CO_3.
2. Bread and cakes rise by the action of carbon dioxide released by the yeast or baking powder.
3. Fire-extinguishers of the soda-acid type.
4. *Foam baths.* The foam consists of bubbles of carbon dioxide or bubbles of air trapped in a shampoo, together with a foaming agent called *saponin.* A mixture of sodium bicarbonate, citric acid, sodium lauryl sulphonate, and a trace of saponin will produce an excellent foam when stirred into hot water.

SULPHUR AND ITS COMPOUNDS

Sulphur is a bright yellow solid that melts on heating and burns with a pale blue flame, forming sulphur dioxide gas (SO_2), which has a suffocating smell.

$$\text{Sulphur} + \text{from the} = \text{sulphur dioxide}$$
$$\text{oxygen}$$
$$\text{air}$$

$$S \quad + \quad O_2 \quad = \quad SO_2$$

Sulphur is an important ingredient of lotions for the skin and hair.

HYDROGEN SULPHIDE

Hydrogen sulphide (H_2S) is a foul-smelling poisonous gas formed when hydrochloric acid is added to iron sulphide. The presence of the gas is also in evidence near rotting cabbages and bad eggs.

SULPHIDES

These are the compounds that are formed from hydrogen sulphide. Some have the power of dissolving or softening hair, and are the active ingredients of depilatories or hair-removers. Sodium sulphide, Na_2S, barium sulphide, BaS, and calcium thioglycollate are the most important sulphide hair-removers. These preparations are also used to remove hair from animal hides before their manufacture into leather.

Sulphide dyes are prepared from a No. 1 solution of sodium sulphide and a No. 2 solution consisting of soluble metal salts of silver, copper, cobalt, nickel, tin, lead, or mercury. (See Chapter 17 for details of sulphide dyes.)

SULPHURIC ACID

Sulphuric acid (H_2SO_4) is an important acid. It is manufactured from sulphur dioxide, which is produced by burning sulphur in oxygen. Sulphuric acid is used in the manufacture of many chemical compounds and is one of the raw materials used in the manufacture of soapless detergents.

Properties of concentrated sulphuric acid

1. A heavy oily liquid, also called 'oil of vitriol';
2. A very strong, corrosive acid;
3. When mixed with water, the solution becomes very hot and may even boil.

Note. Always add the acid in a thin stream while stirring. *Never* add the water to the acid.

4. Sulphuric acid reacts with bases or alcohols to form two kinds of salts: sulphates or acid hydrogen sulphates.

Base or alcohol + Sulphuric acid = sulphates or acid hydrogen sulphates

The acid hydrogen sulphate salts can join with bases and alcohols to form ordinary sulphates:

Base or alcohol + acid hydrogen sulphate = sulphate + water

e.g.

Sodium hydrogen sulphate + sodium metal = sodium sulphate

Lauryl hydrogen sulphate + sodium metal = sodium lauryl sulphate

DETERGENTS

The word *detergent* is used to describe a substance that cleans surfaces or removes dirt. Dirt consists mostly of tiny solid particles clinging to the natural grease coating of the hair or fibre. The following are some of the main substances employed as detergents in hairdressing:

1. *Solvent detergents* or 'dry' cleaners. These are liquid solvents such as petrol or carbon tetrachloride in which the garment or hair postiche is immersed. The solvent dissolves the greasy coating of the hair and suspends the dirt. The garment or hair is then dried quickly by the rapid evaporation of the solvent. The term 'dry cleaning' tends to be misleading, since 'wet' liquids are being used in the process.
2. *Dry powder* absorption detergents are used for certain dry shampoo preparations consisting of a mixture of talc and chalk. Their detergent power depends on the absorption of the greasy material in a similar manner to the absorption of ink by blotting-paper.
3. *Soap detergents.*
4. *Soapless detergents or surfactants.*

The chemistry of soap and soapless detergents will now be considered in greater detail.

SOAP DETERGENTS

Soluble soaps are produced by boiling vegetable or animal oils or fats with sodium hydroxide or potassium hydroxide. Glycerine is also formed as a by-product (its main uses are described in Chapter 15).

Animal or vegetable oil or fat + sodium hydroxide = hard soap + glycerine

Plate 17 shows a soap pan in which the oil is boiled with the alkali. The main raw materials used in toilet-soap manufacture are palm kernel, olive oils, beef and mutton tallow or fats, together with potassium or sodium hydroxides. The process of soap-making is called *saponification*. Sodium hydroxide forms 'hard' soap used for household purposes; potassium hydroxide produces 'soft' soap for toilet purposes. The perfume, colouring matter, and soap chips are subsequently mixed together in the toilet soap mixer.

Experiment 1

Dissolve 9 g of sodium hydroxide pellets in 100 cm³ of water in a 1,000-cm³ beaker, add 50 cm³ of olive oil. Bubble in steam from a boiler and gently heat the beaker with a small flame for about 30 to 60 minutes. Withdraw the heat if frothing occurs (Figure 16.2).

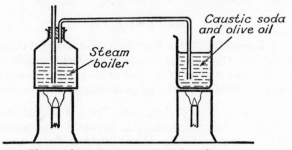

Figure 16.2. Laboratory preparation of soap

Dissolve 40 g of common salt in 100 cm³ of water. This will produce a saturated solution of brine, which is now added to the cool soap mixture prepared above. The solid soap will appear floating on the top of the solution. It is removed by filtration and the soap residue dried on filter papers.

During the process of saponification the oils are split up into *glycerine* and *fatty acids*, such as palmitic and stearic acids. The fatty acids join with the alkali sodium hydroxide forming the salts sodium stearate or sodium palmitate:

$$\text{Oil}\begin{cases}\text{fatty acid}\\\text{and glycerine}\\\text{ester}\end{cases} + \begin{array}{c}\text{sodium}\\\text{hydroxide}\end{array} = \begin{array}{c}\text{sodium fatty}\\\text{acid salt or}\\\text{soap}\end{array} + \text{glycerine}$$

Soap can be prepared by the direct combination of the fatty acid and alkali. This method is used for preparing vanishing-creams, which consist basically of soft soap and water:

$$\begin{array}{c}\text{Stearic}\\\text{acid}\end{array} + \begin{array}{c}\text{potassium}\\\text{hydroxide}\end{array} = \begin{array}{c}\text{potassium stearate}\\\text{soft soap}\end{array} + \text{water}$$

Experiment 2

Dissolve 3 g of potassium hydroxide pellets in 160 cm³ of water, add 30 g of stearic acid, and heat the mixture to 60°C, whilst stirring. Remove the heat and stir the mixture vigorously until it is cool. Note the soapy touch of your preparation and see if it forms a lather with water.

Preparation of soap-type shampoo:

>20 g soft soap
>25 cm³ industrial ethyl alcohol
>75 cm³ distilled water

Dissolve the soft soap in the alcohol, add the water and a few drops of perfume. Filter the mixture if it appears cloudy.

Preparation of spirit shampoo:

>0·5 g soft soap
>3 drops 0·880 ammonium hydroxide
>50 cm³ industrial alcohol
>50 cm³ distilled water

Dissolve the soap in the alcohol. Add the ammonium hydroxide to the water and mix the two solutions. Filter the mixture if it appears cloudy, and add a suitable perfume.

SOAPLESS DETERGENTS OR SURFACTANTS

Soapless detergents or surfactants are produced by the following methods, using sulphuric acid in each case, to produce a *hydrogen sulphate* or *sulphonate* compound. In some cases the surfactant formed is a sulphate.

1. From castor and olive oils

Castor or olive oil are treated with concentrated sulphuric acid, forming the *sulphonated* castor or olive oils. The mixture is neutralized with sodium hydroxide:

Olive or castor oil + sulphuric acid = sulphonated castor or olive oil + alkali = neutral sulphonated castor or olive oils

Sulphonated castor oil is also known as Turkey-red oil. It is useful for its detergent properties, and is also used to protect previously waved hair from the further action of ammonium thioglycollate cold-wave lotion. Sulphonated olive oil is a useful detergent and ranks as one of the first surfactants ever to be made in a laboratory (1831).

2. From coconut oil

Coconut oil or glyceryl laurate is the ester of lauric acid:

Coconut oil = glycerine + lauric acid

(*a*) The oil is changed into *lauryl alcohol* by a process of *reduction* using methyl alcohol and hydrogen.

(*b*) The lauryl alcohol is then treated with concentrated sulphuric acid, forming *lauryl hydrogen sulphate* or *sulphonate*.

Coconut oil or glyceryl laurate $\xrightarrow{\text{Reduction}}$ lauryl alcohol $\xrightarrow{\text{sulphuric acid}}$ lauryl hydrogen sulphate

(*c*) If the acidic lauryl hydrogen sulphate is now neutralized with *different bases*, we obtain different neutral surfactants. The bases used for this neutralization process are ammonia, sodium, hydroxide, triethanolamine, and monoethanolamine.

1. Lauryl hydrogen sulphate + ammonia = ammonium lauryl sulphate
2. Lauryl hydrogen sulphate + sodium hydroxide = sodium lauryl sulphate
3. Lauryl hydrogen sulphate + triethanolamine = triethanolamine lauryl sulphate
4. Lauryl hydrogen sulphate + monoethanolamine = monoethanolamine lauryl sulphate

Summary:

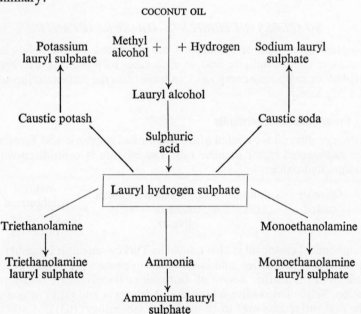

3. From a petroleum by-product

A liquid hydrocarbon petroleum by-product known as *alkane* or *alkyl benzene* is treated with concentrated sulphuric acid and made into acidic alkyl sulphonates or hydrogen sulphates. This is followed by neutralization with various bases, producing a variety of surfactants.

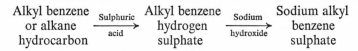

Alkyl benzene or alkane hydrocarbon →(Sulphuric acid) Alkyl benzene hydrogen sulphate →(Sodium hydroxide) Sodium alkyl benzene sulphate

Summary:

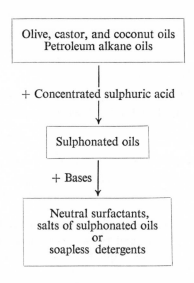

Olive, castor, and coconut oils
Petroleum alkane oils

+ Concentrated sulphuric acid

Sulphonated oils

+ Bases

Neutral surfactants,
salts of sulphonated oils
or
soapless detergents

USES OF MORE IMPORTANT SURFACTANTS

Soapless detergent or surfactant	Appearance	Uses
Triethanolamine lauryl sulphate	Clear colourless liquid or paste	
Monoethanolamine lauryl sulphate	Clear viscous liquid	For shampoos and industrial detergents
Ammonium lauryl sulphate	Viscous amber liquid	
Sodium lauryl sulphate	White powder	

Soapless detergent or surfactant	Appearance	Uses
Alkyl sulphate	Paste	General detergents for all industries, e.g. soapless detergent powders, and laundry preparations
Alkyl benzene sulphonate	Viscous liquid	
Sodium alkyl benzene sulphonate	White powder	
Sulphonated castor and olive oils	Viscous yellow liquids	

PREPARATION OF A SOAPLESS-TYPE SURFACTANT SHAMPOO

1. Shampoo powder:

Ingredient	Formula A	Formula B
Sodium lauryl sulphate	48 g	50 g
Borax	40 g	nil
Sodium sesquicarbonate	12 g	50 g

Mix the powders in a large tin and add perfume.

2. Liquid shampoo:

Take one part triethanolamine lauryl sulphate and mix with either four or five parts of water and perfume. If a medicated shampoo is required, add the indicated quantities of one of the following substances:

Thymol 0·1–2 per cent   Menthol 0·05 per cent
Terpineol 0·40 per cent   Camphor 0·25 per cent

The viscosity of the shampoo can be increased by dissolving 1 per cent of common salt or borax in the water before mixing with the surfactant.

VARIOUS TYPES OF WATER

Hairdressing salons receive supplies of water from various sources, either from a mountain reservoir supply or from a spring or deep well. It is therefore important to consider the main types of natural waters that can be supplied to a hairdressing salon.

The following represent the main types of natural waters together with their *suspended* and *dissolved* impurities.

1. *RAIN-WATER*

Rain-water is the purest form of water obtainable, provided it has fallen through the *clean* air of the country and away from the sea. Town rain-water is liable to contain suspended dirt particles and may also contain dissolved gases and even acids. Rain-water is a soft water, and is ideal for washing the hair in hard-water districts.

2. *RIVER AND LAKE WATER*

This is rain-water that has flowed over the rocks and soil of a river bed. Rain-water that has passed over limestone is a very hard water compared to rain-water that has flowed over granite. Thames water is hard because the river flows over limestone, whereas the rivers of Snowdonia, which flow over slates and volcanic rocks, provide soft water. The normal domestic water supply is mainly from a river or mountain lake source.

3. *SPRING OR DEEP WELL WATER*

This type of water is recognized by its particular sparkling clarity and freedom from suspended matter, produced by the slow filtration of rain and river water through the sand and clay strata of the earth. Such water may contain dissolved salts and become hard.

Certain mineral waters are obtained from springs and wells, for example, at Bath, Harrogate, Leamington, and Vichy. These waters contain dissolved and suspended impurities. They are supposed to have curative properties but have no application to hairdressing practice.

4. *SEA-WATER*

Sea-water contains many dissolved salts of sodium, potassium, and magnesium. The main ingredient is sodium chloride (approximately 2·5 per cent). This salt with its hygroscopic property has previously been described, together with its action on the hair fibre (see Chapter 6).

WATER-SOFTENING

Water that produces easily with soap a lather that persists for at least two minutes is called *soft* water. Hard water will not readily give a lather with soap, because certain salts are dissolved in it. Hard water is divided into two main kinds, namely: (*a*) temporary, and (*b*) permanently hard water.

TEMPORARY HARDNESS

Temporary hardness is caused by calcium and magnesium *bicarbonates* that have entered the water by the action of rain-water containing dissolved carbon dioxide flowing over chalk or limestone.

$$\begin{array}{c}\text{Magnesium}\\\text{or calcium}\\\text{carbonate}\end{array} + \begin{array}{c}\text{carbon}\\\text{dioxide}\end{array} + \text{water} = \begin{array}{c}\text{magnesium}\\\text{or calcium}\\\text{bicarbonates}\end{array}$$

$$\begin{array}{c}MgCO_3\\\text{or}\\CaCO_3\end{array} + CO_2 + H_2O = \begin{array}{c}Mg(HCO_3)_2\\\text{or}\\Ca(HCO_3)_2\end{array}$$

This equation has already been given in describing the action of carbon dioxide on lime-water. Temporary hard water is softened by *boiling*, when a calcium carbonate deposit or *scale* is formed. This reaction is the reverse of the equation shown above.

$$\begin{array}{c}\text{Calcium}\\\text{bicarbonate}\\\text{(soluble)}\end{array} \overset{\text{Boiling}}{=} \begin{array}{c}\text{calcium}\\\text{carbonate}\\\text{(insoluble)}\end{array} + \begin{array}{c}\text{carbon}\\\text{dioxide}\end{array} + \text{water}$$

$$Ca(HCO_3)_2 = CaCO_3 + CO_2 + H_2O$$

PERMANENT HARDNESS

Permanently hard water contains dissolved calcium and magnesium sulphates that have entered the water from rocks as the rain-water flowed over them. This hardness *cannot* be removed by boiling.

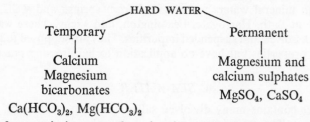

$$\begin{array}{ccc} & \text{HARD WATER} & \\ \text{Temporary} & & \text{Permanent} \\ | & & | \\ \begin{array}{c}\text{Calcium}\\\text{Magnesium}\\\text{bicarbonates}\end{array} & & \begin{array}{c}\text{Magnesium and}\\\text{calcium sulphates}\end{array} \\ Ca(HCO_3)_2, Mg(HCO_3)_2 & & MgSO_4, CaSO_4 \end{array}$$

Soft water in its purest form is rain-water collected in a rain-water butt, or water that has travelled over insoluble granite rocks. Soft water can be obtained by any of the water-softening methods described later.

DISADVANTAGES OF HARD WATER

1. Curd or calcium soap formation is one of the main disadvantages of hard water. When sodium stearate or soap is added to hard water a flocculant insoluble sticky calcium stearate salt is produced.

$$\begin{array}{c}\text{Sodium}\\\text{stearate}\\\text{soap}\end{array} + \begin{array}{c}\text{calcium}\\\text{salt}\\\text{hard water}\end{array} = \begin{array}{c}\text{calcium}\\\text{stearate}\\\text{curd}\\\text{(insoluble)}\end{array} + \begin{array}{c}\text{sodium}\\\text{salt}\\\text{soft water}\end{array}$$

Thus soap is wasted, and the curds or calcium soap scum cling to the hair fibres, making it look dull. Scum may also cling to textile fibres, making white materials grey. Skin blemishes can be caused if the soap curd clogs the skin pores.

2. Scale deposits in pipes, boilers, and heaters cause blockages and waste of fuel through overheating, resulting in expensive repairs to the water system.

ADVANTAGES OF HARD WATER

1. Hard water has a pleasant taste.
2. The dissolved salts are important for teeth and bone formation. These advantages do not compare with the numerous and expensive disadvantages of hard water.

METHODS OF SOFTENING WATER

Hard water usually contains both temporary and permanent forms of hardness. It is rare to find natural water with *one* type of hardness only.

1. **Soapless detergents** or **surfactants** are most suitable detergents for use in a hard-water area. They do not form insoluble curds, because the calcium salt of the surfactant is soluble:

$$\text{Sodium lauryl sulphate} + \text{calcium salt hard water} = \text{calcium lauryl sulphate (soluble)} + \text{sodium salt soft water}$$

Soapless detergent surfactant shampoos are most suitable for hairdressing salons with a hard-water supply. Similarly surfactant washing powders are most useful in hard-water districts.

2. **Slaked lime** or **Clarke's method** is used for softening water on a large scale for use in industry or by town water authorities:

$$\text{Calcium bicarbonate} + \text{lime} = \text{calcium carbonate} + \text{soft water}$$

3. **Washing soda** or **sodium carbonate**, Na_2CO_3, is an excellent water-softener for domestic laundry purposes. It is useful for softening bath water in the form of bath salts. There is no advantage in using perfumed bath salts in a soft-water area; the perfume effect can be produced by a good bath oil or *essence*.

$$\text{Calcium salt hard water (soluble)} + \text{sodium carbonate} = \text{calcium carbonate (insoluble)} + \text{sodium salt soft water}$$

4. **'Calgon'** is the trade name for **sodium hexametaphosphate,** a soluble salt that softens water without forming a scum. The changes that

take place are chemically complex and difficult to explain. 'Calgon'

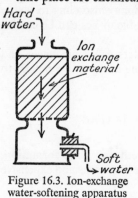

is an ingredient of some surfactant soapless washing powders and is useful for softening bath and washing-up water in hard-water areas and for rinsing the hair after washing.

Figure 16.3. Ion-exchange water-softening apparatus

5. **The ion-exchange process,** or 'Permutit' process, consists of passing hard water through a *mineral ion-exchange* material that exchanges the calcium and magnesium for sodium ions (Figure 16.3). The softening or ion-exchange process continues until no more sodium ions remain.

$$\frac{\text{Sodium ion}}{\text{exchange}} + \frac{\text{calcium salt}}{\text{(hard water)}} = \frac{\text{calcium ion}}{\text{exchange}} + \frac{\text{sodium salt}}{\text{(soft water)}}$$

The ion-exchange material is *regenerated* by means of sodium chloride or common salt:

$$\frac{\text{Calcium ion}}{\text{exchange}} + \frac{\text{sodium}}{\text{chloride}} = \frac{\text{sodium ion}}{\text{exchange}} + \frac{\text{calcium}}{\text{chloride}}$$

The ion-exchange or 'Permutit' process is the ideal water-softening process for use in hairdressing salons. The water-softener unit is fitted into the main water system and is comparatively simple to maintain.

COMPARISON OF SOAPS AND SOAPLESS DETERGENTS

Soap	*Soapless detergent*
Alkaline, pH 9–10	Neutral, pH 7
Form *insoluble* calcium soap scum in hard water	Does not form a scum in hard water
Cannot be used in acid solutions	Can be used in acid solutions
Slight antiseptic properties	Moderate antiseptic properties
Prepared from caustic soda and oils	Prepared from sulphuric acid and oils

EMULSIFYING WAXES

Many hair-conditioning creams and cosmetics contain fatty alcohols and fatty acids that have been *sulphonated* or converted into surfactant compounds with properties similar to soapless detergents, namely, the ease with which they produce a *cream*. A number of emulsifying waxes and emulsifying agents of varying composition used for cosmetic and pharmaceutical preparations are produced by A. Boake Roberts & Co. Ltd ('Abracols' and 'Emulsene'), Glovers Ltd ('Collones'), and Croda Ltd (lanolin derivatives). The application of these materials to cosmetic preparations will be described in Chapter 18.

★ ★ ★

SUGGESTIONS FOR PRACTICAL WORK

In addition to the experiments described in this chapter, the following experiments may also be performed:

1. The determination of the hardness of water.

   Dissolve 20 g of soft soap in 200 cm³ of methylated spirit. Filter the solution if cloudy and make up the soap solution to a total volume of 1,000 cm³ using distilled or de-ionized water. The soap solution prepared is one of known strength, i.e. 20 g soft soap in 1 litre of water; it is called a *standard* soap solution. A 50-cm³ burette is filled with standard soap solution and 50 cm³ of distilled water measured by a pipette is placed in a 250-cm³ conical flask. The soap solution is added 1 cm³ at a time and the flask is well shaken after each addition. Record the number of cm³ of soap solution used when a lather is obtained that persists for two minutes. Repeat the experiment using 50-cm³ portions of water from different localities and water that has been softened by the methods described in the chapter.

   The amount of standard soap solution used gives an indication of the comparative hardness of the different water. Work out the number of cm³ in a standard soap solution using various kinds of water, e.g., distilled or de-ionized water; tap water; water from locality A; water from locality B; water plus $MgSO_4$ (magnesium sulphate); boiled water; water plus washing soda; 'Permutit' softened water; water plus 'Calgon'; water plus lime.

   Note. Students living in soft-water areas can prepare artificial hard water from lime-water through which carbon-dioxide has been bubbled until the solution is clear and to which a little magnesium sulphate has been added.

2. Prepare the following, using the formulae and methods described in Chapter 18: bath salts, bath essence, talcum powder, and a vanishing-cream.

3. If your salon is supplied with hard water, note the effect of using soap shampoo for washing hair and compare it with the effect of using a soapless detergent shampoo. Salons supplied with soft water should experiment with the use of soap and soapless detergent shampoos and compare the relative advantages and disadvantages of the detergents.

QUESTIONS ON CHAPTER 16

1. Explain the term *detergent*, giving examples of the main type of detergents. Describe briefly the method of manufacture and important properties of soaps and soapless detergents.

2. What substances cause hardness in water and how do these substances enter the water? Describe the action of soap and soapless detergent on hard water. Describe two methods of softening water.

3. Describe briefly the raw materials used in the process of soap manufacture. Outline the method you would use to make a soap shampoo. Compare the advantages and disadvantages of using soap and surfactant shampoos.

4. What are surfactants? Describe the preparation of a medicated surfactant shampoo. If your salon has a soft-water supply, what type of detergent shampoo would you use? Give reasons.

5. What is the action of soap on hard water? What are the main disadvantages of hard water in a hairdressing salon? Describe how you may overcome these disadvantages.

6. Write short notes on the following: (a) sodium stearate; (b) triethanolamine lauryl sulphate; (c) calcium hexametaphosphate; (d) sodium sesquicarbonate; (e) ion-exchange resins.

7. Write short notes on the following: (a) distilled water; (b) temporarily hard water; (c) soft water; (d) permanently hard water; (e) hydrogen oxide.

8. Describe the preparation of carbon dioxide gas in the laboratory. Describe its effect on lime-water. Give some uses of this gas. Outline the methods by which carbon monoxide can be formed, and describe its effect on the human body.

9. Briefly describe how you would determine whether the water in your newly acquired salon is hard or soft. What methods would you apply in order to overcome hardness in water?

10. Write brief notes on the main chemical ingredients of the following: (a) surfactant shampoo; (b) liquid soap shampoo; (c) bath essence; (d) bath salts; (e) Turkey-red oil.
    What is the purpose of using bath salts in a hard-water area?

11. What is the action of sulphuric acid on vegetable and mineral oils? Give reasons for the increasing use of these products.

17 HAIR CHEMISTRY AND DYES

Our present knowledge of the physical and chemical structure of hair is mainly due to research on wool, an outstanding fibre similar in structure to human hair.

STRUCTURE OF HAIR AND WOOL FIBRES

The outside of the wool fibre is covered with overlapping scales which point towards the tip of the fibre. This outer layer of the fibre is called the *cuticle*. The inner part consists of spindle-shaped *cortex* cells which give strength to the fibre (see Plate 22).

Plates 20 and 21 show the surface patterns on wool fibre and human hair, as seen through the microscope. The surface patterns clearly distinguish between the two fibres. Surface patterns are used in the identification of various animal hairs and wools.

PROTEINS

Among the many organic chemical compounds produced by living organisms the following classes of organic compounds are of considerable importance:

Carbohydrates. These are composed of carbon, hydrogen, and oxygen. They are the main ingredients of sugars and starch.

Oils and fats. These are made of carbon, hydrogen, and oxygen but contain more carbon than carbohydrates. They are useful as body fuels in the form of butter and lard. (See Chapter 15.)

Proteins are the most complex of all organic compounds and are made up of the elements carbon, hydrogen, oxygen, sulphur, and nitrogen, i.e. CHOSN. They are the main ingredients of such substances as lean meat, muscle, eggs, and hair.

Experiments

To indicate the chemical elements present in hair protein:

1. *Carbon and hydrogen*

Carbon and hydrogen may be detected in hair by mixing finely chopped dry hair with *dry* copper oxide and heating the mixture in a test-tube (Figure 17.1). The *carbon* present in the hair is *oxidized* by

187

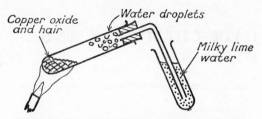

Figure 17.1. Test for carbon and hydrogen in hair

means of the copper oxide to carbon dioxide; this will turn lime water milky. The *hydrogen* is *oxidized* to water by means of the copper oxide, the water formed condensing in the cooler parts of the tube.

$$\frac{\text{Carbon in}}{\text{hair protein}} + \frac{\text{oxygen from}}{\text{copper oxide}} = \text{carbon dioxide}$$

$$\frac{\text{Hydrogen in}}{\text{hair protein}} + \frac{\text{oxygen from}}{\text{copper oxide}} = \text{water}$$

2. *Nitrogen*

Nitrogen may be detected by heating finely chopped hair with sodium hydroxide or soda-lime, when ammonia gas is produced and is recognized by its smell or the way in which it turns moist litmus paper blue.

$$\frac{\text{Nitrogen in}}{\text{hair protein}} + \frac{\text{sodium hydroxide}}{\text{or soda-lime}} = \text{ammonia gas}$$

3. *Sulphur*

The presence of sulphur is indicated by boiling chopped hair with caustic soda and holding a piece of lead acetate paper in the vapour emitted; the blackening of the paper then obtained is due to the formation of lead sulphide, which shows that the hair must have contained sulphur.

Alternatively, the chopped hair may be heated with soda-lime and the vapour tested with lead acetate paper.

$$\frac{\text{Sulphur in}}{\text{hair protein}} + \text{soda-lime} = \frac{\text{hydrogen sulphide}}{\text{(blackens lead acetate paper).}}$$

4. *Oxygen*

There is no suitable simple chemical method for detecting the presence of oxygen in hair protein.

The following table gives the approximate percentage composition of the elements present in hair. It also indicates the chemical elements that make up hair protein.

	per cent
Carbon	51
Hydrogen	7
Oxygen	19
Sulphur	5
Nitrogen	18

THE CHEMICAL COMPOSITION OF HAIR

The structure and composition of hair has been examined by X-ray diffraction methods and by studying the products of hydrolysis of hair protein.

Proteins are considered to be made up of smaller units called *amino-acids*. These are produced on hydrolysis of the protein, that is, boiling the protein with either acids or alkalis; intermediate *polypeptides* are also produced during the process.

Protein $\xrightarrow{\text{hydrolysis}}$ polypeptides $\xrightarrow{\text{hydrolysis}}$ amino-acids

Cystine and cysteine are considered to be among the amino-acids that contribute to the making of hair protein.

KERATIN

Human hair is considered to be built up from a very complex protein called *alpha-keratin* (α-keratin). X-ray studies show that hair, nails, hooves, and horn are all made up of the same protein. All these substances are produced by the *dermis* layer of the skin. Some biologists consider that hair and similar keratinoid substances are primarily nitrogenous *waste products* eliminated through the skin.

MOLECULAR STRUCTURE OF HAIR

As previously mentioned, the smallest part of a chemical compound that can exist in the free state is a molecule, which is in turn built up of two or more atoms. The alpha-keratin molecule is a very large molecule of a type resembling a fine chain, called *fibre molecules*. These fibre molecules are thousands of times as long as they are thick and are composed of many different atoms joined together chemically.

Each keratin fibre molecule may be considered to consist of:

i. A long main chain called the *polypeptide chain*;

ii. Side chains attached to the main *polypeptide* chain. These side chains may be acid, basic, or neutral, thus giving alpha-keratin protein the *amphoteric* property of behaving both with *acidic* and *basic* properties.

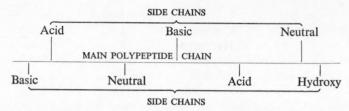

Thus the molecular structure of hair may be considered to be made up of fibre molecules lying parallel to each other. This explains the lengthwise splitting and sideways swelling of wet hair.

THE STRETCHING OF HAIR OR THE 'HAIR SPRING'

Experiments have been performed showing that hair can be stretched in water to one-and-a-half times its initial length. When the stretched hair is released it quickly regains its original length. The experiment can be repeated indefinitely. Examinations of X-ray diffraction photographs of the stretched and unstretched hair show considerable differences.

The *unstretched* hair is called alpha-keratin; the *stretched* hair is called beta-keratin or β-keratin. The change is called the alpha–beta transformation of hair keratin:

$$\alpha\text{-keratin} \xleftarrow{\quad \alpha - \beta \quad} \beta\text{-keratin}$$
$$\text{unstretched hair} \xrightarrow{\quad \text{tranformation} \quad} \text{stretched hair}$$

The process of stretching hair involves changes in the shape of molecule; alpha-keratin may be compared to a *tight spring*, whereas the beta-keratin molecule resembles an extended spring that can be pulled out to more than *twice* its original length.

Plate 19 shows the arrangement of unstretched alpha-keratin with its coiled polypeptide chain. The side chains can also be clearly seen.

THE EFFECT OF WATER ON THE STRETCHING OF ALPHA-KERATIN

Experiments show that as the water content of hair increases the hair stretches more easily. Hair that is soaked with water can be stretched to between one-and-a-half and one-and-three-quarter times its normal length. (See page 23.)

This increase in the elasticity of hair is explained as follows. In the absence of water the side chains cling to their neighbours and seize up the structure. The dry fibre cannot be contracted or stretched to any great extent.

In the presence of water the side chains lose their attraction for each other and slide over each other. The tiny molecules of water protect the side chains from each other's attractive influence and can be regarded as a type of 'molecular lubricants'.

Further experiments show that if a hair is stretched and then dried while in the *stretched* condition, it hardly contracts at all, but once it is wetted it rapidly regains its original length.

THE THEORY OF HAIR SET OR HAIR WAVING

The study of the formation of waves in hair can be considered under the following headings:

   i. Cohesive set or water waving;

  ii. Temporary set or Marcel waving;

 iii. Permanent set, either by the steam waving or chemical cold waving methods.

COHESIVE SET

This is the method of inducing a set in hair by stretching the wet hair and drying the hair in the stretched condition. In the salon, the wet hair is stretched around a roller and the hair dried, resulting in a *water wave* or *cohesive* set. If the hair is wetted by a shower of rain or washed, it rapidly loses its curl and recovers its original length. Therefore the cohesive set or water wave is a *reversible* process.

The mechanism of the cohesive set has already been described as being a process of molecular lubrication by means of the tiny water molecules, followed by 'seizing-up' of the hair in the new stretched condition. The seizing-up is caused by the strong attraction between neighbouring side chains in the absence of water. The process is easily reversed on wetting the hair.

TEMPORARY SET

Experiments have been performed in which hair is held stretched for long periods in cold water. It is found that when the stretching force is removed the hair takes some considerable time to contract to its original length. The longer the time the hair is kept stretched in cold water the *longer* it will take the hair to recover its initial length.

When the experiment is repeated by stretching the hair in *warm* water, or cold water containing an alkali such as caustic soda or borax, it is found that the time taken for the hair to recover its original length is considerably longer than after the cold water treatment. The hair in each case undergoes a *temporary set*.

The temporary nature of this set is indicated when the temporarily set hair is immersed in cold water. It rapidly contracts *part* of the way back to its original length, whereas if the hair is immersed in warm water or in a cold dilute alkali it completely recovers its original length.

The mechanism of the temporary set is considered to be due to the *breakdown* of the keratin cross-linkages, which is facilitated by warm water or cold dilute alkali acting on the beta-keratin. Normal alpha-keratin when stretched into the beta-keratin form recoils back into alpha-keratin when the stretching force is removed. Long periods of stretching tend to weaken this recoiling force and thus prevent the beta-keratin recoiling into alpha-keratin too rapidly.

The term '*relaxation*' is used to describe the process of breaking the cross-linkages of beta-keratin when it is under a stretching force, with the subsequent weakening or loss of its contracting force.

After the breakdown of the cross-linkages a process of re-formation of new, but weaker, cross-linkages takes place. These new linkages are subject to breakdown by warm water or cold dilute alkali.

In the salon the 'temporary set' is produced during the process of waving hair by means of Marcel waving-irons. When the hair is washed with warm water, the temporary set is reversed and the hair recovers its initial length, with subsequent loss of its waves.

PERMANENT SET

If stretched hair is treated with near-*boiling* water or steam, then released from the stretching force, and afterwards immersed in cold or warm water, it will be found to show no contraction to its initial length. If the freed hair is treated with steam or near-boiling water it contracts only *part* of the way back. The hair may therefore be considered as in a state of *permanent set*.

The mechanism of permanent set is due to the following facts:

i. Near-boiling water or steam makes the process of 'relaxation' or breakdown of keratin cross-linkages take place quicker than with cold or warm water;

ii. New cross-linkages are formed which are more *permanent* than those formed during temporary set.

In the salon the permanent set by the action of steam or hot water is given by moistening the hair with water containing alkali, such as ammonium hydroxide, amines, or borax, and applying heat to the tightly wound hair by (*a*) electrical methods using hot permanent-waving machines, or (*b*) by chemical *exothermal* action using sachets of calcium oxide or potassium permanganate, activated by water or various reagents. The heat generated produces the near-boiling water or steam necessary for the permanent set.

After the steaming process the pins or rollers are taken from the hair and the hair combed out. The hair is now reset and given a 'cohesive' set followed by drying. The permanent nature of the permanent set is apparent when the hair is washed in hot water.

The steaming of woollen felt millinery hoods and hats, and the steam-pressing of woollen suits and dresses, are similar processes of permanent set.

COLD PERMANENT-WAVING

Between the main polypeptide chains of the keratin molecule are found cross-linkages or bridges made of two sulphur (S) atoms called *disulphide* (—S—S—) links. During the process of cold permanent-waving a lotion of *ammonium thioglycollate* of pH 7–10 is applied to the stretched hair. This reagent is a reducing agent, that is, it adds hydrogen to the sulphur atoms and breaks the disulphide bridge.

$$
\begin{matrix}
| & & & & | \\
S & & & & S{-}H \\
| & + & 2H & = & \\
S & & & & S{-}H \\
| & & & & |
\end{matrix}
$$

Disulphide bridge   Ammonium thioglycollate   Reduced disulphide bridge

When the disulphide —S—S— bridges break, the beta-keratin molecule undergoes 'relaxation' and the hair can now be moulded into a new shape on a roller under a stretching force.

In order to introduce a permanent set, the reduced hair is now treated with an *oxidizing* agent (dilute 20-volume hydrogen peroxide, sodium perborate, or sodium bromate). The oxidizing agent removes the hydrogen atoms with the subsequent re-formation of permanent disulphide bonds formed at new sites on the keratin chain.

$$
\begin{matrix}
| & & & & | \\
S{-}{-}H & & & & S \\
& + & O & = & | + H_2O \\
S{-}{-}H & & & & S \\
| & & & & |
\end{matrix}
$$

Reduced hair with broken disulphide bridges   Air or hydrogen peroxide (Oxidizing agent)   Re-formed disulphide bridge

The permanent nature of the cold permanent set is indicated by its resistance to initial length-recovery when the hair is washed in hot water.

Sodium bisulphite $NaHSO_3$ can be used instead of ammonium thioglycollate. Certain preparations contain monoethanolamine thioglycollate.

An important application of ammonium thioglycollate is its use as a depilatory in the leather industry for removing hair from the animal

o

hide. Another, is its use in permanently pleating woollen skirts and dresses.

SUMMARY OF THE TYPES OF HAIR SET

Type of set	Method	Mechanism of the set
Cohesive set or water waving or 'shampoo and set'	Wet hair is dried in the stretched condition	Water molecules prevent attraction between the side-chain molecules. The absence of water causes the side-chain molecules to attract each other and weld together in new positions. The process is *reversed* with *cold water*
Temporary set Marcel waving	Long periods of stretching hair wetted with *warm water* or *cold dilute* alkali	(i) Breakdown of side chains in keratin under stress-'relaxation' (ii) Re-formation of new but *weak* side chains. The process is *reversed* with cold water or warm water and cold dilute alkali
Hot permanent set	Wet hair is treated with *steam* or near *boiling water*	(i) Breakdown of side chains of keratin under stress-'relaxation' (ii) Re-formation of *permanent* side chains and linkages that are *resistant* to cold and warm water; the process is not therefore reversible
Cold permanent set	Process of chemical change of the hair (i) reduction with ammonium thioglycollate (ii) followed by oxidation with hydrogen peroxide	(i) Reduction causes the breakage of the *disulphide links*-'relaxation' (ii) Oxidation re-forms the disulphide links in new positions in the keratin under stress (iii) The resultant set is not reversible and resists washing in hot water

SUMMARY OF THE DEFINITION OF SET

Set: change in length of a fibre after treatment.

Cohesive set: set which disappears on release in cold water.

Temporary set: set which persists on release in cold water but disappears on release in boiling water.

Permanent set: set which remains even after release in boiling water.

    The above definitions apply to *length* set in single fibres. They apply equally to *bending* set, in which the hair fibre is set in a *bent* condition, as in hair-waving procedure.

HAIR DYES

Natural hair colour is due to tiny egg-shaped grains of *melanin* pigment in the cortex cells of the hair fibre (see Plate 22). Normal melanin produces black, brown, and yellow hair colour, while red and blonde colours are due to *pheomelanin*. White and grey hair are caused by the absence of melanin pigments.

Hair dyes can alter the natural hair colour in two ways:

(*a*) surface dyes form a surface coating on the hair cuticle which gives the hair a 'dead' lustreless appearance.

(*b*) penetrating dyes penetrate the hair fibre and enter the cortex region. They give the hair a permanent and more natural colour, since the pigments are seen refracted through the transparent cuticle.

The following are the main types of dyes used in hairdressing:

1. *Surface dyes*
   i. Natural vegetable dyes;
   ii. Metallic dyes;
   iii. Temporary colour rinses;
   iv. Plastic bonded colours.

2. *Penetrating dyes*
   i. Henna;
   ii. Colour shampoos;
   iii. Oxidation dyes.

SURFACE DYES

NATURAL VEGETABLE DYES

These include some of the earliest known dyes, namely:

Walnut (*Juglans*) shells before ripening produce a dark brown colour when the juice comes into contact with the hair and skin.

Camomile or *Anthemis nobilis* is also used as a hair dye giving a golden-yellow colour.

METALLIC DYES

These are of two types:

i. *Reduction* metallic dyes which produce a coloured metallic deposit on the hair fibre by the action of a reducing agent such as pyrogallol on copper sulphate or other metal salts.

Experiment

Dissolve 2 g of copper sulphate in 100 cm^3 of water. The reducing solution of pyrogallol is made from 2 g of pyrogallol in 100 cm^3 of water. Specimens of bleached hair are immersed in the copper sulphate solution and 100 cm^3 of pyrogallol solution added. The hair is rinsed and examined for dye permanency by washing in standard soap solution.

ii. *Sulphide* dyes produce an insoluble metal sulphide coating on the hair by the action of sodium sulphide on a metal salt, such as copper sulphate or silver and lead nitrates.

Metal salt + sodium sulphide = metal sulphide + sodium salt
(soluble)   (insoluble)

Experiment

Dissolve 2 g of silver nitrate in 100 cm^3 of water. The sodium sulphide solution is prepared from 4 g sodium sulphide in 100 cm^3 water. Immerse wefts of bleached hair in a mixture of equal parts of silver nitrate and sodium sulphide solutions; wash the hair and test for dye permanency.

Metallic dyes are now rapidly becoming obsolete and are mentioned here because of their historical interest.

TEMPORARY COLOUR RINSES

These are synthetic dyes which are water soluble and therefore produce temporary hair colours. Chemically they consist of sodium salts of sulphonic acids and nitrophenolic compounds mixed with tartaric, or citric acids, which improve the take-up of the dye by the hair.

Experiments

Immerse wefts of bleached hair in 2 per cent solutions of the following dyes: naphthol yellow-S, picric acid, resorcin brown, Ponceau Red, rhodamine-B, methylene blue, and magenta. Each dye solution should contain 2 per cent citric acid. Carry out washing tests in standard soap solution in order to determine the permanency of the dye.

PLASTIC BONDED COLOURS

Water- and spirit-soluble dyes are dissolved in a solution containing plastic or synthetic resins of the type used in hair sprays and setting lotions (see page 209). The colour pigment is then deposited on the hair as a coloured film of plastic which also serves as a hair fixative and is easily washed from the hair.

PENETRATING DYES

HENNA

Vegetable *henna*, from the Egyptian privet plant (*Lawsonia inermis*), produces a coloured dye known as *lawsone* which penetrates the hair fibre to a certain extent giving a fairly permanent hair colouring.

COLOUR SHAMPOO—'SEMI-PERMANENT DYES'

These dyes produce a hair colouring which will last through six to eight shampoos. Chemically they consist of nitrodiamines, nitrated aminophenols, and picramic acid; these dye the hair *directly*, penetrating the cuticle to a certain extent. The dyes are mixed with a soapless detergent, such as triethanolamine oleate, to form a cream. The detergent encourages the fibre to swell and allow the dye to penetrate.

Experiment

Prepare a 2–5 per cent mixture of picramic acid and para-nitrophenylene diamine in triethanolamine oleate, and apply to wefts of light coloured hair. Wash the specimens in standard soap solution to determine the degree of permanency of the dyes.

OXIDATION DYES—PERMANENT DYES

Certain colourless chemical compounds will combine with oxygen and form dark coloured *oxidized* compounds. Such compounds are pyrogallol, aminophenols, and *diamine* derivatives which are known as dye intermediates. These have small molecules which can pass through the pores of the cuticle and enter the cortex. Here they join with oxygen and form *large* molecules of coloured dyes that cannot leave the fibre and are 'locked in', permanently increasing the durability of the hair colour. The oxygen for purposes of oxidation is obtained either from the air (21 per cent) or from 30-volume hydrogen peroxide containing a little ammonium hydroxide.

Colourless dye intermediates with small molecules pass through cuticle. $\xrightarrow[\text{oxygen}]{\text{oxidation with}}$ Coloured dyes of large molecule size, 'locked in' the hair fibre cortex.

The main ingredients of oxidation dyes are para-phenylenediamine, meta-phenylenediamine, para-toluylenediamine, diaminophenol and ortho-aminophenol. These dye intermediates are mixed with a soapless detergent, such as triethanolamine oleate, and sodium sulphite is added to prevent the oxidation of the mixture by atmospheric oxygen.

Note. Oxidation dyes containing diamine derivatives may cause serious inflammation of the skin in some cases and should be used only in accordance with expert advice.

Experiment

Prepare mixtures containing between 2–5 per cent of para-phenylenediamine, or toluylenediamine dissolved in triethanolamine oleate, and add 10 per cent sodium sulphite crystals as a preservative. Apply the mixture to wefts of hair (see Plate 23) and oxidize with 30-volume hydrogen peroxide containing a trace of ammonium hydroxide. Observe the development of the colour and perform washing tests to confirm the permanent nature of the dye.

Note. Handle all diamine compounds with great care, being careful not to spill any of the substance on your skin. Do not attempt to smell diamine compounds since the dust from them is harmful.

DYE REMOVAL OR STRIPPING

Since permanent dyes are applied to the hair by a process of *oxidation* they can be removed, lightened, or stripped by the opposite type of chemical reaction, namely *reduction*. The reducing agent used is sodium formaldehyde sulphoxylate which reduces the coloured dye to a colourless soluble form that is easily washed away. It is interesting to note that dyed furs are tested by means of sodium formaldehyde sulphoxylate. Less effective dye removers are ammonium hydroxide and hydrogen peroxide.

Note. The above mentioned dyes are not for use in a salon and are for experimental purposes on hair samples only.

DISINFECTANTS AND ANTISEPTICS

Antiseptic substances prevent the growth of bacteria and infection of wounds.

Disinfectants are agents that destroy harmful bacteria.

SOME OF THE MORE IMPORTANT ANTISEPTICS AND DISINFECTANTS

Antiseptics	*Disinfectants*
Methylated spirit or ethyl alcohol	Ultra-violet rays
Ether	Heat
Soap	Phenol ⎱ coal-tar derivatives
Soapless detergent surfactants	Cresol ⎰
Hydrogen peroxide	Formaldehyde
Silver nitrate solution	Sulphur dioxide
Mercury salt solution	Potassium permanganate
Iodine	

Cetyl trimethyl ammonium bromide, a quaternary ammonium salt (see page 149) is an antiseptic substance of some importance in hairdressing, since it makes the hair feel soft to touch, it appears as an ingredient of hair reconditioners. It is also used in oxidation dyes as a dye leveller, giving a more even distribution to the dye on the hair fibre.

★ ★ ★

SUGGESTIONS FOR PRACTICAL WORK

In addition to the experiments described in this chapter, the following experiments may also be performed:

1. Investigate the effect of prolonged immersion of samples of hair in the following solutions: (a) ammonium thioglycollate 75 per cent solution; (b) strong caustic soda solution; (c) strong sodium sulphite solution; (d) strong sodium sulphide solution; (e) concentrated hydrochloric acid.
    Wash the specimens and examine them under the projection microscope.
2. Obtain some overstretched hair and normal hair from the same head and examine both under the projection microscope.

QUESTIONS ON CHAPTER 17

1. Give a brief illustrated account of the molecular structure of hair and the theory of hair-waving processes.
2. Explain the following terms: (a) polypeptide chain; (b) disulphide link; (c) 'relaxation'. Describe briefly what happens to the hair during the formation of waves by the cold-wave process.
3. Give a short account of the scientific principles of (a) water waving; (b) steam waving; (c) cold waving processes.
4. What do you understand by the term *elasticity* of hair?
5. Describe two different processes of hair-dyeing. Give an account of the properties of the substances present in the dye reagents.
6. Explain the terms *oxidation* and *reduction*. Give *two* examples of their use in hairdressing practice in each case.
7. Give an account of the main types of hair dyes, discussing their advantages and disadvantages.
8. Write short notes on the following substances, indicating their uses in hairdressing: (a) keratin; (b) sodium sulphide; (c) phenylenediamine; (d) ammonium thioglycollate; (e) sodium bisulphite; (f) pyrogallol; (g) metal salts.
9. What is meant by 'bleaching'? What are some of the suggested causes of yellowing of bleached hair?
10. Explain the following processes: (a) the insertion of permanent pleats or creases in suits; (b) steaming creases in suits; (c) hair-removal or depilatory processes.
11. Write a short account of the group of dyes known as colour rinses and their uses in hairdressing.

18 SOLUTIONS, COSMETICS, AND PLASTICS

SOLUTIONS

When solid sugar is added to water it slowly disappears or *dissolves* in the water forming a solution of sugar in water, the dissolved sugar being called the *solute*.

Solute + solvent = solution

The dissolved solute is in an extremely fine state in the form of *ions* or *molecules* invisible to the naked eye forming a *clear* transparent solution of uniform composition throughout. The solution is said to be homogeneous.

CLASSIFICATION OF SOLUTIONS

(*a*) Solutions of gases in liquids: ammonia gas, NH_3, dissolves in water forming ammonium hydroxide, NH_4OH. Carbon dioxide dissolves in water forming carbonic acid, or soda water.

(*b*) Solutions of liquids in liquids: glycerine dissolves in water; it is used for many skin preparations. Ethyl alcohol is dissolved or *diluted* with water in spirit lotions.

(*c*) Solutions of solids in liquids: this is the most common form of solution, for example, salt in water and washing-soda in water.

IMPORTANT SOLVENTS

Many solvents are employed in hairdressing processes, but each will dissolve only certain substances. For example, salt readily *dissolves* or is *soluble* in water, but is *insoluble* or will not dissolve in petrol.

COLLOIDAL SOLUTIONS

When soap is dissolved in water it forms a *translucent* solution, that is, it allows *some* light to pass through it; the solution is not transparent like water. If the soap solution is filtered, the filtrate continues to be translucent. Such a solution is called a *colloidal* solution. The difference between a true solution and a colloidal solution is in the particle size of the dissolved solutes. The dissolved colloids are present in the

17. 'The last boiling operation' for the manufacture of soap

18. Palm kernels

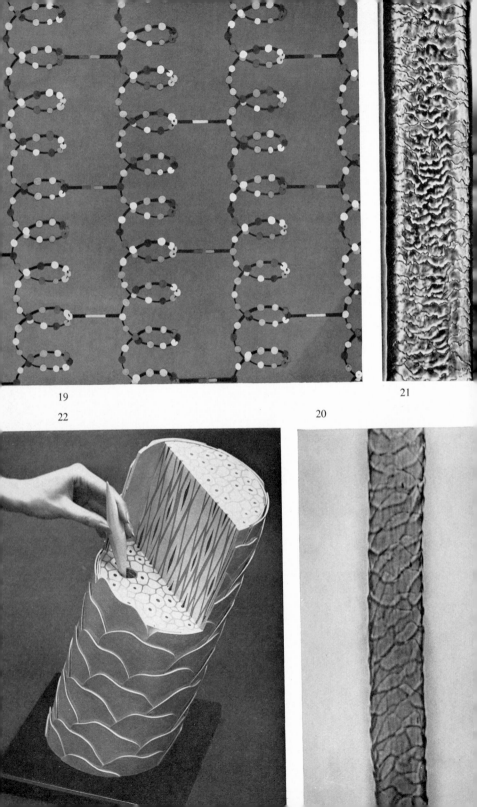

19

21

22

20

23. Testing hair-dye formulations

19. Diagram of keratin with its coiled polypeptide main chain and side chains
20. Photomicrograph of a wool fibre (magnified 100 times)
21. Photomicrograph of a woman's hair (magnified 192 times)
22. Model showing the scales and internal structure of a wool fibre (the hand holds a typical spindle-shaped cortical cell)

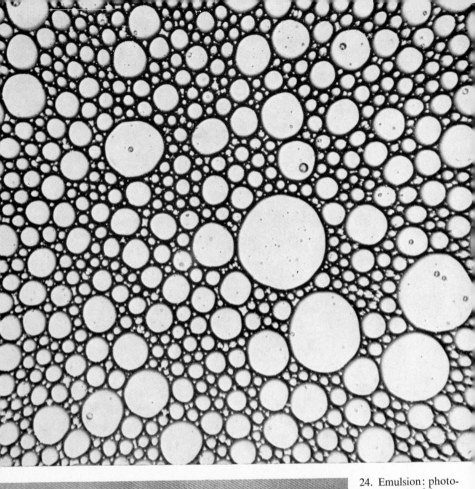

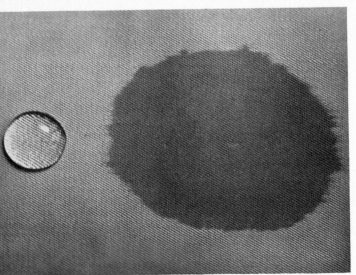

24. Emulsion: photo-
micrograph of fat
globules dispersed
in water

25. Surface tension: th
shows two droplets
material; the first is cle
water, the second is a so
tion of soap and wate
The soap reduces the s
face tension of the wate
resulting in the wetting
the material

solvent as groups of molecules that can pass through a filter-paper. Tea, coffee, soap, and egg-white all form colloidal solutions when dissolved in water.

SOME IMPORTANT SOLVENTS, THEIR SOLUTES, AND APPLICATIONS

Solvent	Solute	Applications
Water, the most common solvent	Most inorganic acids, bases, and salts are soluble in water	Aqueous solutions bring the dissolved solute into intimate contact with the hair or reacting surface
Ethyl alcohol, methylated spirit; inflammable	Dissolves essential oils and castor oil, shellac, lac, and certain dyes	Perfumes and eau-de-Cologne; varnish and hair lacquers; spirit colour rinses; iodine tinctures; removing lacquer stains from mirrors
Carbon tetrachloride; non-inflammable. Poisonous vapour produced when solvent is in contact with naked flames or hot surfaces	Dissolves animal and vegetable oils and fats	For cleaning wigs and postiche; dry-cleaning solvent; fire-extinguishers. *NOTE:* Always use in a well-ventilated room
Petrol; inflammable	Dissolves animal oils and fats	Cleaning wigs and postiche
Chloroform; non-inflammable	Solvent for grease and oils	Anaesthetic; dry-cleaning agent
Trichloroethylene	Solvent for grease and oils	Anaesthetic; dry-cleaning agent
Acetone; inflammable	Solvent for oils and fats, resins, and lacquers, celluloid, collodion, or cellulose nitrate	Nail-varnish remover
Amyl acetate	Solvent for oils and celluloid	Nail-varnish
Ether; highly inflammable	Oils and fats and collodion or celluloid	'Nu-skin'

EMULSIONS

An emulsion is a *suspension* of tiny particles of one liquid in another liquid. Milk is an emulsion consisting of tiny droplets of oil suspended in water. Similarly, an emulsion of olive oil in water can be made by vigorously shaking a few drops of olive oil with water. The emulsion soon settles out into two layers. To prevent this an *emulsifying agent* such as soap or caustic soda may be added, when a permanent emulsion will be obtained.

Emulsions are prepared from two liquids that are *insoluble* in each other, together with an emulsifying agent:

Liquid *A*	Liquid *B*	Emulsifying	Emulsion
e.g. +	e.g. +	agent, e.g. =	of oil
water.	coconut oil	soap	in water

Cosmetic creams and lotions are examples of emulsions. The tiny oil particles can be clearly seen in them when a small quantity of the emulsion is examined through a microscope (Plate 24).

Emulsifying agents

When an emulsifying agent is added to a mixture of oil and water it *lowers the surface tension* between the two liquids and breaks up the oil into tiny oil droplets, forming a creamy liquid. The following are some of the emulsifying agents used in the preparation of emulsions and creams: soap and soapless detergents or surfactants, sodium hydroxide, ammonium hydroxide, sodium carbonate, borax, tri-ethanolamine, and lanolin, together with the emulsifying waxes such as 'Collones', 'Abracols' and 'Lanette' waxes.

COMPARISON OF TRUE SOLUTIONS, COLLOIDAL SOLUTIONS, AND EMULSIONS

True solution	*Colloidal solution*	*Emulsion*
Clear and transparent	Milky and translucent	Creamy and opaque
Solute consists of *ions* or *molecules*; cannot be seen by microscope	Solute consists of *large* molecules; difficult to see with a microscope	*Oil droplets* suspended in water; easily seen by microscope
Passes through filter-paper	Passes through filter-paper	Cannot pass through filter-paper
Example: sugar in water	Example: soap in water	Example: any cosmetic cream

Experiment

Dissolve 3 g of beeswax in 85 cm³ of liquid paraffin heated to 65°C. Dissolve 0·5 g of borax in 12 cm³ of distilled water heated to 65°C.

Add the solution of borax to the warm oils with continual stirring. Stir the mixture vigorously until cool. An emulsion has now been prepared by the use of borax as an emulsifying agent for the liquid paraffin oil and water mixture. Further examples of cream and emulsion preparation are given later in this chapter.

THE CLEANSING ACTION OF SOAPS AND SURFACTANTS

Hair and other fibres when they are dirty become coated with particles of dust and soot clinging to the natural or acquired greasy coating of the fibre. The process of cleansing is based on the following principles:

1. The *surface tension* of the water *is lowered* on the addition of soap or surfactant and this permits more intimate contact between the hair and the cleansing solution (Plate 25). This is called the *wetting* action of the detergent. It can be demonstrated by adding a few drops of detergent to water on which sulphur powder is floating (see Chapter 3).
2. The soap or surfactant detergents *emulsify* the oil and grease, forming an *emulsion* that floats into the solution carrying with it the dirt particles (see Plate 2).
3. The foaming action of the detergent helps to *disperse* or *suspend* the dirt particles (Plates 26 and 27).
4. Final rinsing removes the emulsified oil and grease together with the suspended dirt. *Agitation* or rubbing the hair during the cleansing process helps to dislodge the dirt and emulsified grease. The use of a hot detergent solution improves the cleansing process.

COSMETIC PREPARATIONS

The following formulae are included in this chapter for students to gain experience of *compounding* some simple cosmetic preparations:

SHAMPOO

1. *Soap type*

Soft soap	20 g
Methylated spirit	25 cm³
Water	65 cm³

Dissolve the soap in the methylated spirit, filter if necessary, then add the water and perfume.

2. *Spirit shampoo*

Soft soap	0·5 g
Ammonium hydroxide	8 drops of 0·880
Methylated spirit	50·0 cm³
Water	50·0 cm³

Dissolve the soap in the methylated spirit, add the ammonium hydroxide, filter if necessary, and add the water and perfume.

3. *Surfactant powder shampoo*

Sodium lauryl sulphate	48 g
Borax	40 g
Sodium sesquicarbonate	12 g

Mix the ingredients in a large tin, add perfume, and mix thoroughly.

4. *Surfactant liquid shampoo*

Triethanolamine lauryl sulphate	1 part
Water	4 parts

Add perfume. The addition of 1 per cent sodium chloride or borax increases the viscosity of the shampoo.

HAIR-RINSES

1. Citric acid hair-rinse consists of one teaspoonful of citric acid in a pint of warm water.
2. Acetic acid hair-rinse consists of one fluid ounce of vinegar in one pint of warm water.

HAIR-CONDITIONING CREAMS

1.

'Emulsene' 1219 or Lanette wax SX	15·0 g
Sodium lauryl sulphate	0·5 g
Citric acid	2·0 g
Water	83·0 cm³

Dissolve the citric acid and surfactant powder in water heated to 65°C. Heat the 'Emulsene' 1219 to 65°C. Add the water solution to the melted wax and stir vigorously till cool.

2.

Part A	'Abracol' G.S.P.	15·0 g
	'Abracol' V.P.X.	0·5 g
	Almond oil	5·0 g
	Adipic acid	1·0 g
Part B	Water	78·5 cm³

Heat part *A* and part *B* independently to about 75°C. Add part *B* to part *A* slowly, with continual stirring. Stir until cool, adding the perfume at about 35°C.

'Emulsene' and 'Abracols' are products of A. Boake Roberts & Co. Ltd.

HAIR FRICTION LOTION

Isopropyl myristate	5 cm³
Industrial spirit	95 cm³

Add perfume and antiseptic materials if desired.

SOLID BRILLIANTINE

Almond oil	25·0 cm³
Liquid paraffin	45·0 cm³
Soft paraffin	15·0 g
Spermaceti	7·5 g
Stearic acid	7·5 g

Melt all the ingredients at 65°C, allow to cool, adding perfume at about 35°C.

HAIR CREAM

White beeswax	3·0 g
Liquid paraffin	85·0 cm³
Borax	0·2 g
Distilled water	50·0 cm³

Melt the wax in the liquid paraffin at 65°C. Dissolve the borax in the distilled water heated to 65°C. Mix the solutions and stir vigorously till cool.

HAIR SETTING LOTION

Gum tragacanth	8 g
Isopropyl alcohol	10 cm³
Water	83 cm³

Grind the alcohol and gum together in a glass mortar, add some water and a few drops of terpineol. Grind the mixture thoroughly. Transfer the contents of the mortar to a large bottle, then add the remainder of the water and shake vigorously. Further water may be added until the most suitable consistency of lotion is obtained.

CUTICLE-REMOVER OR SOFTENER

Potassium hydroxide	2 g
Water	80 cm³

Dissolve the potassium hydroxide in the water and add 20 cm³ of glycerine. Handle the potassium hydroxide with care.

ASTRINGENT OR AFTER-SHAVE LOTION

An astringent *tightens the skin* or epidermal tissues, and also closes the skin pores:

Oil of lavender	0·4 cm³
Oil of bergamot	0·4 cm³
Oil of lemon	0·4 cm³
Diethyl phthalate	1·0 cm³
Industrial spirit	65·0 cm³
Water	27·0 cm³

TOILET WATERS

1. *Lavender water*

Oil of lavender	3·0 cm³
Oil of bergamot	2·0 cm³
Oil of rose	0·1 cm³
Oil of cloves	0·1 cm³
Industrial spirit	95·0 cm³

2. *Eau-de-Cologne*

Oil of bergamot	1·0 cm³
Oil of neroli	0·5 cm³
Oil of lemon	0·5 cm³
Oil of rosemary	0·2 cm³
Oil of orange	0·2 cm³
Diethyl phthalate	1·0 cm³
Industrial spirit	97·0 cm³

CALAMINE LOTION

Calamine	15 g
Zinc oxide	5 g
Glycerine	5 cm³
Rose-water	75 cm³

Place the ingredients in a large bottle and shake thoroughly until the suspended material is evenly distributed through the rose-water.

TALCUM POWDER

Talc	85·0 g
Boric acid	5·0 g
Light magnesium carbonate	8·0 g
Magnesium stearate	2·5 g

Place all the ingredients in a large tin, add perfume, and mix the ingredients thoroughly by shaking the tin.

BATH SALTS

Perfume, some sodium sesquicarbonate crystals.

BATH ESSENCE

Bornyl acetate	10 cm³
Terpineol	5 cm³
Industrial spirit	20 cm³
Turkey-red oil or liquid surfactant	65 cm³

Dissolve the pleasant-smelling ingredients in the spirit and add the surfactant to the mixture, stirring.

VANISHING-CREAMS

Stearic acid	18 g
Liquid paraffin	1 cm³
Triethanolamine	2 cm³
Water	80 cm³

Melt the stearic acid and liquid paraffin at 65°–70°C. Dissolve the triethanolamine in the water and heat to 70°C. Add to the oils and stir vigorously till cool. Add perfume when cool. The triethanolamine acts as the emulsifying agent in this preparation.

COLD CREAM

Cold creams *cool* the skin by means of their *high water* content; the water in the cream evaporates from the skin surface.

Cetyl alcohol	2 g
Lanolin	5 g
Soft paraffin	43 g
Olive oil	4 cm³
Rose-water	46 cm³

Heat all the ingredients, except the rose-water, to 70°C, then add the rose-water, stirring the mixture until it is cool. In this preparation the lanolin is the emulsifying agent.

CLEANSING CREAM

Beeswax	9·0 g
Paraffin wax	10·0 g
Cetyl alcohol	1·0 g
Liquid paraffin	45·0 cm³
Borax	0·5 g
Water	35·0 cm³

Melt the oils and waxes, add the borax dissolved in water at 70°C. and stir until cold. Borax is the emulsifying agent in this preparation.

A water-bath is useful for melting the fatty ingredients of creams, etc. and a knife spatula is useful for transferring creams into jars and bottles.

PLASTICS OR SYNTHETIC RESINS

Natural resins such as shellac and rubber have now been partly replaced by modern chemical compounds in the form of plastics or synthetic resins such as *Perspex, celluloid, nylon, Polythene*, and *polyvinyl* plastics.

Plastics or synthetic resins vary greatly in their physical properties, from black *Bakelite* to clear *Perspex* and from rubbery *Polythene* to hard brittle hair-lacquer resin.

Most synthetic resins can be moulded into various shapes, as in the manufacture of trays and toys; others are used for the manufacture of lacquers and paints. Owing to their excellent electrical insulation properties many synthetic resins are used in the making of electrical appliances.

CLASSIFICATION OF SYNTHETIC RESINS

Plastics are divided into two main groups, namely *thermoplastic* and *thermosetting resins*.

1. Thermoplastic resins

These resins can be reshaped or remoulded by the repeated application of heat; they are also *soluble* in solvents such as ethyl alcohol, acetone, chloroform, and ethyl acetate. The following are examples of some important thermoplastic synthetic resins used in hairdressing:

Celluloid and cellulose acetate used in the manufacture of nail varnish and table-tennis balls.

Perspex (polymerized methyl methacrylate) used for electrical fittings, dentures, and aircraft windows.

Polyvinyl acetate (Gelva resin) is soluble in ethyl alcohol; it is used for making hair lacquer, paints, and chewing gum.

Polyvinyl pyrollidone (P.V.P. resin) is soluble in ethyl alcohol containing a little water. It is used in the manufacture of hair lacquer and adhesives.

Dimethyl-hydantoin formaldehyde (D.M.H.F. resin) is soluble in water and in ethyl alcohol. This resin is used for making hair lacquer, hair-setting lotion and for sizing textiles and coating paper. Its ready solubility in water makes it easy to remove from the hair with clean water or during shampooing; the slight hygroscopicity of the resin helps to keep the hair manageable for longer periods of time. Resetting of the hair can be achieved by a moistened comb or brush.

Nylon (polyhexamethylene adipamide) is a thermoplastic resin of many well-known applications, including its use in wigs.

Polythene (polyethylene) is used for various containers; these should not be used for organic solvents.

2. Thermosetting resins

These are resins that *cannot* be reshaped or remoulded by the repeated application of heat. The following are some of the more important thermosetting resins:

Bakelite or phenol aldehyde resin is dark in colour and is used for moulded articles such as trays and beakers. *Urea plastics* are used for plastic table-tops and are resistant to heat and abrasions.

PLASTICIZERS

These are chemical compounds added to a synthetic resin in small amounts to soften the resin and render it less brittle. Materials such as glycerine and triacetin are used in hair lacquers in order to make the resin more pliable and to prevent the flaking of the resin on the hair.

HAIR LACQUERS AND HAIR-SETTING LOTIONS

Hair lacquers are applied to the hair either from a spray bottle or from a pressure spray of the aerosol type. The following formulae show the composition of the commoner types of hair lacquer in general use.

P

Polyvinyl acetate (Gelva resin hair lacquer):

Polyvinyl acetate	6·0 g
Water	10·0 cm³
Ethyl alcohol industrial	100·0 cm³
Triacetin plasticizer	1·5 cm³
Perfume	1·0 cm³

The resin is dissolved in the alcohol and water mixture, followed by the addition of plasticizer and perfume.

Polyvinyl pyrollidone (P.V.P. resin hair lacquer):

Polyvinyl pyrollidone	5·0 g
Ethyl alcohol industrial	100·0 cm³
Triacetin plasticizer	1·5 cm³
Perfume	1·0 cm³

Dissolve the resin in the alcohol followed by the addition of the plasticizer and perfume.

Dimethyl-hydantoin formaldehyde (D.M.H.F. resin hair lacquer):

Dimethyl-hydantoin formaldehyde	5·0 g
Ethyl alcohol industrial	100·0 cm³
Glycerine or propylene glycol	0·5 cm³
Alcohol-soluble lanolin	0·5 cm³
Perfume	1·0 cm³

Dissolve the resin in the alcohol and then add all the other ingredients.

HAIR-SETTING LOTION

The following formula illustrates the use of synthetic resins instead of natural gums, such as gum tragacanth and karaya, in hair-setting lotions:

Water	100·0 cm³
Monoethanolamine	0·4 cm³
Polyvinyl acetate	2·0 g
Dimethyl-hydantoin formaldehyde resin	0·4 g
Perfume	1·0 cm³

★ ★ ★

QUESTIONS ON CHAPTER 18

1. Explain the terms, *dissolving*, *solute*, and *solvent*. Give a brief account of solvents and their properties, indicating their uses in hairdressing practice.

2. What is an emulsion? Give some applications of the use of emulsions in hairdressing.
3. What are soap and surfactant detergents? Briefly describe how detergents cleanse the hair. How would you prepare a medicated shampoo?
4. Write short notes on the following materials: (*a*) carbon tetrachloride; (*b*) acetone; (*c*) triethanolamine; (*d*) ether.
5. Describe the procedure you would adopt in compounding an emulsion or cream from the following formula:

Olive oil	20 cm^3
Liquid paraffin	10 cm^3
Borax	6 g
Water	70 cm^3

Indicate the substance that acts as the emulsifying agent. Draw the measuring instruments you would use.
6. Write short notes on the following materials, and state the main purpose for which each is used in hairdressing: (*a*) liquid paraffin; (*b*) triethanolamine lauryl sulphate; (*c*) carbon tetrachloride; (*d*) borax; (*e*) almond oil.

PART III
Anatomy, Physiology, and Hygiene

19 MOVEMENT

THE SKELETON

The skeleton is the bony framework of the body (Plate 28). Bone is a hard tissue which contains living cells and also inorganic materials such as calcium salts and phosphates. The *axial skeleton* includes the bones of the head and trunk. The *appendicular skeleton* includes the bones of the limbs.

FUNCTIONS OF THE SKELETON

(*a*) The skeleton supports the body and enables it to keep its shape, even during movement. It also helps to keep the organs of the body in their correct positions.

(*b*) It protects many of the softer parts of the body. The brain, an important but delicate organ, is protected by part of the skull known as the *cranium*. The spinal cord is protected by the backbone or vertebral column. The rib-cage, extending from the backbone to the breast-bone, protects the heart and lungs, the main organs in the chest cavity.

(*c*) The skeleton serves as an attachment for muscles, thus enabling movement to take place. The places at which bones can move in relation to each other are known as *joints*. A variety of movement can occur, according to the type of joint.

JOINTS

BALL-AND-SOCKET JOINT

This type of joint involves the rounded end of one bone fitting into a hollow cavity in another. It permits very great freedom of movement such as is possible at the shoulders and the hips. The ends of the bones which meet are covered with cartilage (gristle), and the cartilages are lubricated by *synovial fluid* secreted by the synovial membrane which encloses the joint (Figure 19.1). Ligaments hold the bones together and prevent dislocation during movement.

215

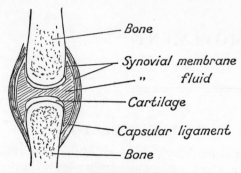

Figure 19.1. Synovial joint

HINGE JOINT

A hinge joint allows movement in one plane only as, for example, at the knee joint and elbow joint.

PLANE JOINT

This occurs where two flat surfaces glide over each other, as for example at the wrist and in the spine (Figure 19.2). In the skull, the bones

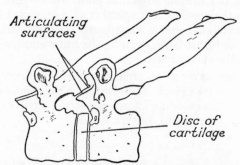

Figure 19.2. Two vertebrae, illustrating plane joint

are fused together (Figure 22.1) except for the lower jaw, thus permitting no movement at all.

MUSCLE

Movement is brought about by the activity of muscles, and those connected to the bones are known as *skeletal* muscles. There are three types of tissue:

1. Voluntary or striped muscle

Voluntary muscle forms the red flesh of the body and is under the control of the will. It is composed of fibres about 4 cm long and 0·1 mm in diameter. They can be recognized microscopically owing to their being striped in alternate light and dark bands (Figure 19.3).

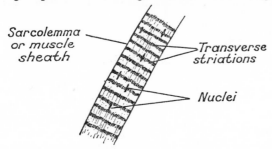

Figure 19.3. Voluntary muscle fibre as seen under the microscope

Each fibre contains several nuclei and is surrounded by a muscle sheath. The fibres are joined together in bundles, and several bundles together form a single muscle. Muscles have different shapes according to their position in the body. Those of the limbs are long, but those in the back are broad and flat. The ends of the muscles are attached by strong tendons (connective tissue) to two definite points on the skeleton. The more fixed point is known as the *origin* and the more movable point as the *insertion*. By contraction, a muscle can become shorter and thicker, thus drawing closer together the two points of attachment. A muscle can only bring about movement in one direction however, and a different muscle must contract in order to effect a return to the original position. The contraction of the second muscle brings about the relaxation of the first.

2. Involuntary or unstriped muscle

This type is not controlled by the will and occurs in various internal organs. It is present in the walls of the stomach and intestines, in the

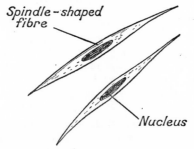

Figure 19.4. Involuntary muscle fibre as seen under the microscope

diaphragm, and in other parts of the body (e.g., lungs, heart, eye, bladder). The presence of this type of muscle enables peristaltic movements in the digestive system and breathing movements to take place without our controlling them voluntarily. These muscles are paler than skeletal muscles, show no cross-striping, and have no muscle sheath. The spindle-shaped fibres are bound together by connective tissue (Figure 19.4).

3. Cardiac muscle

The special muscle which forms the heart walls is known as *cardiac muscle* and is found only in the heart. Cardiac muscle fibres are branched and show very irregular markings, both vertical and horizontal. They have no muscle sheath and are bound together by connective tissue (Figure 19.5). This type of muscle is capable of automatic rhythmic contraction throughout life. The chief muscles of the head and face which influence the shape of the face and

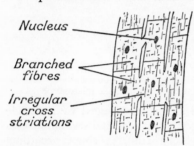

Nucleus

Branched fibres

Irregular cross striations

Figure 19.5. Cardiac muscle fibre as seen under the microscope

therefore indirectly the hair-style of an individual are dealt with in Chapter 22.

MUSCLE TONE

Muscular tissue is always in a state of slight contraction and never completely at rest. This condition is known as *muscle tone*; it means that the muscle is alert and ready to respond to stimuli. Even when the body is resting in sleep the stimulus of an alarm bell will cause some people to leap out of bed in response.

MUSCLE FATIGUE

The energy required for movement is obtained by the oxidation of glycogen stored in the muscle itself and also from a supply of glucose brought by the blood. During prolonged exercise, the supplies of glucose and oxygen needed are increased by a speeding up of the heart-beat, blood circulation, and breathing movements. If the increased circulation does not supply sufficient oxygen, the glucose may be broken down without oxygen (anaerobically), forming acid waste products. The accumulation of these waste products in the muscle may cause a state of fatigue, when the muscular movements become sluggish. A similar effect may result if fats are oxidized instead of glucose, since the combustion of this fuel is not so complete. Muscle fatigue must be followed by rest to restore the tissue to its normal condition.

THE PART PLAYED BY THE NERVOUS SYSTEM IN MOVEMENT

The nervous system is a system of communication in the body, by means of which the movements of the body are controlled. Certain organs of the body, e.g. the eyes, ears, etc., are sensitive and receive stimuli. Others, such as glands and muscles, produce responses to stimuli received. Muscles respond by contracting; glands respond by producing a secretion. By conveying messages or *impulses* to various parts of the body, the nervous system brings about reactions at the correct moment, that is, it co-ordinates the responses. Co-ordination may be due to the nervous system or it may be due to *hormones* which travel in the blood. Hormones are chemical messengers produced by a number of ductless glands in the body and poured straight into the blood.

Co-ordination ensures that the efforts of the body are not wasted. For example, digestive juices are secreted only when food is present in the alimentary canal, thus preventing these secretions from being wasted.

NERVOUS TISSUE

Special nerve cells or *neurones* make up nervous tissue. A typical neurone is a single nerve cell with a number of short branched projections or *dendrites* and one long projection or *axon* which leads to a muscle or gland. The axon may be very long, extending perhaps the full length of a limb (Figure 19.6). Axons are covered by an insulating

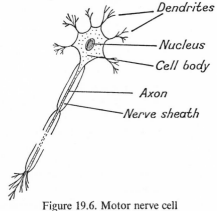

Figure 19.6. Motor nerve cell

layer of fat giving them a white appearance. Collections of axons form the *white matter* of the nervous system. Collections of cell-bodies form the *grey matter*. Nerve cells are the basis of the nervous system, which includes:

(a) *the central nervous system* (C.N.S.): the brain and spinal cord.
(b) *the peripheral nervous system:* the nerves arising from the brain and spinal cord.

In the brain, the cell-bodies or grey matter are concentrated on the outside, but in the spinal cord they are on the inside, with the white matter outside.

NERVES

A *nerve fibre* is made up of an axon and its fatty layer together with a nerve sheath.

A *nerve* is made up of a bundle of nerve fibres.

Some fibres may carry impulses into the C.N.S. from a sense-organ. These are called *sensory* fibres. Others may carry impulses outwards from the C.N.S. to a muscle or gland. Since these effect a response they are known as *motor* fibres.

A nerve may consist wholly of sensory fibres (*sensory nerve*) or wholly of motor fibres (*motor nerve*) or some of each (*mixed nerve*).

CRANIAL NERVES

Nerves may arise from the brain or from the spinal cord. The latter are known as *spinal nerves*, the former as *cranial nerves*.

There are twelve pairs of cranial nerves in the human body, some of which are sensory, some motor, and some mixed. They issue from the brain and supply various parts of the body as follows:

i. *Olfactory*	– nerve of smell—a sensory nerve carrying impulses from the nose to the C.N.S.
ii. *Optic*	– nerve of sight—a sensory nerve from the eyes to the C.N.S.
iii. *Motor-oculi*	– a motor nerve supplying some of the eye-ball muscles.
iv. *Patheticus*	– a motor nerve also to eye-ball muscles.
v. *Trigeminal*	– this nerve has three branches: to the upper and lower jaws and to the eye. It is a mixed nerve containing both sensory and motor fibres.
vi. *Abducens*	– a motor nerve also to eye-ball muscles.

vii. *Facial*   – a motor nerve supplying some of the muscles of the face and responsible for facial expressions.

viii. *Auditory*   – nerve of hearing—a sensory nerve from the ear to the C.N.S.

ix. *Glosso-pharyngeal* – a mixed nerve having sensory fibres leading to the tongue and motor fibres to the muscles of the pharynx.

x. *Vagus*   – a mixed nerve with various branches to the viscera.

xi. *Spinal accessory* – a motor nerve supplying muscles of the neck.

xii. *Hypoglossal*   – a motor nerve supplying the tongue muscles.

The cranial nerves that affect the muscles of the head and face are indicated in the next chapter.

REFLEX ACTION

A reflex action is an automatic response to a stimulus and requires no conscious effort: for example, coughing, swallowing, and sneezing are reflex actions.

Movements concerning organs of the head are usually controlled by the brain, but many stimuli travel through the spinal cord instead. Some impulses received by the brain are relayed to the spinal cord.

The *spinal cord* is a hollow cylindrical mass of nerve tissue protected by the spine. It gives off pairs of spinal nerves, but these nerves arise by two roots (a *dorsal* root and a *ventral* root) which join and pass out between the vertebrae. Stimuli pass into the cord by the dorsal root, which is sensory, and leave the cord by the ventral or motor root. A simple reflex action involves three stages:

1. an impulse travels along the dorsal (sensory) root into the spinal cord;
2. the impulse is relayed to a connecting nerve cell;
3. an impulse passes outwards along a motor nerve to muscles, etc., which bring about the response.

The nerve cells do not actually communicate with each other. The stimulus travels across a gap known as a *synapse* where the dendrites from one neurone interlace with those from the next cell.

EXAMPLE OF REFLEX ACTION

An example of a simple reflex action is the withdrawing of the hand from a hot object. If a hot object is touched the nerve endings in the skin that enable us to detect heat receive the stimulus. This causes an impulse to pass along a sensory nerve by the dorsal root into the spinal cord. It crosses a synapse to a communicating cell, which triggers off one or more motor impulses that travel along motor nerves to the muscles of the arm. The muscles contract in response to enable the hand to be moved away. The path taken by these impulses is known as a simple reflex arc (Figure 19.7). Actually, reflex action is

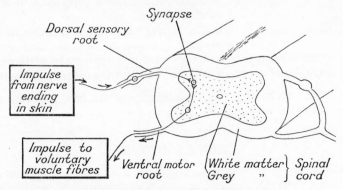

Figure 19.7. The spinal cord and a simple reflex arc

not as simple as described here. Several reflexes are usually associated with one stimulus.

★   ★   ★

QUESTIONS ON CHAPTER 19

1. What are the functions of the skeleton?
2. Name and describe the different types of joints.
3. What kind of joint is present at (a) the knee; (b) the shoulder; (c) the elbow; (d) the wrist; (e) the hip?
4. Describe the microscopic structure of voluntary muscle and involuntary muscle.
5. What kind of muscle is found in (a) the arm; (b) the stomach; (c) the face; (d) the oesophagus; and (e) the heart?
6. Explain the meaning of the terms *muscle tone* and *muscle fatigue*.
7. What is meant by co-ordination?
8. Describe and illustrate a typical motor neurone.
9. Explain the following terms: (a) sensory fibre; (b) motor fibre; (c) central nervous system; (d) grey matter; (e) white matter.
10. Give the names and destinations of the twelve pairs of cranial nerves.
11. Describe the position and structure of the spinal cord.
12. What are the stages involved in a reflex action?

20 NUTRITION

Food is required by man for three purposes:

(a) production of energy;
(b) growth of new tissues;
(c) repair of damaged tissues.

CLASSES OF FOOD

There are three main classes of food: carbohydrates, proteins, and fats.

CARBOHYDRATES

These are foods containing carbon and water and are used for producing energy. They include starches, complex sugars, and simple sugars. Starches and complex sugars need to be converted to simple sugars, e.g. glucose, before they can be utilized by the body. This conversion is brought about by digestion.

Starch is present in bread, potatoes, cereals, pastries and other foods, and has the formula $(C_6H_{10}O_5)n$. The value of n is thought to be high.

Glycogen or animal starch is stored by man in the liver and muscles as a food reserve.

Complex sugars include maltose or malt sugar, lactose or milk sugar, and sucrose or cane sugar. They all have the formula $C_{12}H_{22}O_{11}$.

Simple sugars include fructose or fruit sugar and glucose or grape-sugar, both having the formula $C_6H_{12}O_6$.

PROTEINS

Proteins are the body-building foods. They are present in lean meat, fish, eggs, milk, and cheese, as well as in some vegetables, for example peas and beans. They contain carbon, hydrogen, oxygen, and nitrogen, together with varying amounts of sulphur and sometimes phosphorus. These complex substances are built from units known as *amino-acids*, of which seven or eight are essential to life.

First-class proteins contain all the essential amino-acids and are usually of animal origin.

223

Second-class proteins are deficient in one or more of the essential amino-acids and are usually of plant origin.

Proteins must be converted to amino-acids by digestion, after which selected amino-acids can be used by the body to build up new tissues for growth and repair.

FATS

Fats can be oxidized for energy production. Surplus fats are used as a food-reserve, since they have a high calorific value, that is they yield far more energy than the same weight of carbohydrate or protein. They contain the elements carbon, hydrogen, and oxygen, but the hydrogen and oxygen are not in the same proportions as in water and carbohydrates.

Every fat is composed of two parts, a *fatty acid* and *glycerin*, and fats are converted to these substances by digestion in the body. Surplus fat is laid down beneath the skin and is also deposited around the kidneys. These reserves can be used for tissue respiration in times of need (e.g. starvation). Surplus carbohydrates and proteins can be converted to fat and laid down beneath the skin.

DIGESTION

In order to be of value to the body, food must be broken down into simpler substances by enzymes present in the digestive juices. Enzymes convert carbohydrates, proteins, and fats into soluble substances which can then be absorbed and utilized. The changes take place in a special part of the body known as the *alimentary canal*.

THE ALIMENTARY CANAL

The alimentary canal or food canal is a tube running through the body from mouth to anus. Its walls are muscular and by movement can push food along the canal. The alternate contractions and relaxation of the muscles constitute peristalsis. In man, the parts of the alimentary canal are the mouth cavity, pharynx, oesophagus, stomach, duodenum, jejunum, and ileum (small intestine), colon (large intestine), and the rectum which ends at the anus (Figure 20.1).

DIGESTIVE JUICES

Digestive glands secrete digestive juices which are mixed with the food in the alimentary canal. Some glands are actually in the lining of the alimentary canal, for example, the gastric glands in the stomach lining and the intestinal glands in the ileum. Others are associated with the canal and have special ducts along which their secretions pass into the food tube. These include the salivary glands, with ducts opening into the mouth cavity, and the pancreas, with the pancreatic duct opening into the duodenum (Figure 20.1). The liver sends a secretion of bile along the bile duct into the duodenum (Figure 20.1) but this does not contain any enzymes. It is an emulsifying agent.

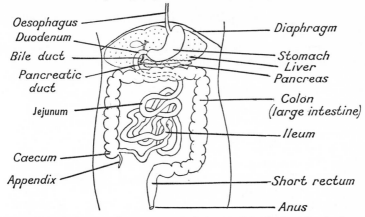

Figure 20.1. The human alimentary canal. Only the abdominal portion is shown. The liver and pancreas are not parts of the canal; they are merely associated glands.

ENZYMES

An enzyme is a chemical substance which can only be produced by a living body and is destroyed by heat. There are several different enzymes and each one acts on one particular type of food only, causing it to change chemically. The following enzymes are associated with human digestion:

ENZYMES ACTING ON CARBOHYDRATES

(a) *Ptyalin*, present in saliva from the salivary gland, converts cooked starch to maltose in the mouth.
(b) *Amylase*, in the pancreatic juice converts cooked or uncooked starch to maltose in the duodenum.
(c) *Invertase* and *maltase* in the intestinal juice convert complex sugars to simple sugars in the ileum.

ENZYMES ACTING ON PROTEINS

(a) *Rennin* curdles milk in young mammals.
(b) *Pepsin*, present in the gastric juice from the gastric glands, converts proteins to proteoses and peptones in the stomach.

Q

(c) *Trypsin* in the pancreatic juice from the pancreas converts peptones to polypeptides in the small intestine.

(d) *Erepsin* in the intestinal juice from the intestinal glands converts polypeptides to amino-acids in the small intestine.

ENZYMES ACTING ON FATS

Lipase in the pancreatic juice converts fats to fatty acids and glycerin in the duodenum.

Fats, however, are first emulsified by bile from the liver to make it easier for the lipase to reach the fat and break it down.

SUMMARY OF DIGESTION

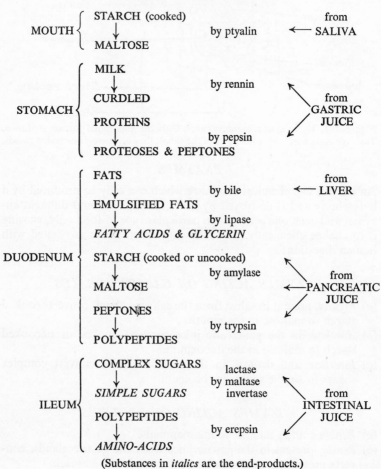

(Substances in *italics* are the end-products.)

ABSORPTION

The soluble end-products of digestion, namely, glucose, amino-acids, fatty acids, and glycerin, are absorbed into the blood for distribution in the body.

Glucose and amino-acids pass directly into the blood through capillaries in the small intestine. The lining of the small intestine is thrown into folds which appear as minute finger-like projections called *villi* (Figure 20.2). In these villi are numerous blood capillaries which receive the digested food.

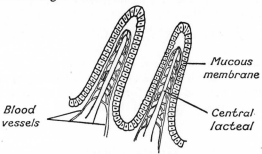

Figure 20.2. Villi (longitudinal section)

Fatty acids and glycerin enter the lymph system first and later enter the blood-stream from the thoracic duct which empties into the jugular vein in the neck. Some fats are so finely emulsified that they are absorbed directly into the blood-stream.

IMPORTANCE OF FOOD

A suitable diet helps to maintain the health and efficiency of the body, and must include the three types of food, proteins, carbohydrates, and fats, and in addition, water, mineral salts, and vitamins.

CARBOHYDRATES

Carbohydrates are the chief source of energy in the body. By oxidation of glucose, energy is set free, as illustrated by the following equation:

$$\underset{\text{(glucose)}}{C_6H_{12}O_6} + \underset{\text{(oxygen)}}{6O_2} = \underset{\substack{\text{(carbon} \\ \text{dioxide)}}}{6CO_2} + \underset{\text{(water)}}{6H_2O} + \text{energy}$$

PROTEINS

Proteins are the body-builders. The amino-acids to which they are converted are selected for re-forming into suitable proteins such as keratin for the growth of the hair.

FATS

Fats are used for energy production, but surplus fats are used as a food reserve which can be utilized in times of need to supply energy.

WATER

Water is present in the protoplasm of the body cells and is present in blood plasma. The various chemical changes taking place in the body occur in solution as illustrated by the following equation:

$$C_{12}H_{22}O_{11} + H_2O \xrightarrow{\text{MALTASE}} C_6H_{12}O_6 + C_6H_{12}O_6$$

(malt sugar)   (water)   (glucose)

Many foods contain water; e.g. fruits contain sugar and also water, potatoes contain starch and water. Water is needed for transporting materials in the body as well as for building up new protoplasm. It is therefore a very necessary part of the diet.

MINERAL SALTS

These are inorganic materials required for a healthy body. Substances present in these salts are required for various purposes:

Iron is needed for the composition of haemoglobin in the blood, without which oxygen could not be transported.

Calcium and *phosphorus* help to make strong bones and teeth.

Sodium chloride is present in all body fluids.

Iodine is necessary for the correct functioning of the thyroid gland, which controls the rate of metabolism in the body.

VITAMINS

Vitamins are chemical substances vital for the maintenance of health. Their absence leads to certain disorders known as *deficiency diseases*. Several vitamins have been isolated and they occur, in small quantities, in many of the foods we eat. Some of the more important ones, their occurrence, and the effects of deficiency are briefly shown in the table on page 229.

As long as a mixed diet is taken, the necessary vitamins and mineral salts will usually be automatically included, along with carbohydrates, proteins, and fats, and the body will be kept healthy.

VITAMINS

Name	Occurrence	Deficiency diseases
Vitamin A	Milk, animal fats, green vegetables	Skin disease Eye disease Lowering of resistance
Vitamin B several members of this group	Most foods, particularly eggs, milk and cereals	Dermatitis Disorders of digestive system Inflammation of nerves, i.e. polyneuritis or beri-beri
Vitamin C	Citrus fruits, blackcurrants, green vegetables	Skin eruptions Anaemia Scurvy
Vitamin D	Animal fats, fish oils, eggs, green vegetables	Rickets
Vitamin E	Wheat germ	Sterility—at least in rats
Vitamin K	Green vegetables	Tendency to bleeding

ELIMINATION OF WASTE

Waste matter of various types must be eliminated from the body if health is to be maintained. Waste products include:

(a) indigestible remains of food (roughage);
(b) water;
(c) surplus amino-acids;
(d) carbon dioxide from the oxidation of food.

SOLID WASTE LEFT OVER FROM FOOD

After food has been digested in the alimentary canal and absorbed chiefly in the small intestine, a certain amount of solid indigestible matter remains. This material passes into the colon or large intestine and is prepared for evacuation by the body. Most of the water present in it is absorbed by the colon so that only semi-solid waste (known as *faeces*) reaches the rectum and is expelled at intervals from the anus. A large proportion of the dry faeces consists of bacteria and cells from the lining of the intestine.

WATER

Surplus water is expelled from the body in a number of ways:
A certain amount is breathed out from the lungs in the form of water vapour (see Chapter 21).

Some is evaporated from the sweat glands in the skin (see Chapter 23).

The bulk of the water, however, is excreted through the kidneys and bladder in the form of *urine*.

The *excretory organs* are a pair of kidneys lying in the abdominal cavity. A kidney duct or ureter passes from each kidney to the bladder at the lower end of the abdomen (Figure 20.3). The kidneys act as filters and the surplus liquid passes down the ureters to the bladder. Here it is stored until it can be released at suitable intervals through the urethra. Urine is not just surplus water. It also contains salts and the waste products from surplus amino-acids and from the breakdown of tissue protein.

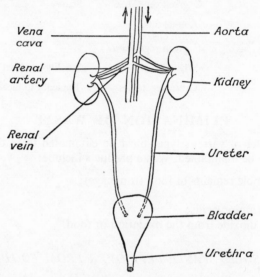

Figure 20.3. Excretory organs and the blood supply to the kidneys

SURPLUS AMINO-ACIDS

Any unwanted amino-acids are carried in the blood to the liver, where an enzyme, *deaminase*, breaks them down further into acids and ammonia. The ammonia is converted to *urea*, of which there is about 2 per cent in normal urine.

CARBON DIOXIDE

In tissue respiration, carbon dioxide and water are produced which may travel to the lungs to be breathed out. Some of the carbon dioxide may combine with ammonia in the liver to form urea and thus leave the body via the kidneys and bladder.

★ ★ ★

SUGGESTIONS FOR PRACTICAL WORK

Experiment

To show that cooked starch is digested by ptyalin in saliva:

1. Make some starch solution by mixing a little powdered starch to a paste with cold water and adding this paste to boiling water, stirring until clear. Allow it to cool.
2. Place some drops of iodine solution on a white tile, and add one drop of starch solution to one drop of iodine solution to show the characteristic blue-black colour produced.
3. Rinse out the mouth with warm water before collecting some saliva. Add the saliva to a little dilute starch solution in a test tube.
4. Withdraw drops of this mixture every thirty seconds, adding each drop to a drop of iodine. Observe that the iodine stains blue-black at first, but gradually stops changing colour because the starch has been converted to sugar.
5. If some of the solution is now boiled with Fehling's solution, a brick-red precipitate will result, indicating the presence of sugar.

QUESTIONS ON CHAPTER 20

1. For what purpose is food required by the body?
2. Give an account of the composition and uses of (a) carbohydrates; (b) proteins; and (c) fats.
3. State the formulae for (a) a simple sugar, and (b) a complex sugar, and name two examples of each.
4. What is digestion, and why is it necessary?
5. What is an enzyme? Name the chief enzymes of the human digestive system and state their functions.
6. Describe how food is absorbed into the blood-stream.
7. Which foods provide (a) the chief source of energy; (b) body-building materials; and (c) food reserves?
8. For what purposes does the body require (a) water, and (b) mineral salts?
9. How does the body eliminate (a) water; (b) solid remains of food; (c) unwanted amino-acids; and (d) carbon dioxide?

21 RESPIRATION AND CIRCULATION

RESPIRATION

Respiration is a twofold process involving:

(a) external respiration, or the interchange of the gases oxygen and carbon dioxide, and

(b) internal respiration, or the combustion of fuel in the tissues in order to produce energy.

ORGANS OF BREATHING

In the human body, the respiratory organs are the *lungs*, which lie in the chest cavity. Each lung is encased in a double membrane, the *pleural membrane*, which adheres closely to the lungs and also to the inside of the thorax (Figure 21.1). The membrane produces pleural fluid which helps to reduce friction during breathing movements.

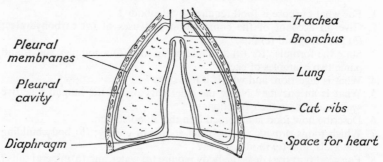

Figure 21.1. The lungs and pleural membranes (the heart is omitted)

RESPIRATORY PASSAGES

Air is breathed into the lungs from the atmosphere by way of a series of respiratory passages, starting at the nose and mouth (Figure 21.2). The nostrils lead into the nasal passages, which are lined with small hairs to filter out dust and dirt that might otherwise reach the lungs. These passages are also lined with a vascular mucous membrane whose secretion also traps dust. Contact with this vascular membrane

232

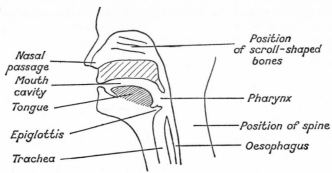

Figure 21.2. Section through part of the head and neck to show
the respiratory passages

warms the air, and since evaporation takes place from the surface, the
air is also moistened.

The *nasal passages* meet the mouth cavity in an area at the back of
the mouth known as the *pharynx*. From this region, the windpipe or
trachea passes into the chest cavity alongside the food-pipe or *oesophagus*. The *epiglottis* prevents food particles from entering the windpipe.
It is important that the windpipe should remain open, and it is therefore supported by a number of incomplete rings of gristle (cartilage).
These rings are incomplete where the trachea comes in close contact
with the oesophagus so that the latter is not damaged during peristalsis.

At the beginning of the trachea nearest the mouth, special cartilages
form the *larynx*, which encloses the vocal cords (Figure 21.3).

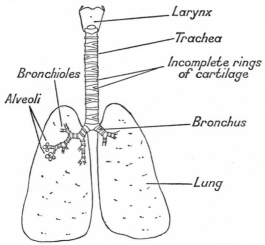

Figure 21.3. The larynx, trachea, and lungs

The trachea extends for a few inches before dividing into the two *bronchi*, each of which is subdivided into *bronchioles*. These very fine branches eventually end in small air-sacs or *alveoli*.

MECHANISM OF BREATHING

The movements of respiration cause air to be alternately drawn into the lungs (inspiration) and forced out again (expiration). These movements are brought about by the activity of the diaphragm and the intercostal muscles.

The chest cavity is an airtight compartment bounded by various bones and muscles.

The *diaphragm* is a dome-shaped muscle forming the floor of the chest. The ribs and intercostal muscles, together with the breastbone and part of the backbone, form the walls of the chest, and the neck seals off the top of the cavity.

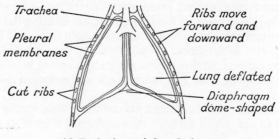

(*a*) Expiration—air breathed out

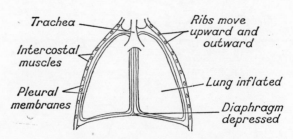

(*b*) Inspiration—air breathed in

Figure 21.4. The mechanism of breathing

INSPIRATION

When the diaphragm muscles contract, the floor of the chest is flattened, thus increasing the size of the cavity and creating a vacuum (Figure 21.4). This in turn causes air to be drawn into the lungs through the respiratory passages, and the lungs expand. The contraction of the intercostal muscles raises the ribs and causes a further increase in the size of the cavity, thus increasing inspiration.

EXPIRATION

When the muscles relax, the size of the chest cavity is decreased and air is forced out again by the same route by which it entered.

EXTERNAL RESPIRATION

The respiratory movements result in an alternate inhalation and exhalation of air. Air is a mixture of gases, both elements and compounds. The composition of inhaled air is approximately as follows:

	per cent
Oxygen	21·0
Nitrogen	78·0
Carbon dioxide	0·04
Rare gases	1·0
Water vapour	variable

Exhaled air, however, contains:

	per cent
Oxygen	17
Nitrogen	78
Carbon dioxide	4
Rare gases	1
Water vapour	increased

A proportion of the oxygen is therefore retained by the body for the purpose of oxidizing fuel in the tissues. The oxygen passes into the blood to be transported to the tissues, in the form of oxyhaemoglobin. The alveoli of the lungs are in close contact with blood capillaries, thus enabling the oxygen to enter the blood-stream (Figure 21.5). At the

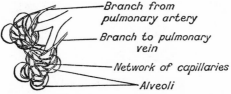

Figure 21.5. Alveoli and associated blood capillaries

same time, carbon dioxide passes from the blood into the lungs to be breathed out. This is known as the *exchange of gases.*

INTERNAL RESPIRATION

On reaching the tissues, blood gives up its oxygen for the purpose of tissue respiration.

Soluble foods such as glucose are oxidized and release energy which is needed for the activities of the body. The production of a certain amount of heat energy also helps to maintain a constant body temperature. The glucose is converted by oxidation into carbon dioxide and water, which are waste products. These pass back into the blood plasma, are returned to the lungs, and are breathed out. The water is exhaled as water vapour. The following equation indicates the change which is brought about by the oxidation of glucose:

$$\underset{\text{(glucose)}}{C_6H_{12}O_6} + \underset{\text{(oxygen)}}{6O_2} \longrightarrow \underset{\text{(carbon dioxide)}}{6CO_2} + \underset{\text{(water)}}{6H_2O} + \text{energy}$$

The part played by the blood is an important factor in respiration.

THE BLOOD

Blood is a liquid tissue. The fluid is a watery solution containing numerous cells both red and white (Figure 21.6). The red cells of the blood outnumber the white cells by about five hundred to one; hence the blood appears red.

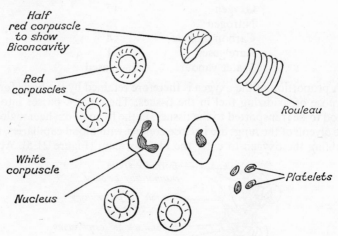

Figure 21.6. Human blood cells

RED CELLS OR ERYTHROCYTES

Structure

A red cell is a small circular biconcave disc without a nucleus. Although appearing red in the mass, erythrocytes are yellow when seen singly, owing to the presence of haemoglobin, a compound of iron with an affinity for oxygen. They are manufactured in the bone marrow and live for about three or four months, after which time they die and break up.

Function

Erythrocytes are the oxygen-carriers of the body. The oxygen combines with haemoglobin to form an unstable compound, oxyhaemoglobin, which readily yields oxygen to the tissues. Blood containing oxyhaemoglobin is said to be oxygenated, but after the oxygen has been released it is said to be de-oxygenated.

WHITE CELLS OR LEUCOCYTES

Structure

These are irregular-shaped cells with a nucleus and are subdivided into two types:

(a) *Granulocytes*. These are granular cells which move by amoeboid movement, a flowing action of the protoplasm.

(b) *Lymphocytes*. Non-granular cells incapable of amoeboid movement.

Function

The leucocytes help to keep the body free from disease in two ways. The granulocytes ingest bacteria, bits of dirt, splinters, and other foreign bodies in the blood, thus destroying them. They will also ingest damaged tissue, thus helping a wound to heal. The lymphocytes cannot ingest bacteria, but produce antibodies which counteract the effects of harmful bacterial toxins.

BLOOD PLATELETS

Structure

These are very small cells or fragments of cells in the blood.

Function

Platelets play a part in the clotting of blood to seal a wound, and this helps to prevent bacterial infection.

PLASMA

Composition

The plasma is the aqueous solution that contains the cells. It is composed of water in which are dissolved salts and organic materials, including plasma proteins.

Function

Glucose, fats, and amino-acids are carried in solution and distributed to the tissues in various parts of the body. Waste products such as carbon dioxide and urea are removed from the tissues and transported in solution, carbon dioxide mainly to the lungs, and urea mainly to the kidneys.

In addition, hormones, enzymes, and other substances are distributed by the plasma. One of the plasma proteins, *fibrinogen*, is necessary for the clotting of blood. Sodium bicarbonate, one of the salts dissolved in the plasma, acts as a *buffer*, that is, it prevents sharp changes in the alkalinity of the blood.

SUMMARY OF FUNCTIONS OF THE BLOOD

Part of blood	*Function*
Erythrocytes	Carry oxygen from lungs to tissues as oxyhaemoglobin
Leucocytes {Granulocytes {Lymphocytes	Ingest bacteria and foreign bodies Produce antitoxins
Platelets	Help in sealing of wounds by clotting
Plasma	Transports: hormones, enzymes, excretory products, soluble food Buffering Clotting of blood Distribution of materials to tissues

THE HEART

The heart is a hollow muscular pumping organ lying in the thorax between the two lungs (Figure 21.7). It is composed of a special type of muscle—cardiac muscle (see Chapter 19). It is divided into four chambers, two thin-walled *auricles* at the base and two thick-walled *ventricles* at the apex. The apex is directed downwards and points slightly to the left.

There is no communication between the left and right sides of the heart, but each auricle communicates with the ventricle on the same

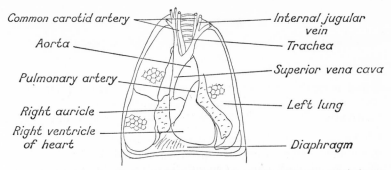

Figure 21.7. Dissection to show heart, great vessels, and lungs *in situ*: certain bones and muscles, etc. have been removed (*after Gray*)

side (Figure 21.8). Blood flows through these chambers in a definite sequence, always leaving the ventricles by arteries and entering the auricles by veins. The left side of the heart deals with oxygenated blood and the right side with de-oxygenated blood.

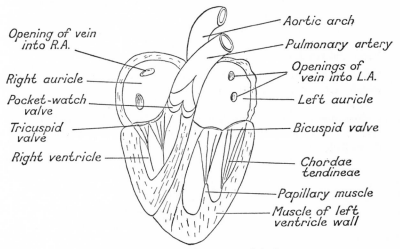

Figure 21.8. Internal structure of the heart

VALVES OF THE HEART

Any backward flow of blood is prevented by valves which are present between the auricles and ventricles. On the left side the *mitral* valve and on the right side the *tricuspid* valve serve to control the flow of blood. In addition, there are pocket-like *semi-lunar* valves guarding the two main arteries which leave the heart.

BLOOD-VESSELS

The blood circulates in a series of closed tubes or blood-vessels.

Arteries and arterioles

These normally carry oxygenated blood, with the exception of the pulmonary arteries which carry de-oxygenated blood.

An artery is a muscular tube with a wall composed of three layers:

(1) an outer protective layer of connective tissue;
(2) a middle layer of muscle which is strong and elastic;
(3) a smooth inner lining of endothelium (Figure 21.9).

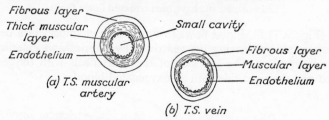

(a) T.S. muscular artery

(b) T.S. vein

Figure 21.9. Artery and vein (transverse section)

Veins and venules

These carry de-oxygenated blood, except for the pulmonary veins which carry oxygenated blood.

A vein is composed of the same three layers as an artery, but the middle muscular coat is much thinner and less elastic than that of an artery. The veins in the limbs have valves that prevent any backward flow of blood (Figure 21.10).

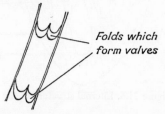

Folds which form valves

Figure 21.10. Vein (longitudinal section) to show valves

Capillaries

Capillaries are very fine branches of arteries and veins forming a network in various tissues of the body. Their thin walls are frequently composed of only a single layer of cells (endothelium). They enable lymph (tissue fluid) to escape and carry various substances to the tissues and remove waste products from the tissues.

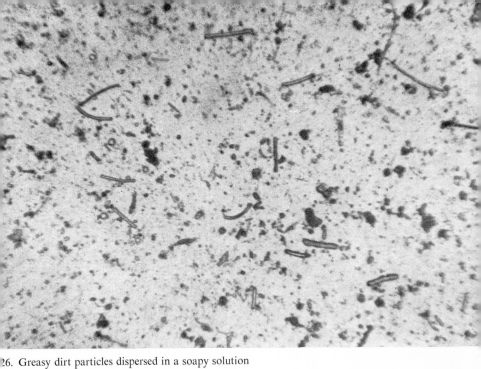

26. Greasy dirt particles dispersed in a soapy solution

27. Greasy dirt particles in plain water

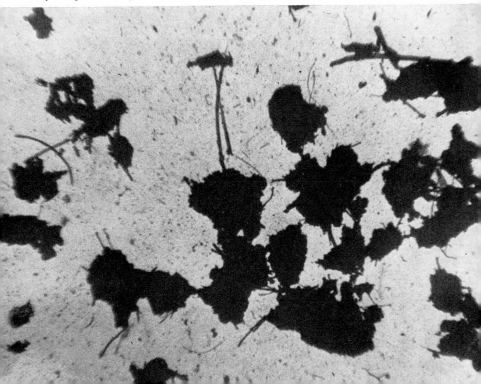

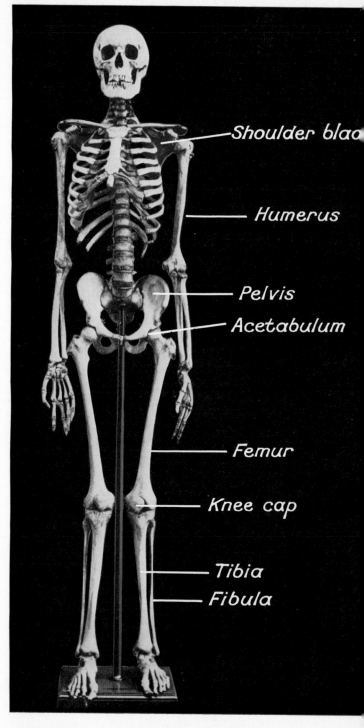

28. The human skeleton

Shoulder blad[e]

Humerus

Pelvis

Acetabulum

Femur

Knee cap

Tibia

Fibula

DOUBLE CIRCUIT

Blood circulates round the body in a double circuit (Figure 21.11). The first circuit distributes oxygenated blood from the left ventricle of the heart to the body, and returns it de-oxygenated to the right auricle of the heart. The second circuit distributes this de-oxygenated blood from the right ventricle of the heart to the two lungs, and returns it oxygenated to the left auricle.

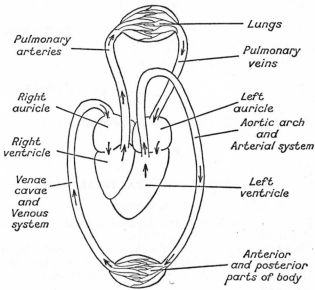

Figure 21.11. Diagrammatic representation of double circuit: direction of flow indicated by arrows

IMPORTANCE OF CIRCULATION TO THE HAIR

Since the blood is the transport system of the body, it enables the roots of the hair to be nourished. This encourages growth, and the average rate of growth is roughly half an inch per month.

BLOOD-VESSELS ASSOCIATED WITH THE HEART

The main arteries leaving the heart are the *aortic arch* from the left ventricle and the *pulmonary artery* from the right ventricle. The main veins entering the heart are the *venae cavae* entering the right auricle and the *pulmonary veins* entering the left auricle (Figure 21.12).

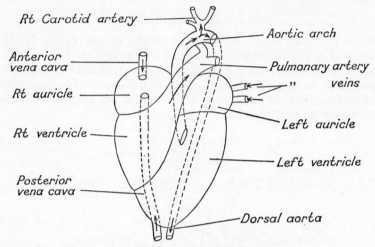

Figure 21.12. The heart and associated blood-vessels

★ ★ ★

SUGGESTIONS FOR PRACTICAL WORK

1. Examine fresh blood under the microscope.
   (a) Obtain a drop of blood by pricking the finger with a needle sterilized by passing it through a naked flame.
   (b) Place the drop at one end of a clean dry slide, and using another clean slide, produce a thin film of blood by drawing the drop along. Examine this thin film under the microscope. Identify and draw red corpuscles.
   (c) Stain the dried film with Leishmann's stain (four drops left for one minute, followed by four drops of distilled water for twenty-five minutes), wash off the surplus stain, and allow the film to dry. Examine it under the microscope. Identify white corpuscles, which now have stained nuclei. Draw examples with nuclei of different shapes.
2. Dissect a sheep's heart from the front. The structure is very similar to that of the human heart.

QUESTIONS ON CHAPTER 21

1. Why is respiration essential for living creatures?
2. Describe the respiratory passages and the organs of breathing in man.
3. Explain the difference between external and internal respiration.
4. What is meant by the gaseous exchange and where does this take place?
5. Give an account of tissue respiration and explain how the waste products are removed.

6. State two ways in which the blood system helps respiration.
7. Give an account of the chief blood-vessels associated with the heart.
8. Describe the structure of the heart.
9. Explain what is meant by the 'double circuit' in the circulatory system of man.
10. Show by means of a diagram the relative positions of the heart and lungs in the thorax.
11. How are bacteria prevented from entering the lungs?
12. What are the differences between arteries and veins?
13. How does expired air differ from inspired air? Account for these differences as far as you can.

22 ANATOMY OF THE HEAD

THE SKULL

The skull is the bony framework of the head and face and influences the shape of the face, and therefore, indirectly, the hair-style suitable for each individual. The skull is composed of a number of bones joined together, all of which are immovable except the lower jaw. The joints are called *sutures* and the edges of the bones are serrated for greater strength and rigidity.

There are two groups of bones—those forming the cranium, a protective 'box' for the brain, and those providing the framework of the face.

BONES OF THE CRANIUM

There are eight cranial bones (Figure 22.1):

A single *frontal* bone at the front of the skull forms the forehead and upper orbits. In the middle of this bone at the front is the *nasal notch*, an indentation into which fit the nasal bones.

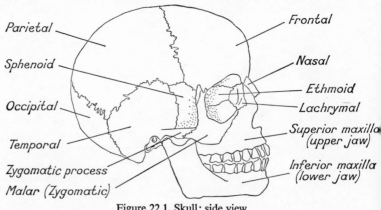

Figure 22.1. Skull: side view

A pair of *parietal* bones forms the roof and the upper sides of the skull.

A pair of *temporal* bones forms the temporal regions, i.e. the lower part of the sides of the skull.

244

A *sphenoid* bone, which lies at the base of the skull and has wings that lie between the frontal and temporal bones.

An *ethmoid* bone lies between the orbits at the roof of the nose, and forms part of the side-walls of the nose.

A single *occipital* bone forms the lower part of the back of the skull.

BONES OF THE FACE

Most of these are paired bones (Figure 22.2):

A pair of *nasal* bones form the bridge of the nose, and these fit into the nasal notch of the frontal bone.

A pair of *lachrymal* bones form part of the orbits at the inner angle of the eye.

A pair of *malar* bones form the cheek-bones. Processes from these join processes from the temporals (*zygomatic processes*) to form the bony arches of the cheeks.

A pair of *palate* bones form the roof of the mouth and the floor of the nose.

A single *vomer* bone forms part of the bony partition of the nose.

A pair of *turbinate* bones are small scroll-shaped bones inside the nose.

Two *superior maxillae* form the upper jaws and contain the upper teeth. They also form the floor of the orbital cavities, and the outer walls of the nasal cavities.

A single *inferior maxilla* or *mandible* forms the lower jaw and contains the lower teeth. This is the only movable bone of the skull (see Figures 22.1 and 22.2).

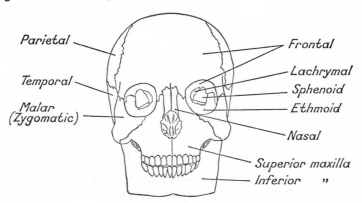

Figure 22.2. Skull: front view

THE CHIEF MUSCLES OF THE HEAD
AND FACE

The muscles are attached to the bones of the skull and receive their nerve supply chiefly from the fifth and seventh cranial nerves.

The *occipito-frontalis*, overlying the occipital and frontal bones, has anterior fibres which raise the eyebrows and wrinkle the forehead (Figure 22.3), and posterior fibres which move the scalp.

The *temporal* muscles at the sides of the head raise the lower jaw.

The great *masseter* muscles and the *buccinators* are at the sides of the face and help in mastication.

The *pterygoid* muscles are also important in mastication, but lie deeper.

The *orbicularis oris* is the sphincter muscle of the mouth and closes the lips. The muscles of the mouth raise and lower the angles of the mouth and separate the lips.

The *orbicularis oculi* are two circular muscles surrounding the eyes and close the eyes tightly.

Muscles of the nose wrinkle the nose. Special muscles at the back of the eyeball move the eyeballs from side to side, and up and down.

Most of these muscles are superficial (see Figure 22.3), but the temporals, masseters, and pterygoids are deeper than the others.

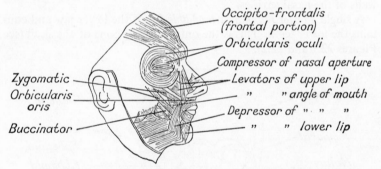

Figure 22.3. Muscles of the scalp and face: right side (*after Gray*)

NERVES OF THE FACE

Of the twelve pairs of cranial nerves (see Chapter 22), the *fifth* and *seventh* pairs are the chief ones which influence facial movements (see Figure 22.4).

THE FIFTH NERVE

The *trigeminal*, the fifth nerve, has three main branches:

(1) A maxillary branch, which is sensory, supplies the upper teeth, part of the nose and cheek, and part of the orbit.
(2) A mandibular branch (motor) supplies the lower teeth and lower jaw, and the muscles of mastication (temporals, masseters, and pterygoids).
(3) An ophthalmic branch (sensory) supplies the upper part of the orbital cavity and also the skin of the nose, forehead, and scalp.

THE SEVENTH NERVE

The *facial*, the seventh nerve, is responsible for facial expressions. It branches to various muscles:

(1) to the neck (cervical branch);
(2) to the forehead and eyebrows (temporal branch);
(3) to the buccinators (buccal branch);
(4) to the orbicularis oris (buccal branch);
(5) to the muscles of the nose (zygomatic branch).

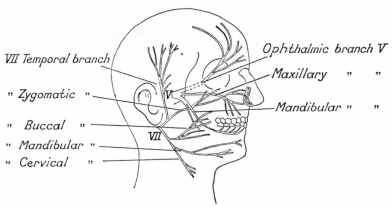

Figure 22.4. Main branches of cranial nerves *V* and *VII*

THE BLOOD SUPPLY OF THE HEAD AND FACE

MAIN ARTERIES (SUPERFICIAL)

The chief arteries of the head arise from the common *carotid* artery on each side of the neck (see Figure 22.5). It divides in the neck into an internal and an external carotid artery, the internal passing through a canal in the temporal bone and entering the skull. The external carotid artery divides into three branches to the head and face:

(1) The facial artery crosses the angle of the mouth and branches into the nose.
(2) The temporal artery branches to the side of the head.
(3) The occipital artery branches to the back portion of the head.

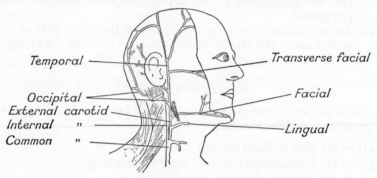

Figure 22.5. Main arteries of right side of head (*after Gray*)

MAIN VEINS

The head is drained by the internal and external *jugular* veins on each side. The internal jugular veins drain the deep parts of the head, receiving branches from the face and tongue. The external jugular veins drain the sides of the face, receiving branches from the temporal and occipital regions (see Figure 22.6).

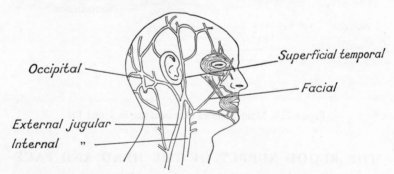

Figure 22.6. Main veins of right side of head and neck (*after Gray*)

* * *

QUESTIONS ON CHAPTER 22

1. Name the bones which constitute the cranium and indicate their positions.
2. How many bones are there in the facial region of the skull? Name them.
3. Which are the chief cranial nerves influencing facial movements?
4. Tabulate the chief muscles of the head and face and their functions.
5. Name the three branches of the trigeminal nerve. Which parts of the face do they supply?
6. Show by means of a diagram the chief arteries and veins of the head.

23 SKIN AND HAIR

All mammals, including man, are characterized by a covering of hair on the body. The hairs grow from the skin, and in man those growing from the scalp (the skin covering the head) are longer and stronger than those on other parts of the body.

STRUCTURE OF THE SKIN

The skin forms a protective covering over the surface of the body, and is attached to the underlying muscles by a layer of subcutaneous fat. It can be divided into two layers, the *epidermis* or outer skin and the *dermis* or true skin.

EPIDERMIS

Five layers of cells form the epidermis (Figure 23.1) and can be distinguished according to the type of cell as follows:

(a) Stratum corneum (horny layer)

The outer layer is composed of flat scale-like cells which are constantly being rubbed off by friction.

(b) Stratum lucidum (clear layer)

Next is a layer of cells which have no nuclei and thus have a clear appearance.

(c) Stratum granulosum (granular layer)

This is composed of nucleated cells with a granular appearance. These three layers are all dead and horny, because their protoplasm has been converted to keratin.

(d) Stratum aculeatum

Soft protoplasmic cells form the next layer, but included are a number of prickle cells, so-called because tiny outgrowths from the cells give them a prickly appearance.

(e) Stratum basale

The *stratum basale*, or Malpighian layer, is arranged as an orderly row of cells. This is the germinal layer from which new cells are produced. These deeper cells are pushed up to the surface to replace those which are worn away on the outside. Pigment, which determines the colour of the skin and hair, is present in this layer.

These five layers of the epidermis have no blood-vessels running through them and practically no nerve supply.

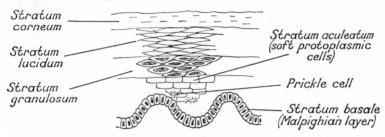

Figure 23.1. The five layers of the epidermis. The relative thickness of the layers varies.

DERMIS

The true skin is made up of tougher, more elastic tissue containing numerous blood-vessels and nerves. Its surface has numerous projections or *papillae* which jut up into the epidermis causing ridges on

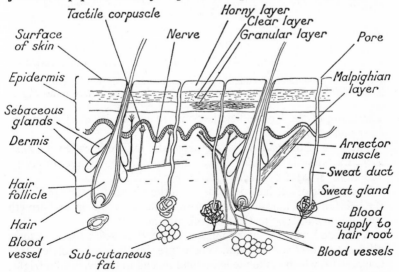

Figure 23.2. Section of skin through scalp

the skin surface. The ridges vary in each individual, and hence no two people have the same fingerprints. It is in the papillae that nerve-endings and capillary loops may be found. The nerve-endings of touch end in rounded bodies or *tactile corpuscles*, while nerves of pain, cold, and heat have delicate branched endings. Sweat-glands, hair-follicles, and sebaceous glands are found in the dermis (Figure 23.2).

HAIR

Hairs grow from small pits in the skin known as *hair follicles*. The follicles are lined with epidermis. The development of a hair usually starts by part of the epidermis pushing downwards to meet a small portion of dermis which forms a hair papilla. It is from this *dermal papilla* that the hair grows. Nourishment required for growth is carried in the blood, and blood capillaries are found in the dermal papilla. The epidermal cells in immediate contact with the papilla form the *hair bulb*, and this thickened bulb fits over the hair papilla (Figure 23.3).

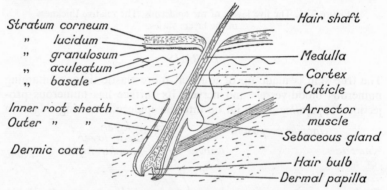

Figure 23.3. (Longitudinal section) Part of skin through hair follicle. The hair root is embedded in the skin. The hair shaft projects from the surface (*after Gray*)

The lining of the hair follicle is arranged in two layers, forming an *inner* and an *outer root sheath*.

The part of the hair projecting from the follicle is called the *hair-shaft*. Each hair is a slender tube composed of an outer layer or *cortex* and an inner layer or *medulla* (pith) (Figure 23.4).

The colour of the hair depends upon the pigment in the epidermis. If a hair falls out, a new hair may grow in the same follicle, and growth will continue as long as the root remains healthy.

Associated with the hair follicles are small muscles, the *arrectores pilorum* or *arrector muscles*. These are involuntary muscles (see Chapter 19) which make the hair stand on end in the event of a fright, and also produce goose-pimples.

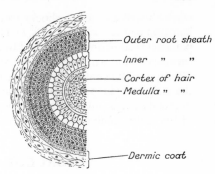

Figure 23.4. (Transverse section) Half of a hair follicle. The cortex and medulla constitute the hair. The inner and outer root sheaths are epidermal (*after Gray*).

Outer root sheath
Inner " "
Cortex of hair
Medulla " "

Dermic coat

FACTORS AFFECTING HAIR GROWTH

A hair grows to a certain length, then stops growing, becomes loose, and falls out. It is replaced by a new hair growing from the same follicle. The rate of hair growth is affected by age, sex, diet, glandular secretions, general health, and the state of the nerves.

Age and sex

The rate of growth is faster in women than in men and is usually fastest in young people. With age, natural thinning may occur in both sexes, and it is believed that after the age of sixty-five long hairs do not usually make any further growth.

Hairfall may occur as a genetical trait, particularly in males, and this hereditary baldness is not confined to the aged, but may develop in young men. Hereditary baldness is much less frequent and less extensive in women.

Diet

Malnutrition may affect hair growth. Since hair contains keratin, a type of protein, a diet deficient in proteins will affect growth. Hair growth cannot be induced, however, by an improved protein diet, in the case of baldness. A cure for baldness has yet to be discovered.

Glandular secretions

The endocrine (ductless) glands, for example the thyroid gland, play a part in influencing hair growth and hair loss. In certain glandular conditions the skin may become dry, the hair lack lustre, and hairfall may occur.

General health and the nervous system

The general health of the body and the state of the nervous system may show their effects on hair growth. Growth appears to be slower during illness but quicker during convalescence. Excessive worry or mental work as well as sudden shocks to the nervous system may cause exhaustion of the scalp and lack of hair growth. *Alopecia* (circular bald patches) is sometimes attributed to nervous factors, though the actual cause is unknown. There is no specific treatment and recovery is usually spontaneous. Alopecia due to traction causes hair loss around the scalp margin, particularly if the hair is fine. This is due to the use of metal curlers and stiff hair brushes. Hairfall may result from diseases of the scalp, some of which are dealt with in Chapter 25.

SEBACEOUS GLANDS

Small flask-shaped glands, the *sebaceous* glands, open into the hair follicles and secrete a special type of oil, known as *sebum*, into the follicle. This secretion lubricates the skin and hair. It keeps the skin soft and the hair glossy and helps to prevent the hairs from breaking. The sebum also picks up dust and germs which must constantly be removed by brushing and washing the hair. Sebum is thought to have a toxic effect on some bacteria.

SWEAT GLANDS

Coiled tubular sweat glands (*sudoriferous glands*) lie in the dermis, and ducts from these glands pass through the epidermis to the skin surface, where they open in small pores. These glands secrete a watery solution composed of about 98 per cent water and less than 2 per cent of dissolved substances including mineral salts, sodium chloride, urea, etc. Heat is required to evaporate this secretion from the body surface. In small amounts it is not noticeable and is known as *insensible perspiration*, but when we are conscious of it, it is known as *sensible perspiration*. Because the amount of dissolved material is so small, sweat glands are not considered important as excretory organs. Their main function is helping to regulate the body temperature by using up body heat for evaporation.

FUNCTIONS OF THE SKIN

1. *EPIDERMIS*

(a) *Cornified dead layer* of epidermis. This forms a protective layer which prevents invasion by bacteria and also forms a waterproof covering to the body.

(b) *Granular living layer* of epidermis. This produces new cells which are constantly being pushed nearer to the surface to replace those that are being lost.

2. *DERMIS*

Accommodates hair follicles, sebaceous glands, sweat-glands, blood-vessels and nerve-endings, and arrector muscles.

(a) Hair follicles

These contain the hairs which grow from the hair papilla at the base.

(b) Arrector muscles or hair-raisers

Contraction of these muscles causes the hair to stand on end.

(c) Sebaceous glands

These produce sebum that lubricates the skin and hair.

(d) Sweat glands

These play a part in regulating the body temperature. In man the temperature is constant at 98·4°F.

Heat is produced in the body by combustion of food. At the same time, heat is lost from the body by conduction, convection, radiation, perspiration, respiration, and evacuation of waste.

Conduction takes place by the transmission of heat to clothing and other objects in contact with the skin (see Chapter 5).

Convection is brought about by the movement of air in contact with the body.

Radiation results in the transmission of heat to the air surrounding the body.

Perspiration causes heat to be lost by the evaporation of sweat from the pores of the skin.

In *respiration* warm air is breathed out from the lungs.

In the *elimination* of waste, heat is lost from the body in faeces (solid waste from the digestive system) and urine.

The sweat-glands help to regulate the body temperature by increasing the evaporation of sweat if the body is overheated, and reducing it if the body is cool. During exercise, heat production is increased and this is balanced by increased sweating. During rest, heat production is decreased and this is balanced by decreased sweating and by contraction of the blood-vessels in the skin. The adjustment between heat production and heat loss is controlled by the heat-regulation centre in the brain.

(e) Blood-vessels

Blood capillaries bring food and oxygen to the skin. Capillaries loop into the hair papillae and bring nourishment and oxygen to the roots of the hair. The blood also removes any waste products which are present.

Blood-vessels near the surface of the skin may contract when neces-sary to decrease heat loss by radiation and conduction, and the skin becomes paler. When the body is over-heated, as for instance during a fever, the blood-vessels near the skin are dilated, the skin reddens, and heat is lost by radiation.

Capillaries in contact with the sweat glands bring waste products to them.

(f) Nerve-endings

The nerve-endings in the skin give us the sensation of touch. These sensations vary and we can distinguish heat, cold, and pain, as well as sensations produced by deep pressure and by light touches.

The nerve-endings of touch are rounded tactile corpuscles. Those enabling us to distinguish between heat, cold, and pain have delicate branched endings.

(g) Subcutaneous fat

The layer of fat below the skin attaches it to the underlying muscles and also provides an insulating layer.

SUMMARY OF FUNCTIONS OF THE SKIN

Epidermis	Horny zone	Protection from bacterial invasion
	Living zone	Growth
	Pores at surface	Evaporation of sweat
Dermis	Hair follicles	Growth of hair
	Sebaceous glands	Production of sebum for lubrication
	Arrector muscles	Raising the hair
	Sweat-glands	Heat regulation Excretion (slight)
	Elastic connective tissue	Makes skin supple
	Blood-vessels	Nourishment of skin Removal of waste Heat regulation
	Nerves	Sensation of touch
	Subcutaneous fat	Insulation Attachment for muscles

★ ★ ★

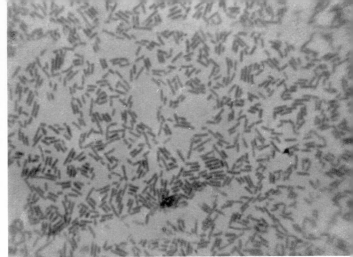

29. Large number of bacilli, as seen under the microscope (magnified 1,000 times)

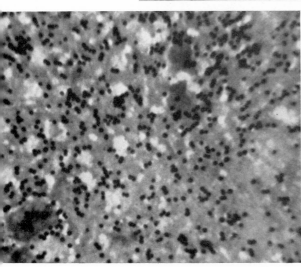

30. Cocci present in pus from a boil, as seen under the microscope (magnified 1,000 times)

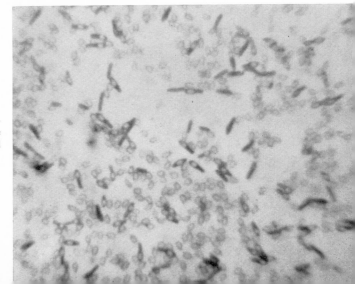

31. Spore-forming bacteria, as seen under the microscope (magnified 1,000 times)

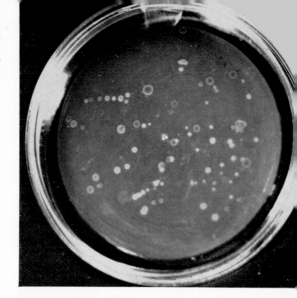

32. Bacterial colonies grown by drawing a human hair over a sterile culture medium (actual size)

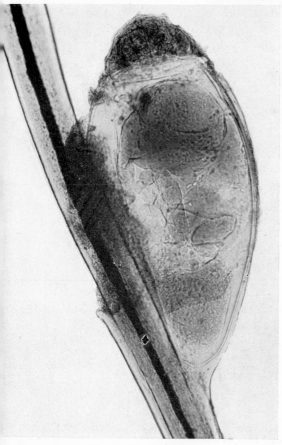

33. Nit on human hair (highly magnified)

SUGGESTIONS FOR PRACTICAL WORK

Examine sections of human skin under the microscope. Identify and draw the various parts.

QUESTIONS ON CHAPTER 23

1. Name and describe the different layers of the epidermis.
2. Describe the dermis or true skin.
3. Give an account of the development and growth of a hair. How is the hair (a) nourished; and (b) lubricated?
4. What are sebaceous glands? Give an account of their position and function.
5. Describe the appearance, position, and function of the sweat-glands.
6. In what ways can heat be lost from the body? How is heat produced in the body?
7. In the case of fright, what causes the hair to stand on end?
8. Give an account of the importance of blood-vessels in the skin.
9. Describe the ways in which the body temperature is regulated.
10. What is a tactile corpuscle?
11. Show, by means of a labelled diagram, the structure of the human scalp in section.
12. State four things which affect hair growth and explain the effects on the rate of growth.
13. What is *alopecia*? State two possible causes of this condition.

24 BACTERIA AND VIRUSES

BACTERIA

Bacteria are minute, colourless, unicellular organisms invisible to the naked eye and difficult to see at all unless stained. They have no apparent nucleus but the nuclear material is thought to be scattered throughout the cytoplasm. They are measured in microns or μ (1 μ = 1/1,000 mm or 1/25,000 in.). Their size varies from 0·2 μ for some bacilli to 40 μ for some spirilla. Despite their small size, each bacterial cell is a complete and independent unit of life which can carry out the normal functions of life, such as nutrition, growth, respiration, and reproduction.

Respiration takes place through the surface of the cell, oxygen entering and carbon dioxide leaving. Oxygen is required for breaking down food material to liberate energy and enable the cell to carry out its functions.

Food enters in solution through the cell wall and growth takes place if the temperature is favourable, but low temperatures inhibit growth. Reproduction takes place by simple transverse fission (Figure 24.1). The cell becomes constricted in the middle, the constriction deepens and finally the organism separates into two halves.

(a)   (b)   (c)   (d)

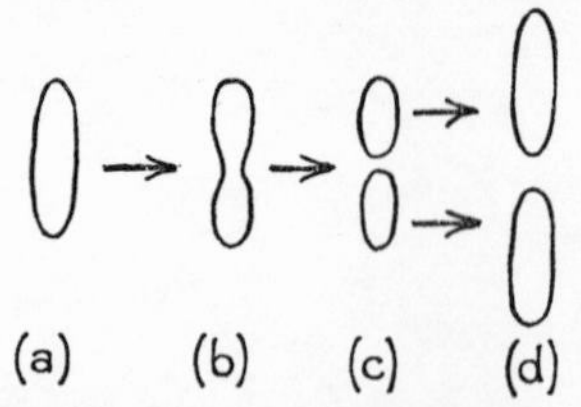

Figure 24.1. Stages in bacterial division: (a) bacterium ready to divide; (b) constriction appears; (c) bacterium separates into two halves; (d) each half grows and the cycle is then repeated

When conditions in general are favourable, the process takes place every twenty to thirty minutes, resulting in a phenomenal number of individuals in twenty-four hours—hence the need for attention to personal hygiene. A group which has developed from one single bacterium in this way is known as a colony and is visible to the naked eye. One can often recognize an organism by the appearance of its colony (Plate 32).

Bacteria can be classified according to their shape as follows:

> *Cocci*—spherical or nearly so:
>   (*a*) *Streptococci*—in chains;
>   (*b*) *Diplococci*—in pairs;
>   (*c*) *Staphylococci*—in bunches.
> *Bacilli*—straight rods.
> *Spirilla*—curved rods.
> *Spirochaetes*—corkscrew-shaped or tightly coiled.

CLASSIFICATION OF BACTERIA
ACCORDING TO SHAPE

MOVEMENT

The cocci are non-motile, but some bacilli and spirilla are provided with long thread-like processes or flagella which cause movement by lashing in a fluid medium. The spirochaetes travel by undulating or by rotary movements. Flagella, when present, may be single at one or both ends, or in a group at one or both ends. Some bacteria, for example the one that causes typhoid fever, have flagella all over the surface of the cell (Figure 24.2).

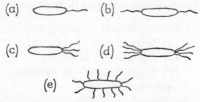

Figure 24.2. Bacteria, showing flagella: (*a*) single flagellum at one end; (*b*) single flagellum at each end; (*c*) several flagella at one end; (*d*) several flagella at each end; (*e*) numerous flagella all over

PATHOGENS AND NON-PATHOGENS

Many bacteria are harmless (non-pathogenic); some are actually helpful to man (commensal); but a large number are *pathogenic*, that is, cause various diseases. They are present everywhere, in dust, in soil, in water, in the air, and on most objects. Some live in or on the human body and may be normal inhabitants of the mouth, nose, throat, skin, and scalp. Certain varieties of cocci may gain entrance to the hair follicles and cause suppurating (pus-forming) infections such as boils, pimples, abscesses, and carbuncles (Plate 30). To prevent the spread of infection in the hairdressing salon, tools and equipment must be kept scrupulously clean. Brushes and combs, etc., must be washed and sterilized regularly.

TRANSMISSION OF DISEASE

Besides entering the hair follicles, bacteria can also enter the body by breaks in the skin, by being breathed in, and by being taken in with food. Those entering the hair follicles may cause boils, etc. Those entering cuts and scratches in the skin may gain access to the bloodstream and thus be circulated to various parts of the body. A variety of infections may be caused by this method, e.g. gangrene. Bacteria breathed in through the nose or mouth may cause infections of the respiratory passages and lungs, e.g. pneumonia, etc. Food that has not been prepared in a hygienic way may carry germs (pathogenic bacteria) into the digestive tract and may result in food-poisoning and other infections.

AVOIDANCE OF DISEASE

Avoidance of diseases transmitted by bacteria is helped by attention to personal hygiene and also by the right amounts of exercise and rest, so that the resistance of the body to disease is not lowered by being run-down.

Skin, pores, and hair-follicles should be kept clean. Combs should have blunt teeth which will not scratch the scalp. Metal combs have the advantage that they can be sterilized with boiling water, but they have certain disadvantages.

SPORE-FORMATION

Some pathogenic bacteria are very hardy and can even resist boiling water for more than an hour, though most are killed by temperatures above 70°C. Some form spores that can remain dormant for years. The spore may lie in the centre of the cell, or towards one end or actually at the end (Figure 24.3). When conditions become favourable,

Figure 24.3. The positions of bacterial spores: (a) central spore; (b) spore towards one end; (c) spore actually at the end

the spore germinates by rupturing its thick membrane and becoming an active bacterium once more (see Plate 31).

CONDITIONS NECESSARY FOR BACTERIAL GROWTH

The essential requirements of bacteria are a supply of food, moisture, and oxygen, a favourable temperature, absence of light, and a slightly alkaline medium.

1. Food is necessary for building up new protoplasm and for supplying energy. The food is taken in as soluble substances which can readily pass into the bacterial cell and enable growth to take place.
2. Water: because food enters in solution, moisture is essential. If water is removed the bacteria are destroyed; drying can therefore be used as a method of sterilization.
3. Temperature is important because it affects growth. Pathogenic bacteria grow best at body temperature (about 37°C). Low temperatures inhibit growth but rarely kill the bacteria. High temperatures above 70°C are usually fatal to bacteria (150°C for one hour destroys all bacteria) but some spores can resist boiling even for long periods.
4. Oxygen is required for respiration. Some bacteria, including most pathogens, require free oxygen, but other types obtain oxygen from the decomposition of organic matter.
5. Darkness favours bacterial growth. Sunlight is fatal to most bacteria, owing to the harmful effects of the ultra-violet rays. Even

diffuse daylight inhibits the growth of most pathogenic types. Bacteria that invade the body are shielded from direct light and therefore survive.

6. The medium in which bacteria grow should be slightly alkaline. The pH (hydrogen ion concentration) of human blood is ideally suitable (see Chapter 14).

VIRUSES

Some organisms are not visible by ordinary microscopic methods, their size being less than 0·2 μ. These are called *ultra-microscopic viruses* and are responsible for a number of infections such as poliomyelitis, smallpox, warts, and shingles. Like bacteria, they may be spherical or rod-shaped, but unlike bacteria they are always found within living cells and have never been cultivated in cell-free media. They have been observed under the electron microscope, but they appear only as minute specks without any visible structure.

STERILIZATION

This is the complete destruction of bacteria and their spores. It therefore involves depriving the bacteria of one or more of the conditions they need; for example, exposing them to strong sunlight or depriving them of moisture.

Sterilization and cleanliness in the salon are extremely important. Personal cleanliness, and also the cleanliness of the whole environment as well as sterilization of tools, etc., are essential.

The methods used for sterilization can be termed physical or chemical.

PHYSICAL STERILIZATION

1. Dry heat

(a) *Naked flame.* This can be used for sterilizing small metal articles, but not sharp instruments.

(b) *Hot-air oven.* All bacteria and their spores are destroyed by heating to 150°C in a hot-air oven and maintaining it at this temperature for one hour. Glass containers can be sterilized in this way; so also can oils and fats and some chemical substances that are not decomposed at this temperature.

Dry heat is not as effective as moist heat because it does not penetrate so well.

2. Moist heat

(a) *Water boiling at 100°C.* This will destroy all forms of bacteria almost immediately and will usually destroy spores in five to fifteen minutes. This method can be used for small apparatus, e.g. metal combs and curlers, etc. It is unsuitable for razors because it tends to blunt the delicate cutting edge. Towels and personal linen may be boiled.

(b) *Pasteurization.* Pathogenic bacteria in milk are destroyed by heating it to about 65°C (145°F) and maintaining at that temperature for half an hour, before cooling it rapidly and refrigerating.

(c) *Steam at 100°C.* Steam as it rises from the surface of boiling water is known as live steam or streaming steam, but exposure to live steam must be repeated several times in order to destroy sporeforming bacteria. This enables the spores to germinate between successive treatments and they are then destroyed. Textiles can be disinfected by this method.

(d) *Steam under pressure.* This is carried out in an *autoclave* (like a large pressure-cooker), which allows the pressure to build up, resulting in temperatures greater than 100°C. The actual temperatures depend upon the pressure:

5 lb per square inch: 110°C
10 lb per square inch: 115°C
15 lb per square inch: 120°C

The usual conditions are 10 lb per square inch pressure for fifteen minutes. This rapidly destroys bacteria and their spores owing to the coagulation of the bacterial protoplasm.

This is a very efficient method of sterilization because the moist heat has much deeper penetration than dry heat. Certain chemical solutions are not damaged by this method. Rubber gloves and capes can also be sterilized by steam.

CHEMICAL STERILIZATION

Many chemical substances can interfere with bacterial activity. These substances are named according to the exact effect that they produce:

A *disinfectant*, germicide, or bactericide is a substance that completely destroys bacteria.

An *antiseptic* merely inhibits the growth of bacteria; as soon as the effect wears off, the bacteria become active again.

All disinfectants can be diluted to form antiseptics, but all antiseptics are not disinfectants.

PROPERTIES OF SOME OF THE MORE COMMON DISINFECTANTS AND ANTISEPTICS*

Hydrogen peroxide (H_2O_2)

This is a colourless liquid that will mix with water in all proportions. Solutions of various strengths are used in hairdressing (see Chapter 13). It decomposes slowly into water and oxygen, but more quickly on heating, or in contact with alkalis or with body tissues. This decomposition is illustrated by the equation:

$$2H_2O_2 \longrightarrow 2H_2O + O_2$$

The oxygen released during the decomposition combines with bacterial protoplasm, thus destroying it.

Potassium permanganate ($KMnO_4$)

This is a dark purple crystalline solid which yields a characteristic purple solution with water. It is commonly used as a deodorant for drains, etc.

Mercuric chloride ($HgCl_2$)

This is a white crystalline solid, fairly soluble in water, very poisonous, and a powerful antiseptic. It can be used for disinfecting the hands and skin, in dilute solutions (1 in 1,000 to 1 in 4,000). It attacks metals, and therefore must not be allowed to come into contact with metal combs, etc.

Iodine (I_2)

This is a grey crystalline solid with a metallic appearance. The crystals are almost insoluble in water, but are soluble in potassium iodide and alcohol. In solution, it can be applied to cuts and scratches. The alcohol in the solution causes a stinging sensation. A $2\frac{1}{2}$ per cent solution is known as *tincture of iodine*.

Phenolic compounds

Phenol is a colourless crystalline solid with a characteristic smell. It turns pink on exposure to light or air. A 5 per cent solution in water is useful for sterilizing brushes, etc. Other phenolic substances include sanitary fluids, lysol, etc.

Formaldehyde

This is a colourless gas, which in solution with water gives formalin. Formalin when heated gives off the gas, which has the power of sterilization. It is used in some forms of cabinet sterilizers that are currently popular in many hairdressing salons for sterilizing combs, brushes, curlers, etc. (See Figure 6.8—page 51.)

* See also Chapter 17.

DRAINS AND TRAPS

The aim of good drainage is the removal of waste matter by suitable pipes without allowing the air from the sewer and drains to gain access to the interior of the building. One reason for this is that bacteria are usually present in the sewer air.

WASHBASINS

All washbasins in a hairdressing salon should discharge into the open air or to the surface of a gulley. They must be provided with an over-flow as well as a waste outlet and should have a suitable trap.

TRAPS

A trap is a U-shaped bend in a waste pipe, which retains some water and so prevents any passage of air through it (Figure 24.4). The upper surface of the pipe should dip below the water-level so that a water-seal is formed. The seal prevents gases from the drain from passing back into the room.

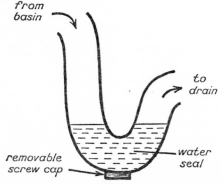

Figure 24.4. Simple trap with water seal

The trap should be as simple as possible with a smooth interior sur-face which will not collect dirt. The water retained in the seal should be completely changed during flushing. Basins used in the salon can be flushed once a day with hot soda-water to prevent any blockages arising. Each trap should also be provided with a removable screw-cap so that the trap can be cleaned if it becomes blocked with hairs and grease, etc.

★ ★ ★

QUESTIONS ON CHAPTER 24

1. Explain the difference between a disinfectant and an antiseptic.
2. What are pathogens and why do they thrive in the human body?
3. Name the chief ways in which bacteria can gain access to the human body.
4. What kind of infections may be spread by brushes and combs if these are not sterilized?
5. Describe the general characteristics of bacteria, including their shapes and methods of movement.
6. What conditions are required for the growth and multiplication of bacteria?
7. Give an account of sterilization by (a) dry heat; and (b) moist heat.
8. How would you sterilize the following articles: brushes, combs, curlers, towels, rubber gloves, your hands?
9. What is meant by a cabinet sterilizer?
10. Explain the terms 'trap' and 'seal'.

25 PERSONAL HYGIENE

It has been seen in Chapter 19 that the skin plays an important part in the regulation of the body temperature, especially by the evaporation of sweat from the body.

Since sweat is a solution containing dissolved organic and inorganic substances, it must not be allowed to remain on the skin, or it may clog the pores and interfere with subsequent heat regulation. In addition, when mixed with shed epidermal cells and sebaceous material it may cause a 'scurf' on the skin, which must be removed regularly with soap and water. A daily bath is therefore advisable or at least a daily wash-down, using plenty of friction to remove loose cells from the skin.

IMPORTANCE OF BATHS

The effect on the body varies with the temperature of the water.

Warm baths are of the greatest importance for general health and cleanliness. A rough towel helps to remove shed cells and, by stimulating circulation, brings more nourishment to the surface, thus improving the complexion.

Cold baths stimulate the nervous system and lead to increased heat production. After the initial shock of the cold water, the body feels warmer.

Tepid baths are also mildly stimulating.

Hot baths raise the body temperature and increase the sensitivity of the body to changes in the surrounding temperature. Therefore care has to be taken not to catch a chill.

CARE OF THE HAIR

WASHING

Washing at least once a fortnight is necessary to remove accumulated sebum, dirt, and bacteria. If *dandruff* (*seborrhoea* or *pityriasis*) is present, frequency of washing should depend on whether the condition is 'greasy' or 'dry'. Inflammation occurs owing to bacterial infection, and the superficial horny layers of the skin are shed. In the treatment of greasy seborrhoea, hair should be shampooed every three or four days, but for dry seborrhoea a shampoo every ten days will suffice, since excessive shampooing only aggravates the condition.

BRUSHING

This stimulates the sebaceous glands, thus making the hair soft and glossy. Brushing also cleanses the hair by removing dust and scurf, and ensures that no parasites obtain a foothold.

A good brush should have stiff bristles set separately and not too close together.

COMBING

Combing prevents the hair from matting. Combs should have blunt teeth which will not scratch the scalp; this would make way for bacterial invasion.

CARE OF THE HANDS AND FEET

The avoidance of cracks and roughness ensures that bacteria do not invade the tissues. Wearing rubber gloves prevents damage to the skin by chemical substances used in certain occupations such as hairdressing. Nails should be kept short and clean: dirty nails provide breeding-grounds for bacteria.

The skin on the feet should be well-dried after washing. This is particularly important between the toes, since warmth and moisture encourage bacterial and fungal development.

CARE OF THE MOUTH AND TEETH

The teeth are covered by a layer of strong enamel (Figure 25.1) but this can be dissolved by the action of acids. The production of acids may result from the decay of particles of food left on the teeth; thorough brushing is therefore necessary after meals. If this is not possible, a crisp apple will help to remove fragments of food.

Tooth enamel is strengthened by fluoride (which may be incorporated in toothpaste). Brushing at night before retiring is most important. The brush should be kept sterile by thorough rinsing and allowing it to dry in the air.

Dental decay allows bacterial toxins to enter the blood-stream, thus poisoning the system.

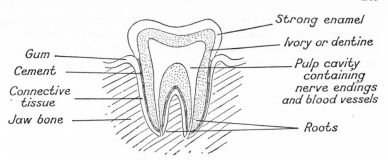

Figure 25.1. Longitudinal section of a tooth with two roots. Blood capillaries and nerve-endings enter the pulp cavity via the roots

IMPORTANCE OF EXERCISE AND REST

For the efficient working of the body the tissues, particularly muscles, require regular exercise.

EXERCISE

Exercise stimulates blood circulation, which in turn results in better nutrition. Food is carried to various parts of the body and waste products are removed, and thus the skin is kept clear. Respiration is increased by exercise, and more oxygen is therefore taken in. The improved blood circulation results in more oxygen reaching the brain and nervous system, and thus alertness is increased.

Exercise also stimulates internal movements, such as movements of the bowel thus preventing constipation. If waste matter remains in the bowel, pressure on nerve endings may cause some discomfort.

If muscles are not used, they become flabby, resulting in bad posture. This may hinder the activities of other parts of the body.

REST

Intervals of rest are essential to allow the body to rid itself of accumulated waste products which might interfere with muscular movements. Periods of sleep rest the body.

POSTURE AND DEPORTMENT

Bad posture interferes with important processes, such as respiration and circulation, by compressing the chest. Muscles maintain posture as well as bringing about movement. For example, the abdominal muscles keep the internal organs in their correct positions. Flabby muscles lead to bad deportment.

The spine influences posture. In both sitting and standing positions, the spine should be kept straight and the head held erect. Shoulders, hips and elbows should be kept level (Figure 25.2). In the sitting position, there should be right-angles at the hips and knee joints.

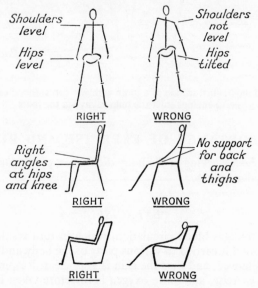

Figure 25.2. Correct and incorrect posture

CLOTHING

For civilized man clothing has to a large extent done away with the necessity for a covering of hair, since it serves a similar purpose. It affords protection to the body against the elements (wind, rain, sun, etc.), against dirt and bacteria and against insect bites, as well as having an important aesthetic value.

GENERAL CONSIDERATIONS

Clothing should be adapted to suit the climatic conditions and the wearer's occupation. Clothing should be warm but light in weight and should allow the passage of air and moisture so as not to interfere with the functions of the skin. The sweat glands help to regulate the body temperature, but clothing helps in the matter also. To help to conserve body heat, clothing should be made of materials which are poor conductors of heat. Still air is a poor conductor of heat, and the clothing should keep a layer of still air between the clothing and the skin. The secretion from the sweat-glands must be absorbed by the clothing next to the skin to keep the skin dry. At the same time, it must hold the moisture and not allow it to evaporate quickly, otherwise it would chill the body.

MATERIALS USED FOR CLOTHING

Wool

This is obtained from the hair of sheep. It has small tubular fibres with serrated edges and cross striations. Wool is a poor conductor of heat, and in addition is usually loosely woven, thus trapping air between the fibres. Hence it is suitable for wear next to the skin. Wool absorbs moisture quickly but allows it to evaporate slowly, and will therefore absorb sweat without chilling the body. Because it contains natural grease, it is to some certain extent waterproof and can be used for outer garments.

Cotton

In contrast to wool, this is of plant origin: it is obtained from the seeds of the cotton plant. Also in contrast to wool, it is a good conductor of heat and allows moisture to evaporate quickly from its surface. (Woollen garments, when laundered, take longer to dry than cotton.) Hence cotton is not suitable for wear next to the skin. The cotton fibres are flat with twists in them and result in material with a smooth, hard-wearing surface suitable for outer garments such as dresses and overalls. The smooth surface does not attract dust so much as the rougher surface of wool.

Linen

Also of plant origin, from flax plants, linen like cotton is a good conductor of heat, absorbs moisture slowly, and is unsuitable for undergarments. It has a smooth durable texture, even stronger than cotton. Linen fibres are branched cylinders.

Silk

Silken threads are spun by the silk-worm. Silk is a poor conductor of heat, and being soft and smooth also is suitable for underwear. Its fibres are very fine. It is, however, an expensive fabric.

Artificial silk or rayon

This is made from plant cellulose. It has similar properties to silk, and is therefore suitable for underwear. It is less durable than silk.

Nylon

This man-made fabric, made from coal, is a poor conductor of heat and a poor absorber of moisture; it is therefore unsuitable for wearing

next to the skin. It is smooth and hard-wearing, however, and is therefore suitable for overalls and other outer garments.

Leather

This comes from animal hides which are tanned or cured to preserve
them. Being waterproof, it is used mainly for footwear and gloves. It
can be used for jackets, etc., but needs ventilation-holes.

Fur

This is a very warm material, since the fur traps a layer of still air
between the hairs, and the leather backing also keeps in the heat.

Rubber

Rubber is extracted from the rubber tree as a liquid which sets into a
pliable material. It is a waterproof material, and if used for raincoats
requires ventilation-holes. Cottons and other durable materials may
be impregnated with rubber to make them waterproof.

ECTOPARASITES

A *parasite* is a living creature which obtains its food supply by living
on another living creature. Some parasites, such as tapeworms, live
inside their 'host'. Others live on the surface of the body, and these
are known as *ectoparasites*. Some of the ectoparasites connected with
human skin are animal parasites, e.g. head lice and body lice, and
plant parasites, e.g. ringworm.

HEAD LICE

These insects live amongst the hairs on the head and suck blood from
the scalp. The female louse is about 2 mm in length (1/12 in.) and lays
batches of eggs called *nits* (Plate 33). The nits are white and oval in

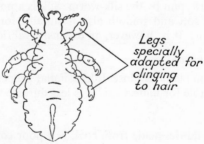

Legs
specially
adapted for
clinging
to hair

Figure 25.3. Male head louse as seen under low power of the microscope

shape and are fixed to the hairs by a sticky secretion. They mature in about a week.

The adult male (Figure 25.3) is slightly smaller than the female. The lice cling to the hairs on the head by specially adapted feet.

BODY LICE

There are two types:

(a) Clothes louse

This parasite (Figure 25.4) is slightly larger than the head louse. It attaches itself to underclothing by means of its claws, the female laying large batches of eggs in the folds of the clothing. The eggs take nearly two weeks to hatch and another two weeks to mature. The mature louse sucks blood, causing irritating spots. It may also transmit various types of fever to man.

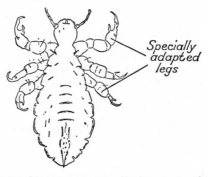

Figure 25.4. Male body louse as seen under low power of the microscope

(b) Crab louse

This is smaller than the other two types and may occur on parts of the body covered with short hairs, e.g. the armpits. The brown nits are attached to the hair by a kind of cement as in the head louse.

SCABIES

Scabies is a skin disease caused by the 'itch-mite', a small parasite that burrows under the skin and causes intense irritation. The burrows usually occur in parts of the body where the skin is wrinkled, for instance between the fingers and on the skin at the front of the wrist. Scratching causes the disease to spread to other parts of the body and may also lead to additional infection by bacteria. The disease can easily spread to other people by contact.

T

DEMODEX FOLLICULORUM

Demodex folliculorum is a minute spider-like organism sometimes found in blackheads. Because of its large abdomen it has a worm-like appearance (Figure 25.5). Blackheads are due to an unclean condition

Long pointed abdomen

Figure 25.5. *Demodex folliculorum* (face-mite) as seen under high power of the microscope

of the hair follicles, which causes sebaceous material to accumulate in the follicle.

RINGWORM OF THE SCALP

A plant growth or fungus is the cause of ringworm. It produces small rounded red patches on the head. These patches become bald and scaly with stumps of broken hairs. The fungus reaches the root of the hair and interferes with its nutrition, thus causing baldness and breakages.

The disease is highly contagious, and care must therefore be taken with the use of combs, brushes, towels, etc.

RECOGNITION OF SOME CONTAGIOUS SKIN DISEASES

Skin diseases may be caused by bacteria or by other organisms. The following conditions may be encountered in a hairdressing salon, and since they can be spread by contact, it is important that the hairdresser is able to recognize the signs.

RINGWORM OF THE SCALP

This contagious disease is recognized by the presence of circular bald patches on the scalp. Contact with the broken hairs and scales covering these areas may spread the infection.

PEDICULOSIS

This is the condition of being infested with lice. The adult head lice are not usually visible, but the eggs laid by the female can be seen and are frequently laid in the hair just behind the ears. The nits can be distinguished from scurf because they are firmly attached to the hairs.

IMPETIGO

This condition is caused by germs in the skin. Blisters develop on the face, particularly around the mouth, nose, and eyes. When these dry up, yellowish scabs appear and the affected parts itch. The disease can be spread not only by direct contact, but also by contact with towels, etc., that the infected person has used.

FAVUS

Honeycomb ringworm or favus is a fungoid disease that is rare in England. When it does occur, a number of cup-shaped discs are formed. Each disc is pierced by a hair. Pus-producing crusts are formed which have an orange or yellow colour. This disease is thought to occur more in animals than in human beings.

VENTILATION AND HEATING IN THE SALON
FACTORS AFFECTING CONDITION OF AIR

The condition of the air in a room affects the people in it. Four factors influence the comfort of the individual: (*a*) temperature; (*b*) humidity; (*c*) purity; (*d*) movement. The supplying of fresh air to replace polluted air in a room is termed *ventilation*.

Temperature
Heat is produced in the human body by tissue respiration and by muscular activity. Heat is lost from the body by expiration, conduction, radiation, and evaporation of moisture from the sweat-glands. Heat production and heat loss are balanced by the heat-regulating mechanism of the body.

A suitable temperature must be maintained in the salon for the comfort of clients and workers. In cold weather, some form of artificial heating will be necessary and this heating should assist ventilation. Heat can be supplied in various ways:

Convector heaters should be sited under windows, since the warm air rises and by mixing with the cooler air near the windows ensures a more even temperature.

Radiators tend to produce a fairly even temperature in heating a large room.

Gas fires are clean and smokeless. Some gas fires do not assist ventilation much, but certain gas radiant-convector heaters have a special ventilation control.

Under-floor heating is good, but may prove tiring for the feet of those working in a salon.

Infra-red heaters mounted high on a wall provide warmth in a defined area.

Some *central-heating systems* provide warm air which is also filtered.

Fan-heaters are very good because they circulate the air and the temperature can be regulated.

Humidity

Humidity concerns the amount of moisture in the atmosphere and depends on temperature. If the air is too dry, the mucous membranes lining the respiratory passages become dry and irritated. If the air is too moist, the body cannot be cooled by evaporation from the sweat glands, and discomfort results.

Good ventilation helps to remove water vapour from the atmosphere and is important in a salon, since humidity is normally high.

Purity

The air is a mixture of gases and also contains shed epidermal cells from the skin, particles of hair, bacteria, and other impurities. The carbon dioxide content is increased by breathing. In addition, in the salon there may be lacquer fumes and other gases which must be removed from the air by ventilation.

Movement

Movement of air appears to be necessary for human comfort. Moreover, the air in a room must undergo *continuous* change without creating unpleasant draughts.

VENTILATION

The supply of fresh air in a salon may be natural or artificial, but there must be suitable inlets and outlets for air. Windows are natural inlets, and chimneys provide natural outlets. In business establishments such as hairdressing salons, some form of artificial ventilation is often advisable.

One of the chief forms is the *extraction fan*, which withdraws impure air from the room by suction. Suitable inlets must be provided, or else air will be drawn in through cracks, etc., and cause unpleasant draughts. Also, the fans should not be placed near the inlets, or they will draw the air supply from them instead of withdrawing foul air from the room. The extraction fan will remove impurities, reduce humidity, and create movement of air. If a form of heating which assists ventilation is used, the temperature will be controlled also, and the factors affecting comfort will be satisfied.

★ ★ ★

QUESTIONS ON CHAPTER 25

1. Describe the effects on the body of (a) a warm bath; (b) a cold bath; and (c) a hot bath.
2. Why is a rough towel useful for drying the body?
3. Outline the general principles in the care of the hair, giving reasons.
4. Explain why exercise is important to the body.
5. Give a brief account of the hygienic care of (a) the hands and feet; and (b) the mouth and teeth.
6. What is the importance of good posture?
7. Describe the nature and general properties of (a) woollen fibres; (b) cotton fibres; and (c) silk threads.
8. Name some other materials used for clothing and give an account of the origin, properties, and uses of each.
   What is the difference between an endoparasite and an ectoparasite?
9. Give an account of two parasitic conditions associated with the head.
10. Name three contagious diseases you might meet in the salon. How
11. would you recognize each?
12. Name the four factors which create the need for ventilation.
13. Explain how an extraction fan effects ventilation.

26 SIMPLE FIRST-AID

A hairdresser may have a client who is in need of first aid. The following conditions and their simple treatment are some of those likely to be encountered in the salon.

FAINTING

Fainting is a form of temporary unconsciousness due to a decreased supply of blood to the brain. This in turn is due to failure of the heart action. It may be caused by some heart disease or anaemia, but other causes include emotional shocks (joy, sorrow, fear, etc.), exhaustion, lack of food, excessive heat, lack of fresh air, and bleeding.

Before fainting, a person usually feels giddy. At this stage, if the head is pressed gently between the knees, blood rushes to the head and swooning is avoided. If consciousness is lost, however, the patient should be kept lying down with the legs slightly raised on a cushion. Clothing round the neck should be loosened, and also tight clothing round the waist. There should be an adequate supply of fresh air. If unconsciousness persists, a doctor should be called.

NOSE-BLEEDING

The patient should be kept sitting up with the head back. Apply cold pads to the bridge of the nose and the back of the neck.

CUTS AND MINOR WOUNDS

The aim in treating cuts and wounds is three-fold: (a) to stop bleeding; (b) to treat shock; and (c) to prevent bacterial infection.

(a) *To stop the bleeding:* Bleeding can usually be stopped by using pressure on the wound after first applying a clean piece of material.

(b) *Shock:* The symptoms of shock are pallor and coldness, but beads of sweat may stand out on the patient's forehead. A person suffering from shock needs sympathy and reassurance. Extra warmth should be provided by blankets and rugs. Warm sweet drinks, preferably of tea or coffee, help recovery. Milk should be avoided since it may cause vomiting.

278

(c) *Prevention of infection:* Minor wounds and cuts should be dabbed with cotton-wool dipped in a suitable antiseptic. The wound can then be covered with a dry dressing or with a dressing smeared with antiseptic cream such as cetrimide. A pad of cotton-wool should be fixed in position over the dressing.

FITS

Two types may be encountered—hysterical and epileptic.

HYSTERICAL FITS

These are due to some sort of emotional strain, and the patient laughs or screams continuously. Slapping the patient's face usually brings about recovery. Sympathy should be avoided.

EPILEPTIC FITS

Occasionally, a client who suffers from epilepsy may visit a hairdressing salon. Epilepsy is a disease of the nervous system; during an epileptic fit the patient usually falls to the ground with the body twitching and the face distorted. Foaming at the mouth is another symptom. The fit gradually passes off, and the aim of the first-aider is to prevent the patient damaging himself. Furniture should be moved out of the way and a gag should be placed between the teeth to prevent the tongue being bitten.

BURNS AND SCALDS

Burns and scalds are both caused by heat, a burn by dry heat (including electrical burns) and a scald by moist heat. The treatment is similar for both.

Remove clothing from the scalded part, but if it is stuck, cover the area with a large soft dressing and get medical attention for the client. Cover a burn at once with a dry dressing and a loose pad of cotton-wool. If blisters have formed, do not break them.

It is probable that the patient will be suffering from shock and this must be treated also (see above).

POISONS

A poison is a substance which may cause harmful effects on the body, damaging the tissues or even resulting in death. A number of poisonous substances are used in hairdressing, and careful labelling and storage are essential. If, however, a poison is accidentally swallowed, it is important to try and remove it from the body and to give an antidote to prevent harmful effects. The following procedure should be adopted:

1. *Send for a doctor,* and give him as much information as possible about the nature of the poison. Save any remains for inspection.

2. *Examine the patient's lips and mouth:*

(*a*) If there is no sign of burning round the mouth, give the patient an emetic to remove the poison from the body. An *emetic* is a substance which produces vomiting. A suitable one can easily be made by dissolving a tablespoonful of salt (or mustard) in a cupful of warm water. Give the patient plenty of warm water to drink to wash out the stomach.

(*b*) If there are signs of burning on the lips or if the tongue is swollen or blistered, this indicates that a corrosive poison has been swallowed. Do *not* give an emetic in this case, as the oesophagus and stomach may be injured, and the strain of vomiting may cause further injury. A corrosive poison may be acidic or alkaline, and each type requires different treatment. Find out the nature of the poison.

ACID POISONS

If the poison is an acid, an alkali is the antidote. The alkali neutralizes the acid, producing a comparatively harmless salt. Suitable alkalis are magnesia and bicarbonate of soda, and either of these can be given in water.

ALKALINE POISONS

If the poison is an alkali, such as strong ammonia, an acid antidote is given. Suitable acidic antidotes include a weak solution of vinegar or lemon juice.

After giving the antidote (for either acids or alkalis), give soothing drinks of milk or olive oil. Treatment for shock will usually be necessary also (see above).

NARCOTIC POISONS (DRUGS)

If the patient becomes sleepy, the poison is probably a narcotic (e.g. chloroform, ether, etc.). In this case, keep the patient awake, or consciousness may be lost. Give drinks of strong black coffee.

ELECTRIC SHOCK

All electrical apparatus in hairdressing salons must be properly earthed. With modern equipment, there is little danger of electric shock if the appliances are properly installed and maintained. However, should an appliance develop a fault and a client receive an electric shock, the following procedure should be carried out:

Before touching the client, turn off the current, but if, for some reason, this is not possible, wear rubber gloves or use some other form of insulating material such as dry woollen cloth. Stand on a dry wooden board or a dry folded coat and pull the client clear of the apparatus. The effects of electric shock may be threefold:

(*a*) unconsciousness and cessation of breathing;
(*b*) shock;
(*c*) electrical burns.

If breathing has ceased, apply artificial respiration, and when breathing has recommenced, treat the client for shock and for any burns that may be present. Get someone to summon medical help.

ARTIFICIAL RESPIRATION

The purpose of artificial respiration is to imitate the natural breathing movements of the body and so induce normal breathing to start again. There are several methods but speed is the essential factor. If time is lost, a life may be lost.

THE HOLGER-NIELSEN METHOD

This method can be carried out as follows. Remove the casualty into the fresh air and then lay him face downwards with the arms forward and the head resting on the hands. Loosen any tight clothing at the neck and waist, but do not remove any clothing, because this helps to keep the patient warm and lessens shock.

Kneel in front of the casualty's head and spread your hands over the shoulder-blades with your thumbs touching. Keeping your arms straight apply light pressure to a count of three seconds, then slide your hands down to the patient's elbows on the count of four. To counts of five, six, and seven, raise the patient's arms and shoulders, rocking back a little. Lay the arms down again to the count of eight and replace your hands on the back ready to repeat these movements. Continue this series of movements repeatedly until normal breathing is restored or until a doctor pronounces life extinct.

FIRE PRECAUTIONS

All containers, and particularly those with inflammable substances, should be clearly labelled and stored carefully, preferably in a metal bin. All electrical appliances, such as hair-dryers, etc., should be properly installed and maintained and *must* be properly earthed. Some sort of fire-fighting appliance should be kept in every salon, in addition to sand.

In the event of a fire in the salon, call the fire brigade and try to ensure the safety of all the occupants. Evacuate all the clients, then while waiting for the fire brigade try to extinguish the fire by use of a fire-fighting appliance.

Water can be used for free-burning fires, but electrical fires must *not* be treated with water because of the hazard from electric shock. A carbon dioxide extinguisher may be used on electrical fires.

If oily substances have caught fire *inside* a salon, an asbestos blanket or a carbon dioxide extinguisher may be used.

FIRST-AID KIT IN THE SALON

This should contain the following:

Burn dressings;
Cotton-wool;
Absorbent lint;
Bandages: 2-inch or 3-inch for head,
          1-inch or 1½-inch for fingers;
Antiseptic cream such as cetrimide;
Scissors;
Adhesive dressing strip;
2 per cent boric acid lotion;
2 per cent sodium bicarbonate lotion;
Eye-bath.

★ ★ ★

QUESTIONS ON CHAPTER 26

1. How would you deal with a client who (*a*) felt faint; (*b*) actually fainted?
2. What are the three aims in treating cuts and minor wounds?
3. What are the symptoms of shock and what treatment would you give to aid recovery?
4. If one of your clients had an epileptic fit in the salon, what action would you take?
5. If a dye went wrong and your client had hysterics, what would you do?
6. What is the difference between a burn and a scald? How would you treat a serious burn in the salon?
7. If a child accompanying one of your clients showed signs of having swallowed poison, what steps would you take in rendering first-aid?
8. What would be a suitable antidote for poisoning by (*a*) ammonia; (*b*) caustic potash; (*c*) thioglycollic acid?
9. If a client showed signs of having been drugged, what action would you take?

10. Under what circumstances would you give an emetic? How would you prepare a suitable emetic?
11. Why is an emetic *not* given in the case of corrosive poisoning?
12. What are the possible effects of electric shock and how would you treat them?
13. Describe carefully one method of artificial respiration.
14. What should you do if a fire broke out in the salon?

VISUAL AIDS

Chapter 1

Filmstrips:
  Hydrometers   Unicorn Head Visual Aids Ltd
Films:
  How to use a burette   I.C.I. Film Library

Chapter 2

Filmstrips:
  Air Pressure, I and II   Daily Mail
  Liquid pressure   Daily Mail
  Weather forecasting   Daily Mail
  Water on tap   Associated British-Pathé Ltd

Chapter 3

Film:
  Outline of detergency   Unilever Ltd

Chapter 4

Filmstrips:
  Expansion   Daily Mail
  Thermometers   Common Ground
  Bimetal strip   Unicorn Head Visual Aids Ltd
Films:
  Energy from the sun   Rank Film Library
  Gas meter and *Oven thermostat*   Gas Council
  Energetically yours   Central Film Library
  Controlled heat   Petroleum Films Bureau

Chapter 5

Filmstrips:
  Conduction, convection, and   Common Ground
    radiation
  Distributing heat energy I and II   Encyclopaedia Britannica
  Heat   Unicorn Head Visual Aids Ltd
Films:
  Transference of heat, I, II, and III Gas Council

Chapter 6

Filmstrips:
  Refrigeration   Educational Productions Ltd
Films:
  Vacuum distillation   Petroleum Films Bureau
  Distillation   Petroleum Films Bureau
  Change of state   Central Film Library
  Principles of gas refrigerators   Gas Council

Chapter 7

Filmstrips:
Don't be shocked	National Film Board of Canada
Static and current electricity	Educational Productions Ltd

Films:
What is electricity?	Electrical Development Association
Electrical terms	Electrical Development Association
Electrochemistry	Electrical Development Association
Ammeters and voltmeters	Electrical Development Association

Chapter 8

Films:
Electricity and heat	Electrical Development Association
Electricity and light	Electrical Development Association
Electrochemistry	Electrical Development Association

Chapter 9

Filmstrips:
Plug points	Electrical Development Association
Safety in the home	Electrical Development Association
Electrical Appliances	Common Ground
Electricity in your home	Educational Productions Ltd

Films:
Domestic hot water	Electrical Development Association
Domestic electrical installation	Electrical Development Association

Chapter 10

Filmstrips:
Magnetism and electricity	Unicorn Head Visual Aids Ltd
Electricity supply	*Daily Mail*
Generation	Electrical Development Association
Made and conveyed	Electrical Development Association
Magnets	Rank Film Library
Electricity and magnetism	Common Ground
Electricity and movement	Electrical Development Association
A.C. and D.C. Currents	Electrical Development Association
Magnetism	Electrical Development Association
Making electricity, Parts I and II	Electrical Development Association

Chapter 11

Filmstrips:
Light	Rank Film Library
Light	Tartan Filmstrips
Light	Unicorn Head Visual Aids Ltd
Colour	Educational Productions Ltd
Reflection of Light	Educational Productions Ltd
Refraction of light	Educational Productions Ltd
Radiant energy	Educational Productions Ltd

Films:
    Electricity and light   Electrical Development Association
    Colour   I.C.I. Film Library

Chapter 12

Filmstrip:
    Chemical change   Rank Film Library

Chapter 13

Films:
    History and discovery of oxygen   I.C.I. Film Library
    Crystallization   I.C.I. Film Library
    Water cycle   I.C.I. Film Library
    Chemistry of water   Rank Film Library

Chapter 14

Film:
    Ammonia   I.C.I. Film Library

Chapter 15

Filmstrips:
    Chemistry   Unicorn Head Visual Aids Ltd
    Margarine   Unilever Ltd
Films:
    Introduction to oil   Petroleum Films Bureau
    Story in the rocks   Petroleum Films Bureau
    Chemistry of oil   Petroleum Films Bureau
    The oil rivers   Unilever Ltd
    Raw materials and refining   Unilever Ltd
    The double bond   Central Film Library

Chapter 16

Filmstrip:
    Soap-making   Unilever Ltd
Films:
    New detergents   Petroleum Films Bureau
    Water   I.C.I. Film Library
    Water cycle   I.C.I. Film Library
    What is soap?   Unilever Ltd
    Outline of detergency   Unilever Ltd
    Let's look at water   Central Film Library

Chapter 17

Filmstrip:
    Hair and beauty   The Toni Co.
Films:
    Colour   I.C.I. Film Library

Chapter 18
  Films:
    Filtration   I.C.I. Film Library
    New detergents   Petroleum Films Bureau
    Outline of detergency   Unilever Ltd
    Emulsion   Crookes Film Library Ltd

Chapter 19
  Filmstrips:
    The Skeleton I   Educational Productions Ltd
    The Skeleton II   Educational Productions Ltd
    Structure of skin and bone   Educational Productions Ltd

Chapter 20
  Films:
    Simple nutrition   Marmite Ltd
    Introduction to nutrition   H. J. Heinz Ltd
    Calories and proteins   H. J. Heinz Ltd
    Minerals, elements, and vitamins   H. J. Heinz Ltd
    Good food, good health,   Van den Berghs Ltd; from
       good looks   Aims of Industry Film Bureau
    Nothing to eat but food   Unilever Ltd
  Filmstrips:
    Elimination   Rank Film Library
    Nutrition for athletes   Diana Wylie Ltd
    Food and nutrition I and II   *Encyclopaedia Britannica*
    Feeding and digestion in   Common Ground
       mammals
    Food and health   Common Ground
    Carbohydrates and calories   Common Ground
    Fats and proteins   Common Ground
    Vitamins, minerals, and salts   Common Ground
    The food we eat   Educational Productions Ltd

Chapter 21
  Film loops:
    The heart   Educational Productions Ltd
    The circulation of blood   Educational Productions Ltd

Chapter 23
  Films:
    Your skin   Unilever Ltd
    Your hair and scalp   Unilever Ltd
    Industrial dermatitis   Unilever Ltd

Chapter 24
  Film:
    Keep it clean   Food Hygiene—Gas Council
  Filmstrips:
    Housefly and disease   Educational Productions Ltd
    Hygiene in the home   Camera Talks

Chapter 25

Films:

Where there's a will	Dental Hygiene—Unilever Ltd
Let's keep our teeth	Dental Hygiene—Unilever Ltd
A tooth in time	Dental Hygiene—Unilever Ltd
The best of yourself	Personal Hygiene—Unilever Ltd
Room for hygiene	Personal Hygiene—Unilever Ltd
Safe hands	Food Handling—Petroleum Films Bureau
Guilty chimneys	Air Pollution—Gas Council
Windows to the sky	Clean Air Act—Gas Council

Filmstrips:

Medical and dental care	National Film Board of Canada
House pests and parasites	Common Ground
Care of our teeth	Camera Talks
Care of our hair	Camera Talks
Hair and beauty	The Toni Co.
Good grooming	Educational Productions Ltd

Chapter 26

Films:

Treatment for shock	I.C.I. Film Library
Artificial respiration	I.C.I. Film Library
Examination of an unconscious patient	I.C.I. Film Library
Industrial dermatitis	I.C.I. Film Library
Accidents don't happen	T. J. Smith & Nephew —Aims of Industry
Help	T. J. Smith & Nephew —Aims of Industry
Starting from scratch	Petroleum Films Bureau

Film loops:

Holger-Nielsen method of artificial respiration	Educational Productions Ltd

Filmstrips:

First aid I	Visual Information Service
First aid II	Visual Information Service

Charts:

Artificial Respiration: Holger-Nielson method— mouth to mouth	Iliffe Electrical Publications Ltd

SUPPLIERS OF FILM AND FILMSTRIP

Name	Address
Aims of Industry	78 Victoria Road, Surbiton, Surrey
Associated British-Pathé Ltd	2 Dean Street, London, W.1
Camera Talks	23 Darmarle Place, London, W.C.2
Central Film Library	Bromyard Avenue, Acton, London, W.3
Common Ground Ltd	44 Fulham Road, London, N.W.10
Crookes Film Library	Gorst Road, London, N.W.10
Daily Mail	Northcliffe House, London, E.C.4
Educational Productions Ltd	17 Denbigh Street, London, S.W.1
Electrical Development Association	2 Savoy Hill, London, W.C.2
Encyclopaedia Britannica	11 Belgrade Road, London, S.W.1
Foundation Film Library	Brooklands House, Weybridge, Surrey
Gas Council Film Library	1 Grosvenor Place, London, S.W.1
H. J. Heinz Ltd	195 Great Portland Place, London, W.1
I.C.I. Film Library	Imperial Chemical House, Millbank, London, S.W.1
Iliffe Electrical Publications Ltd	Dorset House, Stamford Street, London, S.E.1
John King (Films) Ltd	Film House, East Street, Brighton, Sussex
Marmite Ltd	Seething Lane, London, E.C.3
National Film Board of Canada	1 Grosvenor Square, London, W.1
Petroleum Films Bureau	4 Brook Street, Hanover Square, London, W.1
Rank Film Library, Rank Film Organization	1 Aintree Road, Perivale, Greenford, Middlesex
T. J. Smith & Nephew Associated Co. Ltd.	Bessemer Road, Welwyn Garden City, Herts.
The Toni Co.	Trevor House, 100 Brampton Road, London, S.W.1
Unilever Films	Blackfriars, London, E.C.4
Visual Information Service	12 Bridge Street, Hungerford, Berks.
Diana Wylie Ltd	3 Park Road, Baker Street, London, N.W.1

U

INDEX

(Italicized page numbers indicate that the subject is also referred to on subsequent pages.)